Previously published:—

MERRILLEANA: A Selection from the General Writings of Elmer Drew Merrill. — During his long and active life the Nestor of American Plant Taxonomists has found the time for many studies of a wide and general interest. Though these are often not so well known as his purely taxonomic and administrative activities, they are of a great and permanent value. It seemed fitting to the Editors of CHRONICA BOTANICA to bring out, on the occasion of the 70th anniversary of the birth of their distinguished co-editor, a selection, difficult as this was to make, of his more general writings. As Professor SARTON observed in *Isis*: "The finest, as well as the most profitable, way of honoring a scholar is to publish an edition of his smaller writings, those which are not available in book form but are scattered in many periodicals and collections." The book includes a 'Vita' and 'Bibliographia' as well as certain portraits. — *Chronica Botanica, Vol. 10, No. 3/4 (1946)*; 268 p., 23 illus., $4.00.

Contents: THE ASCENT OF MOUNT HALCON (1907). — AMBOINA FLORISTIC PROBLEMS IN RELATION TO THE EARLY WORK OF RUMPHIUS (1917). — COMMENTS ON COOK'S THEORY AS TO THE AMERICAN ORIGIN AND PREHISTORIC POLYNESIAN DISTRIBUTION OF CERTAIN ECONOMIC PLANTS, ESPECIALLY *Hibiscus tiliaceus* (1920). — ON THE FLORA OF BORNEO (1921). — DIE PFLANZENGEOGRAPHISCHE SCHEIDUNG VON FORMOSA UND DEN PHILIPPINEN (1923). — AN APPEAL FOR SIMPLIFIED LITERATURE CITATIONS (1925). — CORRELATION OF THE INDICATED BIOLOGIC ALLIANCES OF THE PHILIPPINES WITH THE GEOLOGIC HISTORY OF MALAYSIA (1926). — LEPROSY BOWS TO SCIENCE (1929). — ONE-NAME PERIODICALS (1931). — ON LOUREIRO'S *Flora Cochinchinensis* (1935). — SCUTTLING ATLANTIS AND MU (1936). — PALISOT DE BEAUVOIS AS AN OVERLOOKED AMERICAN BOTANIST (1936). — ON THE TECHNIQUE OF INSERTING PUBLISHED DATA IN THE HERBARIUM (1937). — ON THE SIGNIFICANCE OF CERTAIN ORIENTAL PLANT NAMES IN RELATION TO INTRODUCED SPECIES (1937). — DOMESTICATED PLANTS IN RELATION TO THE DIFFUSION OF CULTURE (1938). — *Index Kewensis* IN IMPROVED LOOSE LEAF LEDGER FORM (1939). — A SIMPLE CHANGE IN NAME (1941). — MAN'S INFLUENCE ON THE VEGETATION OF POLYNESIA, WITH SPECIAL REFERENCE TO INTRODUCED SPECIES (1941). — SOME ECONOMIC ASPECTS OF TAXONOMY (1943). — RAFINESQUE'S PUBLICATIONS FROM THE STANDPOINT OF WORLD BOTANY (1943). — SIR DAVID PRAIN (1857-1944) (1944). — IN DEFENSE OF THE VALIDITY OF WILLIAM BARTRAM'S BINOMIALS (1945). — FURTHER NOTES ON TOBACCO IN NEW GUINEA (1946).

• Professor MERRILL, the "American Linnaeus," is known most widely for his taxonomic work and for his administrative activities in Manila (as director of the Bureau of Science) and in this country (as dean of the College of Agriculture at the University of California, director of the New York Botanical Garden, and administrator of botanical collections at Harvard University and director of the Arnold Arboretum). From this collection of some of his more general writings it is clear that he has also the gift of grasping the broad general significance of his detailed botanical work and of interpreting it not only for other botanists but also for fellow scientists in such fields as geography and anthropology and for the general reader. (GEOGR. REVIEW)

• Uno de los más hermosos y útiles, sin duda, es el que le rinde la prestigiosa revista CHRONICA BOTANICA. Con el título de *Merrilleana* dió a luz un bellísimo volumen de unas 250 páginas y abundantes ilustraciones, en el cual se reimprimen 23 trabajos del Dr. MERRILL de gran interés y publicados en diferentes revistas, algunas de difícil acceso. Hay trabajos reproducidos íntegramente, de otros sólo vienen las partes más sobresalientes. Los editores han sabido escoger con mucho tino los trabajos más adecuados, omitiendo aquéllos muy técnicos, que interesan solamente a un grupo reducido de especialistas. La mayoría de los artículos, aunque tienen por centro común la botánica, son de índole más general e interesarán también a muchos lectores que no sienten predilección por la scientia amabilis, como geógrafos etnólogos, médicos, agrónomos, etc. (LOOSER *in* REVISTA CHILENA HIST. GEOGR.)

• Altogether, this is a distinguished and commendable effort for which great thanks are due . . . (QUART. REV. BIOL.)

CHRONICA BOTANICA, *An International
Collection of Studies in the Method and History
of Biology and Agriculture,* edited by FRANS VERDOORN
● Volume 14, Number 5/6, Pages i-iv, 161-384, Plates 80-93 ●
(Issued Autumn, 1954)

The BOTANY
of
COOK's VOYAGES

● This issue of CHRONICA BOTANICA (which is also available in a limited,
cloth bound edition, at $4.75) completes Volume 14.
● Volume 14 of CHRONICA BOTANICA consists of three issues (*cf.* p. 384).
The second issue of this volume (*i.e.,* Volume 14, No. 3/4) was erroneously
marked "Number 3" on the cover and half title; the running heads, however,
give the issue numbers correctly.
● Volume 15 of CHRONICA BOTANICA (I. W. BAILEY's *Contributions to
Plant Anatomy*) will be issued shortly as a single, buckram bound volume.
● A strong, buckram binding case, stamped in genuine gold, to hold
Volumes 13/14, with the volumes' contents indicated on the spine, will be
available shortly at $1.25.

PRIMITIÆ

FLORÆ INSULARUM

OCEANI PACIFICI,

sive

CATALOGUS

PLANTARUM

in

OTAHEITE, EIMEO, OTAHA,

HUAHEINE & ULAIETEA

A.C. MDCCLXIX, diebus 13 Aprilis — 9 Augusti

collectarum

TEXT FIGURE 1. — Title page of SOLANDER's unpublished manuscript flora of Tahiti and other neighboring Pacific Islands (*vide* p. 329). The descriptions in this flora were transcribed and, to a good extent, made ready for press by BACSTRÖM, from SOLANDER's file of plant descriptions. His cards or slips, written during COOK's first voyage, were originally in Solander cases, but were later bound in a number of small quarto volumes which are at the British Museum (Natural History). — Reproduction of two pages (one has to search for pages without unpublished binomials) from this Flora will be found on p. 199 & 344.

Chronica Botanica, Volume 14, Number 5/6

The BOTANY of
COOK's VOYAGES

and its Unexpected Significance in Relation to Anthropology, Biogeography and History

by

ELMER DREW MERRILL, Sc.D., Ll.D.
Arnold Professor of Botany, Emeritus, Harvard University

1954
WALTHAM, MASS., U.S.A.
Published by the Chronica Botanica Company

FIRST PUBLISHED 1954, BY THE CHRONICA BOTANICA CO.

LIBRARY OF CONGRESS CATALOGUE CARD NUMBER: 54-12803

ELMER DREW MERRILL was born in East Auburn, Maine, in 1876. Upon completing his studies at the University of Maine, he became Assistant Agrostologist with the U. S. Dept. of Agriculture, in Washington, D. C. (1899-1902). In 1902, he left for Manila as Botanist to the Bureau of Agriculture and Forestry. Dr. MERRILL remained in the Philippine islands until 1923, playing an important rôle in the development of the Bureau of Science and of the University of the Philippines, while establishing his reputation as a foremost authority on the Flora of Tropical Asia.

In 1923, the University of California secured his services as Director of its Agricultural Experiment Station and as Dean of its College of Agriculture. After successfully integrating a number of California organizations, which were growing up too loosely knit, Dr. MERRILL was chosen to be Director of the New York Botanical Garden. He held this post from 1930 to 1935.

From 1935 until 1946, he served as Director of the Arnold Arboretum and as Administrator of Botanical Collections at Harvard University. During the Second World War, Dr. MERRILL acted as a consultant to the Secretary of War.

His main publications include: *New and Noteworthy Philippine Plants* (1904, seq.), *Bibliographic Enumeration of Bornean Plants* (1921), *Enumeration of Philippine Flowering Plants* (1923, seq.), *Bibliography of Polynesian Botany* (1924), *Loureiro's Flora Cochinchinensis* (1935), *Polynesian Botanical Bibliography* (1937), *A Bibliography of Eastern Asiatic Botany* (with E. H. Walker, 1938), *Plant Life of the Pacific World* (1945), *A Botanical Bibliography of the Islands of the Pacific* (1946), and *Index Rafinesquianus* (1949). — A collection of his general writings, *Merrilleana*, was published in CHRONICA BOTANICA 10, 3/4 (*cf. supra*).

Dr. MERRILL is the recipient of many honours, among which we may cite: Foreign Member, Linnean Society of London (1933); LL.D., Univ. California (1936); Sc.D., Harvard Univ. (1936); Linnean Gold Medal (1939); Correspondant, Académie Sci. (Institut de France) (1945); Member, Board of Directors, Escuela Agrícola Panamericana (1946); Pres., Section of Nomenclature, Seventh Int. Bot. Congress (Stockholm, 1950); Grand Médaille Geoffroy Saint Hilaire (1950); Sc.D., Yale Univ. (1950); Foreign Member, Swedish Acad. Sci. (1951); Foreign Member, Netherlands Acad. Sci. (1953); Hon. Pres., Eighth Int. Bot. Congress (Paris, 1954).

An outstanding organizer, a leading authority on the flora of the Old World tropics, a recognized expert on problems of botanical taxonomy, nomenclature, and bibliography, Dr. MERRILL has amassed a tremendous amount of unique data and experience. This has been the fruit of a life time arduously devoted to studies in the field, in various herbaria, as well as of the botanical and travel literature. The present memoir could, indeed, have been prepared only by an authority of Dr. MERRILL's broad outlook on the historical, humanistic, geographical, ethnological and economic aspects of plant taxonomy.

CONTRIBUTIONS FROM THE INT. BIOHISTORICAL COMMISSION, No. 2

Made and Printed in the U. S. A.
Designed by Frans Verdoorn

DEDICATED TO

HENRY ALLEN MOE

TABLE *of* CONTENTS

PREFACE:—

Objectives of the Author's Last European Trip 171
   Studies of the WILLIAM ROXBURGH Collections 171
   Studies of unnamed Specimens from Malaysia, India, China and Polynesia 172
   The BANKS and SOLANDER Collections of Captain COOK's First Voyage 172
   On the comprehensive Nature of the classic Collections made in the Pacific Islands by BANKS, SOLANDER and the FORSTERS... 173

The Author's Personal Handicaps 174

Modification of the Author's Original Plans 175
   Most Technical Names originated by SOLANDER and casually used by PARKINSON not listed in *Index Kewensis* 175
   The Historical Importance of early Collections of dated Plant Specimens 175
   The Author's early Studies regarding the Significance of certain widely used Plant Names 175

Old Herbaria and other Sources of Information 176
   Literature on Early Herbaria 177
   The HANS SLOANE Herbarium 177
   The CHARLES DU BOIS Herbarium 177
   Old Herbaria, important but neglected Sources of Information 178

Ancient Antarctic Connections 178

Anti-DE CANDOLLE Theorists 179
   DE CANDOLLE's *Origin of Cultivated Plants* 179

Imagined Wisdom without Understanding 180
   FERNALD on CRAIGIE and HULBERT's *Dictionary of American English on Historical Principles* 181
   G. N. JONES on CRISWELL's LEWIS and CLARK Studies 181

In Defense of the Term "Neogeography" 181
   Fields which suffer most 181
   Neglect of DE CANDOLLE's Work 181
   "Neogeographers" seem to avoid Consultation with well-informed and easily available Specialists in other Fields 182

Acknowledgments 182

Chapter I : INTRODUCTION:—

Captain COOK's Exploring Expeditions in the Pacific Islands 185
   Importance of Polynesian Plants collected during and after Captain COOK's First Visit to Tahiti 185
   Importance of Species of natural Pan-tropic Distribution as well as man-introduced Cultivated Plants and Weeds known to have been present in Tahiti, New Zealand, Hawaii, etc., at the time of Discovery of these Islands 186
   SOLANDER's Manuscript Floras 186
   Two Letters from LINNAEUS to J. ELLIS 186
   The Use of Antiscorbutics on the Voyage of the *Endeavour* 187

On the Limited Distribution of Important Cultivated Plants between the two Hemispheres 188
   "No Pacific Regatta" (MANGELSDORF and OLIVER) 188
   No Popcorn (*Zea*) in India in Pre-Columbian Times 188
   Aboriginal Rafts and Canoes in the Pacific before 1520 189
   Disregard of Early Transportation Conditions 189

Pre-Columbian Advanced Cultures did not reach America across the Pacific 189
   O. F. COOK and HEYERDAHL's Ideas on the Origin of American Agriculture 189
   A preliminary Analysis of certain False Claims 190

The Importance of Early Collections which give us an idea which Species of Exotics were and were not present on a given Island 190
   The Early Botanical Collectors within the Polynesian Triangle did not ignore Cultivated Plants and Weeds 191
   The FORSTERS had not been instructed to ignore the Weeds 191
   The Botanical Evidence clearly indicates that, as of 1769, all Cultigens in the Pacific Islands, with one possible exception, and nearly all Weed Species, were brought in from the West by the early Settlers who occupied the Polynesian Triangle 191

Pioneer large-scale Portuguese Operations after 1500 (Brazil to Goa, and beyond,
via the Cape of Good Hope) 192
> The most important Portuguese Period of Expansion too often ignored by Botanists and His-
> torical Geographers 192
> Dangers of Theorizing as to when a given American Cultigen reached China, India or
> Malaysia 192

Early Portuguese *versus* early Spanish Plant Introduction Work 193
> The Spanish Galleon Route from Mexico to the Philippines, initiated in 1565 193
> Spaniards and Portuguese in the Orient 193

Early Distributional History of *Cocos, Ipomoea* (the Sweet Potato) and *Lagenaria*
(the Gourd) 194

The Collections of BANKS, SOLANDER and the two FORSTERS at the British Museum (N. H.), Materials of Unexpected Interest 194
> Tahiti, the Centre of the Polynesian Culture Area 195
> Plants of economic Importance and Weeds at Tahiti in the 1760's 195
> GLADMIN's *Men out of Asia* 195
> On outrigger and other Types of Canoes in Malaysia and Polynesia 196
> The Atlantis Idea 196
> CHURCHWARD's Mu Idea 196
> From WASHINGTON IRVING's *Knickerbocker History of New York* 197
> Early Man, a very limited Factor in the Distribution of Cultigens and Weeds between the two
> Hemispheres 197
> DE CANDOLLE's List of Cultivated Plants 197
> AKEMINE's Lists of Cultivated Plants 198

Chapter II : BANKS, SOLANDER and the TWO FORSTERS:—
History of Captain COOK's Second Voyage (1772-75) 201
> The FORSTERS, Naturalists of Captain COOK's Second Voyage 201
> The Collections made by the FORSTERS 201
> The FORSTERS and Sir JOSEPH BANKS 203
> The FORSTERS' *Characteres generum plantarum* (1776) 203
> GEORG FORSTER's *Journal* (1777) 203
> The FORSTERS' Drawings 203
> GEORG FORSTER's *Florulae insularum australium prodromus* (1786) 205
> GEORG FORSTER's *De plantis esculentis insularum oceani australis* (1786) 205
> Break between the Earl of SANDWICH and the two FORSTERS 206
> SOLANDER *Nomina Nuda* in GEORG FORSTER's *Prodromus* 206
> Linnaean Binomials misinterpreted and misapplied to Tahitian Species 206
> GEORG FORSTER's Treatment of a number of Vascular Cryptogams 207

Chapter III : The FORSTER HERBARIUM:—
Duplicates of the FORSTER Collections in Older European Herbaria 208
> FORSTER Specimens in the ABRAHAM BÄCK Herbarium 208
> FORSTER Specimens in the Linnaean and Sir JAMES E. SMITH Herbarium 208
> FORSTER Specimens in the THUNBERG Herbarium 208
> FORSTER Specimens in the British Museum (N. H.) Herbarium 209
> FORSTER Specimens at Liverpool and Kew 209

STANSFIELD's Recent Studies on the FORSTER Specimens at Liverpool 210
> Notes on the Destruction of important Herbaria 210
> "General Biologists" and important Historical Records 210
> FORSTER Specimens in the Sir WILLIAM J. HOOKER and other Herbaria at Kew 211

Chapter IV : The REAL SIGNIFICANCE of the BANKS and SOLANDER
TAHITI COLLECTIONS of 1769:—
Tahiti, its Discovery and Flora 212
The Pre-Magellan Inhabitants of the Pacific Islands came out of Asia via
Malaysia 212
Criticism of HEYERDAHL's Theory, according to which Polynesia was populated
by the American Indians 212
> The Common Gourd (*Lagenaria*), the only Cultivated Plant which occurred not only in tropical
> and temperate America, but also in the corresponding parts of the Old World in pre-Col-
> umbian Times 212
> Maize (*Zea*) and Cassava (*Manihot*) in Africa in pre-Columbian Times? 212
> O. F. COOK's *Food Plants of Ancient America* 213

Importance of the BANKS, SOLANDER and FORSTER Collections, practically the
First Botanical Collections made in the Pacific Islands 213
> No dependable Biological Evidence that there was any effective direct Communication across
> the great Ocean until after MAGELLAN's Voyage (1521) 213

The Sweet Potato (*Ipomoea*) in New Zealand and Polynesia 213
THOMAS DAVIS's Voyage and Studies 214

Quiros's Observations in the Tuamotu Islands 215
Heyerdahl and O. F. Cook's Misinterpretations of Agricultural and Botanical
 Evidence 215
Early Introductions by Quiros and Wallis 216
Solander's Tahitian Specimens, Collected in 1769 216
Man-Introduced Economic Species 216
 Artocarpus and Musa 216
 Pueraria 217
 Pachyrrhizus 217
 Cucurbita in Tahiti 218
Weeds 219
 Most Tahitian Weeds of Indo-Malaysian Origin 219
 On Cenchrus echinatus and C. calyculatus 219
 Weeds described in Roxburgh's Flora Indica 220
 Oviedo's Account of Ipomoea batatas, the Sweet Potato 220
 Argemone 220
 The Author's earlier Studies on the Significance of Polynesian Weeds 221
 Seemann's Flora Vitiensis 221
The Fortunate Preservation of the First Botanical Collections, made by Banks,
 Solander and the Forsters, yields Evidence which supports the Theory that
 the Inhabitants of the Pacific Islands came from Malaysia 221
 Tahitian Weeds of Pan-tropic Distribution 222

Chapter V : EARLY TRADE ROUTES in RELATION to PLANT DISTRIBU-
TION:—
Man, since the Close of the Fifteenth Century, the greatest single Factor in
 extending the Ranges of Plants 223
Introduced Plants in North America 223
Introduced Plants in California 225
Introduced Plants in New Zealand 225
 On Phalaris and other weeds 227
Introduced Plants in the Tropics 227
Two Early Trade Routes 229
 To India and Malaysia via Brazil and the Cape of Good Hope 229
 To Cape Horn, via Brazil, thence to Guam and other Parts of the Orient 229
 Weeds of Brazilian Origin in the Orient 229
 Brazil and Mexico, Centers of Origin of many Tropical Weeds 230
The Acapulco-Manila Galleon Line (1565-1815) 231
 G. F. Gemelli Careri 231
Further Notes on Early Voyages and Routes 232
 Bartholomew Dias, Vasco da Gama and Cabral 233
 Early Spanish Control of the Pacific 233
 Drake enters the Pacific (1578) 233
The Time Element in Trans-Pacific Voyages 234
 On early Transportation Conditions 234
 Native, basic Food Plants often lacking in Tropical Areas 234
 The limited Resources of aboriginal New Zealand 235
The Importance of the Marianas Islands 235
The Floras of Guam and the Philippines 235
 Mexican Weed Species in Guam and the Philippines 235
 Many American Weeds and Economic Plants first described on the basis of Specimens collected
  in the Old World 236
 Carter's Misinterpretation of the Distribution of certain American Weed Species 236
 Native Names of Sanskrit or Chinese Origin for Plants introduced into Malaysia 236
 Nahuatl Names for Plants introduced at an early time in the Philippines 236
 Influence of the long continued Acapulco-Manila Galleon Route 237
 An Analysis of the Flora of Manila 237
Critical Notes on Authors who Disregard the Early Trade Routes 237
 The Stonor-Anderson Theory of Maize in Assam in pre-Magellan Times 237
 Roxburgh on Maize in India 237
 Cogniaux on Cucurbita 237
The Distribution of American Weeds 238
 American Weeds now dominant everywhere in the Old World Tropics 238
 The Significance of the Absence of American Weeds in Tahiti, New Zealand and other Pacific
  Islands when these Islands were discovered 238
 Early Plant Introduction Records 239

Chapter VI : DISAGREEMENTS BETWEEN BOTANICAL FACTS and PRE-CONCEIVED THEORIES in VARIOUS FIELDS:—

SOLANDER's Manuscript Floras, Plant Taxonomy, Nomenclature and Historical Geography 240
Weaving not Introduced into America via the Pacific Route 240
Various Aspects of Early Polynesian Culture 241
No Evidence that any Cultivated Plant of American Origin (except the Sweet Potato?) and a few Weeds of American Origin had become established on the Pacific Islands until after European Exploration Commenced 241
   Ipomoea, the Sweet Potato 241
   The Coconut 241
   Lagenaria, the Common Gourd 241
   Gossypium, Cotton 241
   "Floating Barley Seeds" 242
   DE CANDOLLE's Conclusions of 1883 never refuted 242
The Culture which Developed in certain Parts of S. America, C. America, incl. Mexico, founded on an Agriculture based on Cultivated Plants and Domesticated Animals of American Origin 243
   The Polynesian Distribution of the Sweet Potato (*Ipomoea batatas*) 243
   On the History of Pre-Columbian American Culture 243
   Sir DAVID PRAIN on Diffusionists of the PERRY—G. ELLIOT SMITH Group 244
Pre-Columbian American Civilizations based wholly on different Cultivated Plants and Domestic Animals then the Civilizations of the Old World, an incontrovertible Argument in favor of parallel, independent Development of Agriculture in the two Hemispheres 245
The FORSTERs' Collections confirm the Evidence supplied by the BANKS and SOLANDER Collections 245
   Waltheria indica in the Society Islands 245
   On certain Weeds, etc., of American Origin or of a pan-tropic Distribution discovered by the FORSTERS in the Pacific 246
   The lowly *Dentella*, an interesting and convincing Case 246

Chapter VII : A CONSIDERATION of CERTAIN "AUTHORITIES":—

The late O. F. COOK's Writings 248
F. B. H. BROWN's erratic Writings 248
Native Food Plants of the Polynesian Islands 248
Early Plant Introduction Activities 249
Polynesian Agriculture based on Plants and Animals introduced from outside the Pacific Islands 249
F. B. H. BROWN 250
   The Author's Studies of Man's Influence on the Vegetation of Polynesia, with Comments on BROWN's Work, overlooked by HEYERDAHL 250
   BROWN's *Flora of Southeastern Polynesia* 250
   On the Need for a comprehensive Modern Flora of Tahiti 252
GEORGE F. CARTER 252
   HILLEBRAND's *Flora of Hawaii* (1888) misinterpreted 252
   CARTER on the discontinuous Distribution of the Sweet Potato (*Ipomoea batatas*) in Polynesia 253
   CARTER and O. F. COOK's Theories 253
   Dioscorea alata, the Yam or Ajes 254
   Lagenaria siceraria, the Common Gourd 255
   GUPPY's Floating Experiments 257
   CARTER's Floating Experiments 257
   Mrs. TOWLE's Views of GUPPY's Results 257
   Gossypium, Cotton 258
   No Proof that other Food Plants than *Lagenaria*, the Common Gourd (not a basic food plant), were of universal Distribution, in Cultivation in N. and S. America, Africa, Asia and the Pacific Islands in Pre-Historic Times 258
   Cocos, the Coconut 258
   Argemone mexicana, an example of CARTER's Interpretations 259
   On nine "Hawaiian" Species listed by CARTER 260
   CARTER on Maize (*Zea*). — The STONOR-ANDERSON Theory. — Maize first crossed the Atlantic, from Brazil to Goa, via the Cape of Good Hope 261
   Two early recorded Maize Plantings 262
   CARTER asserts that *Lonchocarpus* appears to be "botanically the same plant" as *Derris* .. 262
   Chenopodium ambrosioides, an effective Vermifuge, not a Food Plant 262
   On the Distribution of the aquatic, American *Nelumbo lutea* 262
T. HEYERDAHL and his "Theories" behind the Kon-Tiki Expedition 263
   The Bottle Gourd and Giant Gourd, both Forms of *Lagenaria siceraria* 264
   Cucurbita maxima (the Squash) introduced into Polynesia in the 1760's from Brazil 265

HEYERDAHL on Cotton and Maize 265
HEYERDAHL and O. F. COOK on the Distribution of *Cocos*, the Coconut 265
OVIEDO on the Coconut at the Pacific Coast of Panama 266
BRUMAN's Studies on the Distribution and History of the Coconut 267
F. B. H. BROWN's erroneous Views on the History of the Pineapple and Papaya 267
Introduction of the Pineapple (*Ananas*) in Polynesia 269
Early Explorers as Introducers of Plants and Animals 270
ROSS and FIRTH on HEYERDAHL's Theories 270
CARL SAUER 271
  Lagenaria, a single Species, *versus* 1800 or more cultivated Species which were never common to, nor widely distributed in, both Hemispheres until after the 1490's 271
  Influence of O. F. COOK's erroneous Theories 272
  SAUER's "Cultivated Plants of South and Central America", a valuable review 272
  Botanical and Archeological Evidence shows that Agriculture originated independently in America on the basis of indigenous American Plants and Animals 272
  Results of Dr. JUNIUS BIRD's Excavations at Huaca Prieta (Peru) 272
  Dr. BIRD finds *Canna*, not *Musa* 272
  SAUER's *Agricultural Origins and Dispersals* 273
  Biogeographical Differences between the Old and the New Worlds 273
  On Diffusion of Culture along the Northern Coasts of Asia to America, thence East and South in America (the early peoples could, however, not have brought Asiatic plants with them over the northern route) 273
  No Reason why the Polynesians could not have, occasionally, reached the American Coast, and why they could not have brought with them a few of their cultivated Food Plants of Indo-Malaysian Origin (as *Colocasia*, *Musa*, *Saccharum*, *Dioscorea* and *Cocos*) 274
  The striking North and South Distribution of Cultivated Plants in the Americas 274
  A similar, but less spectacular, North and South Distribution of Old World Cultivated Plants 274
  SAUER on *Oryza sativa*, rice. — E. B. COPELAND's Comments 275
  SAUER on *Cocos*, *Pandanus*, the Sweet Potato, the Peanut, and Maize (the latter credited with helping to make up protein deficiencies) 275
  Excursions in, not "proofs" derived from, Poultry Science. — Comments by Drs. WETMORE, LANDAUER and PUNNETT 277
  SAUER, OVIEDO and WIENER on the distributional History of the Banana and Plantain (*Musa*) 278
  SAUER, L. H. BAILEY, G. W. BOHN, BOUCHÉ, BOIS, COGNIAUX, T. W. WHITAKER, et al., on *Cucurbita* 279
  On *Cucurbita ficifolia* Bouché 281
  SAUER's erroneous Views on: *Acorus calamus*, *Cyperus esculentus*, *Trapa natans*, "*Nelumbium lotus*", and *Sagittaria* "*sagittifolia*" 282
  Lack of Consultation and Coöperation between Geographers and Plant Scientists at the University of California 285
  Little known Crop Plants worth further study by, and of interest to, Workers in Historical Geography 285
  Ustilago Infected Rhizomes and Intumescences 286
  On *Malva parviflora* 287
  MANGELSDORF on SAUER's *Agricultural Origins and Dispersals* 287
EDGAR ANDERSON 289
  The STONOR-ANDERSON "Maize in Assam" Theory 289
  MANGELSDORF-OLIVER's Reply 289
  CARL SAUER on Maize in Asia 289
  The old Silk Route 289
  LAUFER's "The American Plant Migration" 290
  An only partially true Statement about "Pan-Tropic Weeds" 290
  Diffusionists and Independent Inventions 291
  Gossypium (Cotton) in early Polynesia and Peru. — Weaving and Spinning unknown to the Polynesians, but highly developed at Huaca Prieta 291
  ANDERSON and SAUER's Views on DE CANDOLLE's *Origin of Cultivated Plants* 293
  ANDERSON and ROXBURGH on the History of the *Dahlia* 294
  ANDERSON on the Distributional History of *Tagetes*, *Coix lachryma-jobi* and *Gossypium* 294
  ANDERSON and O. AMES on the History of *Arachis*, the Peanut 295
  Notes on *Canavalia*, *Cucurbita*, and *Psidium* 296
  An Objection against unsupported Statements, sweeping Inferences and the Disregard of the Rôle played by the Portuguese and Spanish Colonizing Ventures, following 1500 299
  On Brazilian Cultigens of American Origin which reached the Orient by the old, direct Route to India 301
  CARTER and ANDERSON on *Bixa orellana* 301
JONATHAN D. SAUER's Excellent Study of the Grain Amaranths 301
R. C. BAKHUIZEN VAN DEN BRINK, Sr. 303
  His Studies of "American" Plants in Malaysia 303
  BAKHUIZEN, CHEVALIER, and H. J. TOXOPEUS on *Ceiba pentandra* (Kapok) 304
  BAKHUIZEN, BACKER, O. F. COOK and RUMPHIUS on *Heliconia* 305
  BAKHUIZEN, PIGAFETTA and LAUFER on *Ipomoea batatas* (the Sweet Potato) with Notes on its Introduction in New Guinea 306
  BAKHUIZEN, L. O. WILLIAMS, VAN NOUHUYS, HADDON, HELEN-MAR WHEELER, CHEVALIER, WITTHOFF, EAST, and others, on the History of Tobacco (*Nicotiana*) 307
  On Herbarium Specimens of Cultigens 312

The American *Nicotiana rustica* L. and *N. tabacum* L., both Hybrids, did not reach any part of the Old World until after the Portuguese and Spaniards had established themselves in the Orient, after the 1500's 312

BAKHUIZEN, RUMPHIUS, and MERCADO on *Plumeria acuminata*, a Plant of Mexican Origin which reached the Philippines via the Acapulco-Manila Galleon Route 313

Notes on the History of Cacao (*Theobroma*) and other Plants in the Philippines 314

Leading Historical Geographers often not too familiar with the History of Travel and Exploration 315

Many Ethnologists seemingly not interested in Ethnobotany 315

LEO WIENER 316

His Views on the History of Tobacco and the Smoking of Tobacco 316

WIENER, QUISUMBING, POVEDANO, HERNANDEZ and DE SAHAGUN on the Sweet Potato, *Ipomoea batatas* (camote, kuringatos, quauhcamotli, etc.) 316

WIENER, CARTER and JEFFREYS on Distribution across the Atlantic, in pre-Columbian Times, with special reference to *Manihot* and *Zea* 319

R. B. DIXON on WIENER 319

Further Remarks on the Sweet Potato (*Ipomoea batatas*) Controversy .. 321

W. D. PIERCE's recent, mainly Entomological Studies 321

On Vernacular Names of Economic Plants 323

New Guinea Names for *Nicotiana tabacum*, *Ipomoea batatas*, *Dioscorea alata* and Taitu (*Dioscorea* sp.) 323

BARTLETT's "English Names of Some East-Indian Plants and Plant-Products", with special reference to "arrow-root" 323

H. N. STEVENS on the Prevalent Practice of Writing on Historic Subjects without first Verifying the Sources of Information 324

Apologia 325

Chapter VIII : On the BINOMIALS APPEARING in PARKINSON'S JOURNAL (1773):—

Death of SYDNEY PARKINSON. His Personal Effects turned over to his Brother   326

FOTHERGILL's Foreword to the Second Edition of PARKINSON's *Journal* 327

HAWKESWORTH's Voyages 327

PARKINSON's Binomials in his "Plants of use . . . Otaheite" 328

WARBURG and MARTELLI on *Pandanus "tectorius"* 328

SOLANDER Names in PARKINSON's *Journal* 329

On SOLANDER's Manuscript Flora of Tahiti 329

FOSBERG's Views on PARKINSON's New Names 330

New Generic Names, originated and characterized in the SOLANDER Manuscript, mentioned by PARKINSON 330

Notes on Unlisted Technical Botanical Names 331

Suggestion that the PARKINSON Opus be included in our Official List of Outlawed Titles   331

Chapter IX : The LINNAEAN BINOMIALS USED by PARKINSON:—

Notes on Linnaean Binomials from SOLANDER's Manuscript Appearing in PARKINSON's *Journal* 332

Casuarina 332

Dioscorea alata, the Yam 333

Gossypium, with special reference to the Work of HUTCHINSON and his Associates 335

Problems of Early *versus* Late Distribution of Cultivated Plants 340

Further Notes on *Amaranthus* and *Ipomoea* 341

Broussonetia papyrifera 342

Musa troglodytarum 343

Musa paradisiaca 343

Chapter X : The NEW and MOSTLY UNLISTED TECHNICAL NAMES in PARKINSON'S JOURNAL (1773):—

PARKINSON's Names Taken from SOLANDER's Descriptions or Copied from his Plates 346

Nearly all PARKINSON's New and Unlisted Names are Nomina Nuda or Nomina Subnuda, hitherto not included in *Index Kewensis* 346

Ipomoea batatas (the Sweet Potato) with Notes on CHEESEMAN's Studies 349

Benincasa hispida 350

Lagenaria siceraria, the Common Gourd 350

Epipactis purpurea, the Basis of the Genus *Malaxis* 351

Alyxia scandens 352

Ochrosia parviflora 352

Pandanus tectorius 354

Two *Piper* Species 357

Problems in *Artocarpus* 359

Spondias dulcis 360

Terminalia glabrata 361

Alphitonia zizyphoides, with Notes on BIEHLER and SPRENGEL's Works 362

ADDITIONAL NOTES:—

Further Notes on the History of Maize 364
  Maize not recorded from Cebu in PIGAFETTA's Account of MAGELLAN's Voyage 364
  Panicum miliaceum, the Classical Millet 364
  The Word *Mais* in the POVEDANO Manuscript (1578) 365
  Early Records for the Introduction of Maize into the Old World 365
Maize in Europe 365
  FINAN's *Maize in the Great Herbals* 365
  ANDERSON's Norsemen Hypothesis 366
  OVIEDO, FUCHS, HERNANDEZ, and LOBELIUS on Maize 366
  Maize in Asia 366
"American Fruits" on Murals at Pompeii 367
  CARTER's "Plants across the Pacific" 367
  CASELLA's "La frutta nelle pitture Pompeiane" 367
  Annona squamosa, the Sweetsop 367
  The Pineapple 367
  Mangifera indica, the Mango 369
Bixa across the Pacific 370
Further Notes on *Gossypium* 370
  SILOW's "Problems of Trans-Pacific Migration" 370
Concluding Remarks on the Origin of the Sweet Potato (*Ipomoea batatas*) 371
  WIENER on the Nahuatl Name *Camotl* 371
  On the possible African Origin of the Sweet Potato 371
  A. E. KEHR's Recent Studies 372
COLMEIRO's Bibliography 372
On the possible Importance of certain Classic Arabic Works 373
Postscript 373
INDEX OF AUTHORS 374
COMMON, LATIN AND VERNACULAR PLANT NAMES 377
CONTENTS AND PLATES OF CHRONICA BOTANICA, VOLUME 14 (1950/1954) 384

LIST OF ILLUSTRATIONS

TEXT FIGURE 1: Title page of SOLANDER's unpublished manuscript flora of Tahiti and neighboring Pacific Islands iv
TEXT FIGURE 2: DANIEL CARL SOLANDER, contemporary caricature, ca. 1772 184
TEXT FIGURE 3: A typical page from SOLANDER's flora of Tahiti 199
TEXT FIGURE 4: Title page of the FORSTERS' *Characteres generum Plantarum* (1776) 200
TEXT FIGURE 5: Title page of G. FORSTER's *De Plantis Esculentis* (1786) 202
TEXT FIGURE 6: Title page of G. FORSTER's *Florulae Insularum Australium Prodromus* (1786) 204
TEXT FIGURE 7: *Physalis* (from HERNANDEZ) 224
TEXT FIGURE 8: *Helianthus annuus* (from HERNANDEZ) 226
TEXT FIGURE 9: *Mimosa pudica* (from PISO & MARCGRAVE) 228
TEXT FIGURE 10: *Lagenaria siceraria* (from RUMPHIUS) 256
TEXT FIGURE 11: *Ananas comosus* (from RUMPHIUS) 268
TEXT FIGURE 12: *Zea mays* (from HERNANDEZ) 288
TEXT FIGURE 13: *Tagetes* (from HERNANDEZ) 292
TEXT FIGURE 14: *Arachis hypogaea* (from AMES) 297
TEXT FIGURE 15: *Psidium guajava* (from HERNANDEZ) 298
TEXT FIGURE 16: *Bixa orellana* (from HERNANDEZ) 300
TEXT FIGURE 17: *Nicotiana rustica* (from HERNANDEZ) 308
TEXT FIGURE 18: *Ipomoea batatas* (from PISO & MARCGRAVE) 322
TEXT FIGURE 19: *Dioscorea* sp. (from PISO & MARCGRAVE) 334
TEXT FIGURE 20: *Gossypium hirsutum* (from HERNANDEZ) 336
TEXT FIGURE 21: Another page from SOLANDER's flora of Tahiti 344
TEXT FIGURE 22: *Annona squamosa* (from HERNANDEZ) 368
LIST OF PLATES 80–93 384

Vignettes: on p. i, the younger FORSTER, after a contemporary silhouette; on p. 163 & 164, from HERNANDEZ's *Nova . . . Plantarum* (1651); on p. 183, from *Merrilleana (Merrillanthus* Chung & Tsiang); on p. 383, the *Kon-Tiki,* pen drawing by Express Features Service (London).

PREFACE

In 1951, I was fortunate in being able to spend about six months in London, working, for the most part, at the British Museum (Natural History), but with short intervals at Kew, Edinburgh, Oxford University and brief trips to Leiden and Brussels. This work was made possible by a generous, unsolicited and unrestricted grant from the John Simon Guggenheim Memorial Foundation of New York City. The same grant was renewed for 1952 and has made it possible for me to work up some of my notes.

At the outset, I had several objectives. One of these was to locate as many of the actual WILLIAM ROXBURGH collections, from both India and Malaysia, as I could. ROXBURGH was, in truth, the father of Indian botany. Notwithstanding our knowledge that, when he returned to England on account of ill health in 1813 (he died early in 1815 in Edinburgh), he shipped all of his botanical material to London, the place of deposit of his actual holotypes is, strange as it may seem, still unknown. The really large collections of authentic ROXBURGH specimens are preserved in the British Museum (Natural History), at Kew (in the master set of the WALLICH distribution and others scattered through the general herbarium) and at Brussels (in the MARTIUS herbarium). But, what seems to be the largest of all the ROXBURGH sets, is in the DELESSERT herbarium in Geneva, There are scattered ROXBURGH specimens in some of the other older herbaria of Europe, and we can find some even in certain American institutions (the Gray Herbarium and the Arnold Arboretum). Much of the ROXBURGH material, now at Geneva, was acquired by DELESSERT at the LAMBERT sale in London, 1842. All of the ROXBURGH specimens in the Brussels herbarium were purchased by MARTIUS at the sale of the general herbarium of the Linnean Society of London in 1863. I suspect (but, because of LAMBERT's habit of having all labels rewritten and the original ones discarded, I cannot prove) that the Geneva lot may possibly be the master-set of the ROXBURGH collection. It may have been purchased from the ROXBURGH heirs, following his death in Edinburgh in 1815; and, if so, it contains many holotypes. Many of the specimens in Brussels are labelled in ROXBURGH's own hand, as well as those in the master-set of WALLICH's so-called "Catalogue" (actually Numerical List), for it was WALLICH's habit to preserve original labels, usually in packets attached to the sheets.

In this task of searching out ROXBURGH material, I was much more than reasonably successful. Nevertheless, the BARKER WEBB herbarium, in the Istituto Botanico at Florence, Italy, is still to be examined for ROXBURGH specimens. It will not be possible, however, for me to complete an account of what was actually accomplished on this task.

Typewritten copies of the data compiled to date have been deposited in the libraries of the British Museum (Natural History) ; Royal Botanic Gardens, Kew; the Jardin Botanique de l'Etat, Brussels; the Conservatoire et Jardins Botaniques, Genève; the Rijksherbarium, Leiden; and the Arnold Arboretum. These herbaria, with the exception of the last two, are the ones where many of the historical ROX-BURGH collections are preserved.

Shortly after beginning my study of the status of about one hundred and forty species of vascular cryptogams, described by ROXBURGH (of the named collections of which I was fortunate enough to locate about one hundred isotypes), the unfinished data were turned over to Mr. A. H. G. ALSTON of the British Museum. A much-needed critical study may now be completed by a specialist on this particular group of plants and to stimulate such a study was my first objective. As far as I can determine, no specialist on the Pteridophyta has hitherto ever actually studied a single one of the numerous ROXBURGH collections which are still extant. The inadequate descriptions of the ROX-BURGH pteridophytes were published in 1844(1). A critical study of his specimens at the present time may result in some slight changes in nomenclature.

My second objective was to examine as many unnamed specimens from Malaysia, India, China, and Polynesia, in the general herbarium and among the unmounted material, as possible and to make at least approximate identifications, so that the specimens could be distributed into their proper families and genera. The largest single collection was that made by Mr. C. E. CARR in New Guinea in 1935-36.

While I was engaged on this task, a small bundle of Malaysian and Polynesian specimens was brought to my attention; it proved to represent the unnamed *reliquiae* from the BANKS and SOLANDER collections of Captain COOK's first voyage around the world in 1768-71. The specimens were incomplete: some only in fruit, others sterile. With the limitations of the Linnaean system, Dr. SOLANDER could not place these because of the absence of flowers for study.

Some years earlier, I had given a little attention to the significance of the collections made by Messrs. BANKS and SOLANDER on this famous trip. Therefore, towards the end of my stay in London, when it became evident that I had to limit my working hours as well as my mental and physical efforts, I turned to the very intriguing problem discussed in this memoir: searching out various BANKS and SOLANDER specimens and comparing them with the beautifully prepared, unpublished SOLANDER descriptions, where there seemed to be certain discrepancies. At the same time, I also checked various collections

---

1) GRIFFITH, W. The Cryptogamous Plants of Dr. ROXBURGH, Forming the Fourth and Last Part of the *Flora Indica*. Calcutta Jour. Nat. Hist. 4: 463-520. pl. 26-34. 1844.

The ROXBURGH descriptions (but not the plates) were reproduced by C. B. CLARKE in his reprint of the *Flora Indica*. 754-763. 1874. The nine plates consist of reproductions of nineteen of ROXBURGH'S own, excellent illustrations. Although I have never seen any references to these figures in pteridological literature, I have found them listed in the *Index Londinensis*.

made by the two FORSTERS on Captain COOK's second voyage in 1772-1775, for a number of the new species of the FORSTERS are very inadequately described. I also looked up certain Hawaiian specimens, including that of the *Argemone* discussed below (p. 259), which was collected on Captain COOK's third voyage. When I had completed the purely bibliographic work on the WILLIAM ROXBURGH problem, which has been mentioned above, I turned my attention to the preparation of this memoir.

Part of this manuscript was prepared at the British Museum (Natural History) in November and December of 1951, mainly the section on the taxonomic significance of those SOLANDER names which PARKINSON incidentally published in 1773. Another part was written at the Arnold Arboretum in 1952-53. Still another was put into form at the Escuela Agricola Panamericana near Tegucigalpa, Honduras, from January to March of 1953. Finally, a very small part was completed in camp at Moosehead Lake in northern Maine.

As time passed, it became very evident to me that perhaps I had attempted too large a task by expanding my original programme to cover the actual significance of the combined BANKS and SOLANDER and the two FORSTERS' botanical collections in the Pacific Islands. Yet, the more time and thought I devoted to the matter, the more evident it became that some most significant and irrefutable conclusions could be drawn from these combined collections.

Let one important point be noted here: these classic botanical collections made in the Pacific Islands (including New Zealand) were not prepared by mere amateurs. Both BANKS and SOLANDER were trained botanists. So were the FORSTERS, if we allow certain limitations, albeit the son, when he left England as his father's assistant, was only 17 years old! All of the four men involved did exactly what a modern botanist or collector would do to-day, were he to visit a previously unexplored region. His objective would be to locate and to prepare specimens of as many different species of plants as he could find in all parts of the region visited. Unlike nearly all modern field workers in botany, however, they were just as interested in the cultivated plants and weeds as they were in the indigenous and endemic elements. They accordingly prepared material of all species of the cultivated flora, as a matter of course. We should realize that this was for each of the four individuals their first opportunity of botanizing in the tropics, except for a brief stop in Brazil, and they all realized that they were operating in regions which were botanically wholly unknown.

I must emphasize the above statement for the benefit of some theorists outside of botanical fields, including those who claim brashly that the trained botanists and experienced collectors of to-day figuratively jump from mountain top to mountain top in the tropics. In making such a statement, one author, who should have known better, infers that, in the field, most taxonomists ignore the vegetation of the low lands between the mountains. This is, indeed, not the case. Almost all of us do ignore the cultivated plants, for, from a taxonomic standpoint, there is little to be gained by preparing dried specimens of them. Here economic botany, which must be associated with genetics, rather than taxonomic botany is involved. We taxonomists are content to let the geneticists work in this field, even though, on occasion, we do disagree rather violently with some of their conclusions. Genetics, indeed, has much to contribute to modern taxonomy. The wise taxonomist of to-day will take full advantage of advances in genetics, as well as in paleobotany, morphology, anatomy, pollen analysis (palynology) and several other allied fields. Specialists in these and other fields are now contributing greatly to a better system of classification. Some of the contributions of workers in general biology are also of great importance to our knowledge of plant classification. On the other hand, those who insist upon erecting theories, on the basis of their intensive knowledge of any single one of these branches of biology, with little or no knowledge of or reference to other fields often end by displaying their own ignorance.

Personal Handicaps:— Advances in age often bring with them a corresponding decline in physical and mental capabilities. The memory, likewise, undergoes a decline in sharpness of detail. All of this was brought home to me recently when I wrote an account of the peanut. The variety concerned (*see* p. 295) was found in Inca tombs and was cultivated in China following 1516. When the typewritten draft of this present paper reached me, I was shocked to read in place of "shoestring peanuts" the phrase "shoestring potatoes". In checking on the original holographic copy, I had actually written "potatoes" instead of "peanuts".

This and other slips which I have inadvertently made while preparing the text have shown me that I have come to the end of my writing career and that it is time for me to stop. Here and there, in scanning the final draft of this work, I have detected errors due entirely to lapses of memory. I can but hope that the most serious ones were detected and corrected. It is, therefore, rather consoling to me to find that some much younger individuals, recognized specialists within their own fields, at times, also depend too much on their own memories when, in their eagerness to find supporting evidence for what they wish to believe, they venture too far into marginal areas. There are really many pitfalls which can be avoided only by checking and rechecking of the records in order to be sure that what is accepted as a fact is in reality factual. Otherwise, theorizers may, and too often do, fall into a pit prepared for the unwary who, too often wed to their preconceived ideas, accept erroneous conclusions. I regret that during the preparation of parts of this work, I found it increasingly difficult to consult specialized libraries or herbarium material representing various species with which I became concerned.

Another difficulty, also associated with lapses of memory, was the tendency to forget what had been discussed in earlier chapters, when work was later initiated on another subject. The finished copy has shown that there was altogether too much duplication of certain details, and the reader is asked to forgive any unessential repetition.

In many cases, however, a certain amount of duplication was deliberately made for emphasis.

In turning the final manuscript over to younger colleagues for editing, I gave them authority to eliminate duplications and to soften or modify remarks that they might consider to be too harsh. It is my earnest hope that their efforts, which I appreciate deeply, will make my arguments in this treatise as valuable to critical readers as I would have them be.

When FERNALD edited *Rhodora*, he actually was *Rhodora*, for there was no one who could or would restrain him in his remarkable series of reviews of the work of certain authors who lacked his careful and critical approach. I have, on occasion, wished that I had the pen of a FERNALD. Yet, I realize that there is a limit, beyond which one should not go, in being ultra-critical of the work of others. Nevertheless, it is exasperating in the extreme to read categorical opinions of non-specialists which oftentimes may be from ten to fifty per cent or more in error, because facts are misused or not understood at all. Let those individuals console themselves in finding as many errors as they can in my writings, for this is their privilege. I would be the last one in the world to claim that I have made no errors, either in my past or my present work. A man's best is all that we have a right to expect; but it is certain that some of the wild guesses which I dissect critically in this memoir cannot, with any stretch of imagination, be considered to represent the best that their authors could give.

Modification of the Original Plans:— At the time work on this project was started, in London, late in 1951, it immediately became evident that most of the technical names originated by SOLANDER, and used casually by PARKINSON in 1773, were not listed in *Index Kewensis* or those few that were included had bibliographic references to works by other authors (especially SEEMANN, a century or more later than the publication date of PARKINSON's volume). This memoir, therefore, as originally planned, was of a purely taxonomic nature. As I worked on the data and checked on the actual specimens and descriptions available to me in London, it gradually dawned upon me that here was a lead to something really important. It is admitted by everybody, even by those generally not too well informed in the field of taxonomy, that dated specimens of a plant collected at an early time, still preserved, provide much more dependable evidence than does guessing, wishful thinking, or surmising as to the place of origin of the species in question and also give sound evidence as to when and by whom it was distributed. This is especially true of all cultigens and weeds.

The idea that gradually developed in my mind paralleled, in a sense, what happened somewhat more than forty years earlier, in Manila, regarding the significance of certain widely used plant names which were up to that time, for the most part, casually accepted as of Philippine origin (if, indeed, they were considered at all). I was then compiling data on the native plant names actually in common use. What developed was that there were involved several series of these names having nothing to do with the great bulk of the colloquial ones which were of Malay origin. One series was of Sanskrit origin, one of Chinese, and the largest of Nahuatl (Mexican) origin. It further developed that these three series of names were all applied to obviously man-introduced species. This led me into a rather detailed considera- tion of the historical significance of these exotic plant names, with some attention as to when and how the names, and the plants with which they were associated, became established in the Philippines (*see* p. 236). This was, admittedly, an unconventional type of botan- ical paper, but it was distinctly worth while for those who claim that they are really trying to get nearer to the truth as to what really happened in the transmission of cultivated plants and weeds from one hemisphere to the other. Most of the claims of those who are not botanists prove, on careful analysis, to be false, insofar as the botan- ical evidence underlying philological subjects is concerned.

It is perhaps not strange that some students, in making specific claims, prove just the opposite of what they attempt to demonstrate. Were they actually able to coordinate the data from all fields, and were these data all to indicate a given set of facts, it would be one thing. But as yet, not one of the specialists interested in some of the more unconventional and radical theories has been able to prove those prem- ises which he wanted to believe to be true. This applies most especially to those who dote on pre-Columbian and pre-Magellan exchange of basic food plants across the Pacific from Eurasia to America and *vice versa.*

Old Herbaria and other Sources of Information:— There is one source of important information which I have not tapped, but which I had hoped to exploit in 1952, had not advancing years forced me to forego a second trip which I had planned overseas. I have in mind the early herbaria, of the pre-Linnaean period, which are still extant. There are, naturally, none of these old collections in American insti- tutions, for our herbaria have been built up since about 1800. The older institutions in Europe contain many of these old collections, however. This is particularly true of the British Museum, the Oxford and Cambridge herbaria, as well as similar institutions in Holland, France, Switzerland, Italy (where the art of preparing herbarium specimens originated), Austria and other countries in Europe. Some of these take us back about four hundred years. No matter what the interests of civilized man were, from the times of the Greeks and Ro- mans, herbaria could not be developed until after adequate supplies of paper became easily available, following the invention of printing in Europe. The time period is very short as compared with thousands of years that man has been associated with plants. Yet, this short period is of very great significance, insofar as the time of transmission of plants, from the eastern to the western hemisphere and *vice versa,* is concerned; and we scarcely need to go back of the period of 1492 to 1500, in spite of the wishful thinking of some of our non-botanical colleagues who ardently support the idea that man's cultigens might have been more or less universally distributed between the two hemispheres 2,000 to 3,000 years ago.

There is a fairly extensive series of publications on these ancient herbaria which I have not had time to examine critically. I have scanned several of these, of which one by SAINT-LAGER*(2)* is characteristic. Another special source of information is a paper by CAMUS*(3)*. Probably at least as important as the two works just cited is a continued series of papers, for the most part short, by CARL FLATT VON ALFÖLDI*(4)* issued in both Hungarian and German, during 1902-03.

Some of these ancient but still preserved herbaria are very extensive. That of ALDROVANDI (1522-1605), about which there exists a very extensive literature, is reported to contain about 5,000 specimens. Another important one is that of the BAUHIN brothers, said to have contained originally 4,000 specimens, of which about one-half are still preserved in Basle, Switzerland. This BAUHIN material dates from about 1560 to 1620. The largest old herbarium, of which I have any knowledge, is that of Dr. HANS SLOANE; the material, consisting of at least 100,000 specimens, is preserved in 337 volumes. Dr. SLOANE commenced collecting botanical material while studying for a medical degree (which was granted in 1683) ; he died in 1753. This herbarium was a part of the material intended by him for the nation and thus was an important item involved in the basic collections for the preservation of which the British Museum was established, two hundred years ago. Mr. A. W. EXELL has been kind enough to estimate its size for me. Mr. JAMES BRITTEN's account of the SLOANE Herbarium was intended to be published in 1951 as a part of the 200*th* anniversary celebration of the establishment of the British Museum. But it was found that the BRITTEN manuscript was by no means completed before his death. Accordingly it has required much editorial work which has not been completed as yet. The SLOANE gift was not a direct bequest. He specified that the nation would have the first refusal provided £20,000 be supplied from his estate. These data were recently supplied by Dr. J. RAMSBOTTOM.

The CHARLES DU BOIS herbarium, at Oxford University, contains about 13,000 sheets. DU BOIS was treasurer of the British East India Company from 1702 to 1737. He died in 1740. The DU BOIS material is now partly identified, in terms of modern nomenclature, and the entire herbarium is arranged in generic order, following the BENTHAM and HOOKER system. It contains nearly 4,000 Asiatic species, most of those from India having been identified by Mr. J. SYKES GAMBLE in 1917. I am indebted to Dr. E. F. WARBURG of Oxford University for these data regarding the DU BOIS herbarium. We know about the

2) SAINT-LAGER, J. B. Histoire des Herbiers. Ann. Soc. Bot. Lyon 13: 1-120. 1886.

3) CAMUS, J. Histoire des Premiers Herbiers. Malpighia 9: 283-314. 1895.

4) FLATT VON ALFÖLDI, K. A herbariumok történetéhez — Zur Geschichte der Herbare. Magyar Bot. Lapok 1: 61 seq. 1902; 2: 30 seq. 1903. Also issued in 1903, in German only (there may have been a separate reprint of the Hungarian text), as a 52 p. pamphlet, with index and corrigenda.

contents of the Morisonian and the Dillenian herbaria at Oxford University, thanks to the works of DRUCE and VINES, published in 1897 and 1907.

From these old herbaria (only a few of which I have mentioned), it is possible to determine approximate dates for the establishment or, at least, the presence of a specific weed of American origin in a given part of Europe or Asia, when a specific plant, of tropical American origin, became established in India, and when many of the Indian species became established in the West Indies and elsewhere. This would be a very dull task, even for most botanists, for, in many cases, complete correlations have not as yet been made between the pre-Linnaean and the post-Linnaean nomenclature, and, in certain cases, some of the specimens have never been named under any system of classification. Yet, we should not overlook these almost totally neglected sources, regardless of whether they may or may not support any special theory. As I close my active career, one of my regrets is that I have not been able to exploit these promising possibilities.

Ancient Antarctic Connections:— It has been argued that, for early transantarctic distribution of representatives of such a genus as *Gossypium*, one must prove that, in pre-glacial times, arid conditions prevailed at least in parts of what is now Antarctica. It so happens that the family *Proteaceae*, with some fifty genera currently recognized, is almost wholly restricted to the southern hemisphere. Four of its genera, *Orites* R. Br., *Roupala* Aubl., *Embothrium* J. R. & G. Forst., and *Lomatia* R. Br. have representatives in South America and in the southern parts of the Old World; and in the Old World the whole family is limited primarily to South Africa, Australia, Tasmania, New Caledonia and New Zealand. There, particularly, the existing species are to a high degree characteristic of rather dry habitats, especially in South Africa and Australia. There are many genera, in other families, that are confined to the southern parts of both hemispheres. Hence, under the circumstances, there is no reason whatever to doubt the validity of this ancient Antarctic route of migration of various families and genera of plants; certainly, no experienced phytogeographer would question the validity of this route, for it is as thoroughly established as its more evident equivalent by what is now the Arctic region. Dr. T. H. GOODSPEED has given some attention to this very ancient route in his forthcoming *Nicotiana* monograph (*cf.* p. 309). Of his sixty recognized species of *Nicotiana*, sixteen occur in Australia, the remainder being strictly American, except for those economic and ornamental species which modern man transferred to the Old World, there are no Eurasian or African species other than a few man-distributed ones. I ignore the strange claims of WIENER regarding *Nicotiana* in Africa. He knew no botany and could not yet be aware that *N. rustica* L. and *N. tabacum* L. are hybrids of American origin. The parents of these two hybrids never extended beyond the limits of the Americas, yet the two hybrid forms were spread, more or less all over North and South America, by the American Indians who detected and propagated them simply because both were better for the purposes for which they were used than any of the parent species. There are other data available in such authoritative works as those of REICHE(5) for Chile and COCKAYNE(6) for New Zealand. There is an increasing amount of evidence that certain genera reached the Polynesian islands (as well as the parts of the southern hemisphere above mentioned) directly from ancient Antarctica, but this subject I am forced to leave to others for development. Some very significant data appear in a paper by Dr. VAN STEENIS, just published as these proofs were being read (6a).

Anti-de Candolle Theorists:— It now develops that some leaders, in certain fields, clearly have no confidence in DE CANDOLLE's beautifully balanced, logical, highly critical and classic *Origin of Cultivated Plants*. ALPHONSE DE CANDOLLE, primarily a taxonomist, was unusually well equipped, both by education and experience, to deal with all aspects of this complex subject, excepting only the genetics of cultivated plants, a subject developed for the most part within the present century. He had no preconceived ideas when he initiated his investigations of the wide range of problems involved. He obviously had a logical mind, which is more than we can say for some of our contemporaries who, nonchalantly and on the basis of inadequate training and knowledge, consider him to be unworthy of consideration. Those who deliberately exclude the classic *Origin of Cultivated Plants* from their bibliographies and recommended reading lists simply tempt fate. One gets the impression that they do not wish unsuspecting readers to realize that there is another totally different side of the story. As MANGELSDORF and OLIVER stated the case, in 1951, in their paper "Whence Came Maize to Asia": "Basically . . . the lines are drawn between those who are short on facts and use them uncritically (although with superb imagination) and those who demand evidence and valid reasoning."

These modern proponents of the imaginative theories can in no way be compared with DE CANDOLLE as an authority, for they all argue on the basis of inadequate training in some fields and lack of knowledge and experience in others. The sequence as I see it, with us in America, runs from the thoroughly exposed and discredited ideas of Dr. O. F. COOK on origin and distribution, next, to one of his admirers who knows hardly the rudiments of simple botany, then to one of the latter's disciples or converts who knows even less botany, and finally to a specialist in another field who became infected with COOK's ideas, at second or third hand.

This is where I enter the picture. I know little geography, other than what I have picked up during fifty-five years of active work in plant taxonomy (chiefly in the Asiatic, Malaysian, and Polynesian

---

5) REICHE, K. Grundzüge der Pflanzenverbreitung in Chile. *In* ENGLER und DRUDE. Vegetation der Erde 8: 1-374. Illus. 1907.

6) COCKAYNE, L. The Vegetation of New Zealand, ed. 2. *Op. cit.* 14: i-xxvi. 1-456. Illus. 1928.

6a) STEENIS, C. G. G. J. van Results of the Archbold Expeditions. Papuan *Nothofagus*. Jour. Arnold Arb. 34: 301-374. pl. 1. fig. 1-22. Oct. 15, 1953.

regions) and as a result of my extensive tropical experience in both hemispheres and my extensive travel record in the Old World tropics. My geographical knowledge is supplemented by a limited knowledge of the philology of native plant names, involving some 15,000 different plant names used in the Philippines and several thousand others used in China, Indo-China, Malaysia and many parts of Micronesia and Polynesia. I may also bring to bear an acquaintance with the contents of a wide range of published accounts of travellers and explorers, from ancient times to the decline of sailing ships, in the nineteenth century, a bit of archaeology, anthropology, ethnology, historical geology and allied sciences, as well as considerable first hand information pertaining to tropical phytogeography and ecology in both hemispheres.

I roundly object to and disavow the beliefs of that handful of modern detractors of DE CANDOLLE who cast to the winds his sound ideas on the origin and distribution of cultivated food plants, and substitute unsound theories which are not only strange but utterly illogical. DE CANDOLLE proved his points on the basis of a vast amount of special data, which he was competent by training and experience to evaluate; he presented both sides of the argument, where differences of opinion existed. Our modern dissenters, in general insufficiently trained and experienced, usually choose only what supports the one side of the problem they present.

This unfortunate trend is not due wholly to the ultra-departmentalism that now characterizes our large educational and research institutions. The worst offenders, amongst these theorizers, are found in what I dub "neogeography" (and this is not to be interpreted as a reflection on the various branches of legitimate geography) : it is they who most recklessly cut across a whole series of related fields in most of which they have had little or no experience, and in which they are actually incapable of drawing conclusions. In many cases, as will be shown below, a proper and skilled handling of the facts would prove exactly the contrary of what they have tried to establish.

Imagined Wisdom without Understanding:— At one time during the preparation of the manuscript of this memoir, I became intrigued with the phrase: "Imagined Wisdom without Understanding" as a possible title for the work. But I abandoned the idea because it was not sufficiently descriptive of the included subject matter. Yet, it describes aptly the published opinions of those individuals to whose views I take exception. I became familiar with the phrase through FERNALD's(7) review of W. A. CRAIGIE and J. R. HULBERT's *A Dictionary of American English on Historical Principles,* published by the University of Chicago Press, beginning in 1938. As a title for his utterly devastating review, this very descriptive four word phrase was used. It was an abbreviation of the title of a baccalaureate sermon which, as a boy, he had copied for his father, the full text being: "Wisdom is the principal thing; therefore get wisdom; and with all thy getting,

---

7) FERNALD, M. L. Imagined Wisdom without Understanding. Rhodora 46: 312-315. 1944.

get understanding." He confined his attention to the colloquial or so-called common names of plants appearing in the first half of volume one, speaking of the work as "seemingly authoritative." If other subjects were handled with the same lack of skill and understanding characteristic of the plant names, it might be disastrous to analyze entries in other fields too closely. Yet, the work is accepted as authoritative.

I call attention to yet another case of gross errors that an inexperienced lexicographer made while venturing into the field of plant taxonomy. The volume in question was prepared by E. H. CRISWELL*(8)*. Dr. JONES's*(9)* review of this venture into taxonomy is as devastating as is FERNALD's treatment of the CRAIGIE and HULBERT work. He says, *inter alia*: "When the author ventures into the botanical field . . . he loses the trees in the forest . . . many of his results and conclusions are nothing less than ludicrous", and concluded: "It is a pity that the science of systematic botany has to bear the burden of such unripe scholarship." After reading the review, one cannot escape the conclusion that this thesis should never have been published, as it reflects no credit upon the author, nor upon the competence of those who directed the preparation of the text, those who edited it, or those who published it.

Were I a teacher in botany, or in any of the allied sciences, both of these reviews would be required reading for all students who might wish to take graduate work under my supervision; no better illustrations of misinterpretations could be found.

In Defense of the Term "Neogeography":— Occasionally, I have perhaps over-used the term "neogeography". My use of it should in no way be interpreted as being disparaging to what we might call the normal geographical sciences such as economic, physical, political, social geography, etc., and their ramifications. I use "neogeography" in a very restricted sense, to denote a very active and vociferous school in the United States which, basically geographic in scope, is characterized by having leaders who insist on pontificating in fields in which their ignorance is abysmal. Some of the fields of science which suffer most are: taxonomy, biogeography, other branches of biology, and the history of exploration and commerce. In addition to mistreating these fields, the "neogeographers" exhibit an astounding lack of knowledge of early publications and available manuscripts. The strange thing is that this small group works in a branch of geography recognized as historical geography. In considering the views of two individuals, I find that in their lectures and papers the historical method is scarcely indicated, being replaced by inferences and the citation of references supporting what they want to believe. The most detailed, logical, well documented and fully trustworthy publication on the origin of cultivated plants, to which I referred above, is not even listed in

---

8) CRISWELL, E. H. LEWIS and CLARK: Linguistic Pioneers. Univ. Missouri Linguistic Studies 15: i-ccxii. 1-102. 1940.

9) JONES, G. N. LEWIS and CLARK: Linguistic Pioneers. Rhodora 43: 92-94. 1941.

most of their bibliographies. The result is catastrophic, for the non-trained reader will acquire grossly distorted views.

It is, in reality, a very simple matter to point out weaknesses in the arguments of these theorists. Some of the claims made are actually grotesque. In a number of cases, they apparently never sought advice, when all they would have had to do would be to make a simple telephone call to well informed specialists, in some cases, within the walls of their own institutions. Whether they realize it or not, they do not enhance their own standing, locally, nationally, or internationally; nor do some of their extraordinary claims reflect credit on the institutions they represent. In this "neogeographic" group, as a whole, the impression conveyed, by their often erroneous claims, is that they feel that they must expound their personal beliefs without even trying to correlate what they consider to be correct with known, factual data in allied fields of research. This, to me, is very dangerous ultra-departmentalism. Geography is indeed an inclusive field of knowledge; but, occasionally, it seems a field "in which a noisy man gets prestige", as a former botanical colleague, now at the University of California, expresses it very concisely.

Acknowledgments:— The opinions expressed in this volume are my own, and I assume full responsibility for them. Yet they are, by no means, merely personal ones. All conclusions have been checked by a careful and critical consideration of all the information that has been available to me. In many cases, I have sought the opinions of thoroughly qualified specialists, and not merely of those whom I knew would agree with me. I have expressed my opinions without fear or favor when, in my judgment and that of specialists with whom I have discussed various items, all available data point to an unavoidable conclusion.

I am particularly grateful to Dr. and Mrs. FRANS VERDOORN for the time they have devoted to making my rough draft copy ready for press. On their advice, rather acrimonious criticisms of a number of authors have been, somewhat reluctantly, omitted. Yet, I agree, often all that is necessary is to quote certain passages from their works, for these speak for themselves. Then, I was again fortunate, for Dr. RICHARD EVANS SCHULTES, by no means a tyro in the field of economic and systematic botany in tropical South America, returned from field work just in time to read and improve much of the text, for which I am very grateful. Then I am much indebted to my long-time co-worker, Dr. LILY M. PERRY, for the help given with proof reading, etc., as well as to various members of the Editorial Board of CHRONICA BOTANICA who read sections of the proofs, particularly, Drs. F. R. FOSBERG, J. RAMSBOTTOM and C. G. G. J. VAN STEENIS.

My colleague, Professor P. C. MANGELSDORF not only went through the proofs of this memoir, but kindly made a number of helpful suggestions drawing my attention to the results of various recent, mainly genetical investigations. Dr. C. E. KOBUSKI helped me to read the original rough drafts.

I am under special obligations to several members of the staff of the British Museum (Natural History) who, at my request after my return from a very fruitful half year, spent mostly in that institution in 1951, consulted various BANKS and SOLANDER specimens, unpublished letters and other documents for me. These include Dr. GEORGE TAYLOR, Mr. A. H. G. ALSTON, Mr. A. W. EXELL, Mr. W. T. STEARN, all senior staff members of the Department of Botany, as well as Mr. A. C. TOWNSEND, Librarian of the Museum. Mr. SPENCER SAVAGE, retired secretary of the Linnean Society of London, kindly supplied pertinent information regarding certain specimens preserved, not only in the Linnean herbarium but also in the Sir JAMES SMITH herbarium, both at Burlington House in London. Mr. H. STANSFIELD, of the Liverpool Museum, has kindly assisted me in matters pertaining to the FORSTER botanical material acquired by the Liverpool Botanical

Garden in the very early part of the last century. I am, indeed, most deeply grateful to Mr. I. H. BURKILL, whose knowledge of the history of plant introduction into India and of the origin and dissemination of economic plants in the Indo-Malaysian-Polynesian regions is unsurpassed.

In the United States, important data have been provided by Dr. E. B. COPELAND and Dr. T. HARPER GOODSPEED, of the University of California at Berkeley. Dr. HAROLD ST. JOHN, of the University of Hawaii, and Dr. F. R. FOSBERG, now in Washington, D. C., generously assisted me in relation to certain Polynesian plant problems with which I became involved. Dr. JOSEPH EWAN, of Tulane University, New Orleans, has provided historical data pertaining to the J. R. and G. FORSTER collection preserved in Philadelphia. In tropical America, Dr. LOUIS O. WILLIAMS, of the Escuela Agricola Panamericana at Tegucigalpa, Honduras, with an unusually wide botanical experience both in Brazil and in all the Central American republics, has been of material assistance. Dr. JUNIUS J. BIRD of the American Museum of Natural History has kindly provided special information regarding the plant remains found in his remarkable "dig" at Huaca Prieta, Peru, a site constantly inhabited from pre-pottery times to about 1600 A.D.

It seems most fitting to dedicate this memoir to Mr. HENRY ALLEN MOE, the discerning and sympathetic Secretary of the JOHN SIMON GUGGENHEIM Memorial Foundation, in appreciation of his rare judgment in guiding the selection of GUGGENHEIM Fellows. His unique qualifications and breadth of view I have learned to esteem in my long period of service as a referee for applications for grants in the plant sciences and related disciplines, from residents of Canada and the United States, and as a member of the Selective Committee for applications, in all fields, covering Latin America.

The **SIMPLING MACARONI.**

Like Soland-Goose from frozen Zone I wander.
On shallow Banks grows fat Sol......

Pub accor to Act by JMarly Strand July 13th. 1772

TEXT FIGURE 2. — DANIEL CARL SOLANDER (1736-1782), contemporary caricature, etching, ca. 1772. — "The Simpling Macaroni is an etched whole-length portrait of SOLANDER, standing in profile to our right, holding in one hand a large flowering plant, and in the other a naturalist's knife, on the blade of which is written the maker's name, SAVIGNY.... He appears to be speaking.... It was the day of the Macaronis, who amused the town for a long season with published pictures of dandies and other eccentrics. BANKS and SOLANDER were, of course, lawful prey: with their renown in hitherto undiscovered trifles.... The term signifies 'a compound dish made of vermicelli and other pastes, universally used in Italy. It came into England at the beginning of the last peace' (Macaroni and Theatrical Magazine, October, 1772). The word was introduced at Almack's, and the subscribers came to be described as Macaronis. Originally aimed at luxury and extravagance, it eventually came to mean any person who exceeded the ordinary bounds of fashion and fell into absurdity in consequence. For more upon the Macaronis see *Annals of a Yorkshire House* (London, 1911)..." (EDW. SMITH, The Life of Sir JOSEPH BANKS, London and New York, 1911, p. 176, who reproduces also a caricature of BANKS as "the Fly Catching Macaroni"). — *Courtesy of the Trustees of the British Museum.*

Chapter I

INTRODUCTION

> "As I grow older, I realize how limited a part reason
> has in the conduct of men. They believe what they want
> to—and, although liable to shipwreck, they very generally
> get off with a hole in the bottom of their boat and stick an
> old coat into that". (Chief Justice HOLMES, in a letter to
> HAROLD LASKI).

Among the first botanical collections, made in the Pacific Islands
(including New Zealand), were those prepared by the botanists and
collectors on Captain JAMES COOK's three exploring expeditions around
the world, from 1768 to 1780(1). The collections of the three voyages
were neither small nor insignificant, and three of the collectors were
trained botanists, or, at least, naturalists. The fourth was the
younger FORSTER, a boy, seventeen years old when he sailed from England on COOK's second voyage as an assistant to his father. As I will
show, the long overlooked significance of these early collections actually argues devastatingly against the theories which are currently
being advanced by certain authors, all of whom are botanically untrained and inexperienced. Their views, as would be supposed, differ
widely from any conclusions that one can legitimately draw from a
consideration of the Polynesian plants collected in the decade following
Captain COOK's first visit to Tahiti. An early collection of botanical
specimens, with complete locality and collector information and dates,
is, after all, something tangible. Evidence of this kind is decisive, and
fatal to dreamy and unsupported ideas as to when and by whom a
given exotic species (various cultivated economic ones and weeds)
were introduced into insular areas. These collections are still extant
for consultation, if one doubts the identity of any single species among
those recorded in botanical literature. We could hope for no better
source of information than this.

In this memoir I have ignored the general collections made by
several botanists and collectors on Captain COOK's voyages to various
Atlantic Islands, the Cape Horn and Cape of Good Hope regions,
Australia, Java, New Zealand, and New Caledonia, and have concen-
trated on what plant species were, or were not, present on a given
Pacific Island in the decade following 1769, when the first extensive
collections were made in Tahiti. Dr. VAN STEENIS calls my attention
to the fact that COMMERSON visited Tahiti and prepared botanical collections in 1768, on *La Boudeuse* and *L'Etoile*, a year previous to
Captain COOK's arrival.

---

1) Captain JAMES COOK was killed by natives of Hawaii, Feb. 14, 1779.

I have not concerned myself in the slightest with the indigenous and endemic elements in the flora of any island. On the contrary, my interest has been confined to the very few species of natural pantropic distribution and the man-introduced cultivated plants and weeds which were known to be present in Tahiti, in New Zealand, in the Friendly Islands, in Hawaii, or elsewhere in the Orient, at the time of discovery or when the first botanical collections were studied for a given island. This may brand me as a renegade taxonomist, for why should anyone bother with the taxonomically uninteresting cultivated plants and the common weeds? The first botanists to explore the newly discovered Pacific islands were, unfortunately for some theorists, just as interested in the cultigens and the weeds, which were, for the most part, as new to them as were all of the indigenous and endemic elements. In this memoir (especially in its purely taxonomic parts) I have, of course, had to make exceptions here and there, for PARKINSON did consider certain indigenous and endemic species, as well as the exotic, man-introduced economic species and weeds.

Dr. SOLANDER prepared many manuscripts based on the plants and animals collected by BANKS and himself on Captain COOK's first voyage. His manuscript floras of Madeira, Cape of Good Hope, Java, Eastern Australia, New Zealand, Tierra del Fuego, Tahiti, and other regions then visited, are all preserved in the library of the British Museum (Natural History). Except in a very few cases, the specimens, on which his numerous descriptions were based, are available in its vast herbarium. The percentage of new genera and new species was naturally very high, for BANKS and SOLANDER were the pioneer botanical explorers (except for Madeira, Java and, to a very limited degree, Australia) of the regions above listed. Unfortunately, these SOLANDER manuscripts were never published and, as will be demonstrated later, the two FORSTERS (father and son), who served as naturalists on Captain COOK's second voyage, liberally helped themselves to SOLANDER's manuscript data, when they initiated work on their own collections, after their return to London, in 1776 (FIG. 1).

Of interest in this connection are two letters from LINNAEUS to J. ELLIS. The first of these was dated Uppsala, August 8, 1771, when LINNAEUS learned through ELLIS of SOLANDER's safe return from Captain COOK's voyage around the world; the other, dated December 22, 1771, when he received news, from the same source, of the projected plans for the second expedition (*ia*). It is well known that Dr. SOLANDER (FIG. 2 and PLATE 89) was a very poor correspondent.

"I received about an hour ago, my ever valued friend, yours of the 16th of July, nor did I ever receive a more welcome letter, as it conveys the welcome news of my dear Solander's safe return. Thanks and glory to God, who has protected him through the dangers of such a voyage! If I were not bound fast here by 64 years of age, and a wornout body, I would this very day set out for London, to see this great hero in botany. Moses was not permitted to enter Palestine, but only to view it from a distance: so I conceive an idea in my mind of the

---

1a) SMITH, J. E. A Selection of the Correspondence of LINNAEUS and other Naturalists, 2 vol. 1821.

acquisitions and treasures of those who have visited every part of the globe." (p. 264).

"I have just read, in some foreign newspapers, that our friend Solander intends to revisit those new countries, discovered by Mr. Banks and himself, in the ensuing spring. This report has affected me so much, as almost entirely to deprive me of sleep. How vain are the hopes of man! Whilst the whole botanical world, like myself, has been looking for the most transcendent benefits to our science, from the unrivalled exertions of your countrymen, all their matchless and truly astonishing collection, such as has never been seen before, nor may ever be seen again, is to be put aside untouched, to be thrust into some corner, to become perhaps the prey of insects and of destruction.

"I have every day been figuring to myself the occupations of my pupil Solander, now putting his collection in order, having first arranged and numbered his plants, in parcels, according to the places where they were gathered, and then written upon each specimen its native country, and appropriate number. I then fancied him throwing the whole into classes; putting aside, and naming, such as were already known; ranging others under known genera, with specific differences; and distinguishing by new names and definitions such as formed new genera, with their species. Thus, thought I, the world will be delighted and benefited by all these discoveries; and the foundations of true science will be strengthened, so as to endure through all generations.

"I am under great apprehension, that if this collection should remain untouched till Solander's return, it might share the same lot as Forskall's Arabian specimens at Copenhagen. Thus shall I be only more and more confirmed in my opinion, that the Fates are ever adverse to the greatest undertakings of mankind.

"Solander promised long ago, while detained off the coast of Brazil, in the early part of his voyage, that he would visit me after his return; of which I have been in expectation. If he had brought some of his specimens with him, I could at once have told him what were new; and we might have turned over books together, and he might have been informed or satisfied upon many subjects, which after my death will not be easily explained." (p. 267-268).

It is, I think, of much more than passing interest to note that, on the long voyage of the *Endeavour* (PLATE 81) scurvy was controlled by the intelligent use of antiscorbutics then known. The subject is briefly discussed here because it does have a very definite bearing on certain strange ideas, held by some scientists, as to when advanced cultures, cultivated plants and even weeds were distributed in the Pacific regions.

Among the ninety-five men of all ranks, including the eleven civilians, who left Plymouth on the *Endeavour*, August 26, 1768, which anchored in the Downs, July 13, 1771, after an absence of nearly three years, there were no deaths from scurvy. This was the terrible scourge that often affected the crews of all sailing ships bound on long voyages. On the *Endeavour*, three were drowned, two were frozen to death on Staten Island, and two died of natural causes before the ship reached Batavia, Java, nearly two years after leaving England. The two and one half months that the *Endeavour* remained at Batavia, for necessary refitting, were disastrous; during and following this stay, thirty-one individuals died. These deaths were mostly due to malaria and dysentery, against which preventive methods and cures were then unknown. In the normal course of events, a high percentage of deaths was the expected thing on all long voyages, particularly those from Europe to Asia and Malaysia and return, as well as on the dreadful voyages of the Spanish galleons between Acapulco and Manila and return (*cf.* p. 231).

Aided by BANKS and SOLANDER, two good botanists, Captain COOK and his staff were able to utilize the vegetable resources of the various islands visited in a more effective way than any previous expedition. BANKS and SOLANDER, in this connection, paid attention to all plants they could find. It is worthy of note that SYDNEY PARKINSON, an artist on Captain COOK's first voyage, gave special attention to the economic plants observed by him in Tahiti during the three months which he spent there in 1769 (his observations were published in 1773). The younger FORSTER also gave special attention to the edible plants of the same island during his shorter stay there on COOK's second voyage. He made this subject the basis of his thesis in 1786. We are safe in assuming, I believe, that these two men overlooked very few species in the accessible parts of the region. (PLATE 80).

To quote from Captain COOK's *Narrative*: "Many of my people, officers as well as seamen, at first disliked celery, scurvy-grass, etc., being boiled in the peas and wheat; and some refused to eat it; but as this had no effect on my conduct, this obstinate kind of prejudice, by little and little, wore off; they began to like it as well as the others, and now, I believe, there was hardly a man in the ship who did not attribute our being so free of the scurvy, to the beer and vegetables we made use of at New Zealand; after this, I seldom found it necessary to order any of my people to gather vegetables whenever we came where any were to be got, and if scarce, happy was he who could lay hold of them first." (*cf.* R. S. ALLISON's *Sea Diseases* . . . 1943, where interesting data about the antiscorbutics used on COOK's expeditions will be found).

In 1949 I thought that I had written my last paper on the general subject as to the dates and by whom a very limited number of important economic cultivated plants were distributed between the two hemispheres(2). The score still stands at three or four species only that occurred widely in both hemispheres before 1520. And now I will demonstrate that the same distribution story applies to weeds of American origin, now dominant all over the Old World tropics, and those of Old World origin that have become established in tropical America. In the plant kingdom what species was or was not present on a given island when it was discovered, or was first botanically explored, is most important, for here is a series of comforting or disconcerting facts, depending on what an individual may wish to prove. No matter what one may think of the value, or the lack of value, of dried botanical specimens (which some laboratory workers very lightly brush aside), those who theorize on the ethnology or the ethnobotany of the Pacific Islands, ignoring the plant evidence, do so at great risk.

The same statement applies to those who insist that certain significant species of cultivated food plants had been carried by man, from one hemisphere to the other, long before the time of COLUMBUS and MAGELLAN. No matter what they now think, all of them need to re-evaluate the basis of their positively expressed and supported beliefs. Certainly there never was such a thing as a "Pacific Regatta", as MANGELSDORF and OLIVER have so aptly expressed it in disproving a claim that maize was present in India in pre-Columbian times. As late as 1952, one of the originators of the idea that a popcorn was present in India long before the Europeans reached that part of the world asks "whether it might have crossed the Pacific in very early pre-Columbian times". There was not an inkling that he had any knowledge of the old Portuguese route, from eastern Brazil direct to Goa, initiated in 1500 and continued for 165 years. Unfortunately for this theory, Dr. MANGELSDORF, in 1951, was able to match the kernels of several of the Assamese varieties, in size, shape and color, with a single collection of Colombian popcorns. All that is now needed is

2) MERRILL, E. D. Observations on Cultivated Plants with Reference to Certain American Problems. Ceiba 1: 3-36. 1950.

to survey the popcorn varieties characteristic of the bulge of Brazil, but even such a survey would seem to me to be unnecessary in view of the thousands of Portuguese ships that traversed this old route between 285 and 450 years ago. This Assam popcorn never crossed the Pacific but rather the Atlantic, thence to India (and in relatively modern times, *i.e.*, after 1500)!

Those among the younger theorists (and, for that matter, some of our older, presumably more experienced and better informed specialists) who speculate on when and how man and his commensals reached various parts of the world, take altogether too much for granted in reference to the Pacific region. One sometimes suspects that untravelled individuals (and curiously a high percentage of the theorists involved have had little or no personal experience in the Pacific basin), in these modern days, may be misled in their judgment by thinking how long it now takes to cross, from one side of the Pacific to the other, by modern liners or by air. They forget what the situation was in the days of sailing ships, from the fifteenth through the early nineteenth centuries.

Before MAGELLAN entered the Pacific in 1520, in what we would now call a primitive sailing ship, the situation was much worse, for then there were only primitive rafts and dugout canoes; later, outrigger canoes; followed, still later, by the double canoes (catamarans) with built-up sides. There were more advanced types of ships in Japan, China, Malaysia and India, but of a type which scarcely could make very long transoceanic voyages successfully.

The disregarding of early transportation conditions is, indeed, a convenient method of bypassing debatable assumptions, such as: (1) the transmission of seeds of an Asiatic species of cotton from Asia (India) *direct* to America by man at a very early date (the time has been illogically stretched by some to 2,000 to 3,000 years); (2) the presence of maize in India in pre-MAGELLAN times; (3) a historical geographer's belief that the now dominant weeds of American origin in the Pacific Islands and in Malaysia were there long before the Europeans appeared on the scene; and, (4) the idea (among certain anthropologists and, apparently, accepted by at least some historical geographers) that pre-Columbian advanced cultures in America came across the Pacific (without a single Old World basic food plant or, at least, without more than two or three species).

In sharp contrast to all this is the fantastic idea, developed by O. F. COOK, according to which agriculture was older in America than in the Old World. He believed that the South American Indians, in pre-historic times, occupied Polynesia, taking their basic food plants with them and hinted that they not only reached Malaysia but even Madagascar. In recent times, we have HEYERDAHL following this lead in his *American Indians in the Pacific* (1952).

In this connection it should be noted that, in the Pacific, the islands (at least most of those in the so-called Polynesian triangle) were not occupied, even by primitive man, until relatively late. This Dr. BUCK has rather conclusively shown in his studies of the expansion of the Polynesian people. Failing to find confirmation for erratic beliefs in

Polynesian archeology, the extremists can think only of *direct* communication between Asia (India) and America to explain what they want to believe. Some even eliminate possible visits to the Pacific Islands in transit! That there were occasional and accidental associations between the peoples of Polynesia and America, and even occasional ones between the American Indians and the eastern Polynesian islands, actually must be accepted; but most certainly there was no "Pacific Regatta" in either direction.

While in some of my earlier papers, some erroneous deductions were drawn, partly because of my lack of experience and partly because of my lack of certain documents due to the limited library facilities in Manila, there very likely may be a few unwarranted claims in my paper of 1950 and possibly in this memoir; but such errors are certainly very few, and I have done all in my power to eliminate them. Contrary to my earlier attempts I have seriously tried to limit this work to a consideration of the plant evidence alone, for this is a field in which I am at home.

Were it not that in 1952 certain authors, with at most merely a very superficial knowledge of taxonomy, plant geography, ecology and of the annals of early exploration (to say nothing of the early annals of botany), reached very different conclusions from those expressed in this memoir and elsewhere, there would have been no reason whatever for the preparation of several chapters of this work.

To me, it is most unfortunate that a certain geographer (my classification is "neogeographer") and a geneticist chose to publish popular books on the subject, as recently as 1952. The false claims, made by both writers, actually led me back to this controversial field. These two small volumes were to me an indication of brashness, bred by ignorance, and an invitation to answer certain claims which I consider to be false.

My own factual data, greatly reinforced by the notes I made in 1951 in the archives of the British Museum, are in practically all respects directly opposed to the claims of these authors. As I see this phase of the picture, the contrast is between historical specimens, supplemented by hard facts from early records, on the one hand, and pure imagination and wishful thinking, on the other. One of these authors challenged me to "put up or shut up" and in preparing this, my last work, I am taking up the challenge and I will restate the case as I interpret it. If I be reasonably correct in my ideas, those who oppose my conclusions are guilty of a series of gross errors.

It is frankly not expected that any of those specialists or non-specialists, with whose conclusions I disagree, will be greatly impressed by the new evidence I have developed. It is based on an extensive series of relatively old (175 to 185 years), dried plant specimens which are still preserved and available to all competent individuals for study, in addition to unpublished and very extensive manuscripts, as old as the specimens themselves. The important fact to keep in mind is that these early collections clearly indicate which species of exotics (cultivated plants and weeds) *were* and *were not* present on a given island, at the time or times that the collections were made. It is also not expected that my exposure of the misquotations, partial quotations and misinterpretations of these theorists will have the slightest effect on their beliefs; they will continue on their respective ways heedless of some old dried plants (really comprehensive collections) which some taxonomists prepared nearly two centuries ago, and which their successors fortunately, or perhaps unfortunately, carefully preserved over the years!

It will be useless to argue that these first botanical collectors, within the Polynesian triangle, ignored the cultivated plants and weeds. That, wherever they botanized, they did give proper attention to these groups, now normally more or less ignored, is proven by the completeness of their collections and the SOLANDER and FORSTER descriptive data. Furthermore, it is unnecessary to argue that, when they botanized on islands other than Tahiti, they frankly recorded the fact in a journal entry when they found nothing new. That the botanists, and others, on Captain COOK's first and second voyages, were interested in economic plants, whether introduced or indigenous, is again proven by PARKINSON's consideration of the economic species in 1773 (Captain COOK's first voyage) and the younger FORSTER's doctorate thesis, published in 1786, entitled *De plantis esculentis insularum oceani Australis*, a volume of eighty pages, based on specimens collected, within the Polynesian triangle, on COOK's second voyage.

It has been suggested that perhaps the two FORSTERs, who did the botanical work on Captain COOK's second voyage, may have had instructions to ignore the weeds. Yet, Mr. ALSTON could find nothing in Sir JOSEPH BANKS's correspondence that would confirm this. A comparison of the lists of species, collected on the two voyages, demonstrates that the two FORSTERs, on the second voyage, gave as much attention to the cultigens and the weeds as did BANKS and SOLANDER, on the first voyage. It must be kept in mind that the botanists and collectors, on the three voyages of Captain COOK, naturally operated, in large part, in the rather densely populated areas, where cultigens and weeds are normally abundant; in these populated areas very few plant species would ordinarily be overlooked. This would be particularly true for the coastal areas and the river valley adjacent to Matavai Bay in Tahiti.

My memoir may be summarized by this statement: *the botanical evidence clearly indicates that, as of 1769, all the cultigens in the Pacific Islands, with possibly one exception, and all the more numerous weed species, with possibly two or three exceptions, were brought in purposely or inadvertently from the west by the early people who occupied the Polynesian triangle.* The very few exceptions come from tropical America. Thus, for this extensive area, we need not go back beyond COOK's first voyage, for 1769 was the year in which he initiated the modern period of active plant introduction into the Pacific basin.

Here, I must state, I ignore the independent and earlier introduction of many Mexican species into Guam via the Spanish galleon line commencing immediately after 1565 and extending to 1815. There is every reason to believe that, during the expansion over their extensive area, especially when their long voyages of exploration were being made, an occasional traveller reached the west coast of America and that some returned to their island homes, but *there is no valid evidence that any of the important cultigens of American origin became universally distributed in both hemispheres in pre-Columbian or pre-Magellan times.*

And, most curiously, the pioneer large-scale Portuguese operations from 1500 on (Brazil to Goa, and beyond *via* the Cape of Good Hope) do not change the picture as to tropical Asia — and this stands regardless of any claims for a peculiar type of peanut in southeastern China, maize in India, the common marigold in India, and various *Cucurbita* cultigens here and there in Asia in pre-Columbian times. In this last case it is evident that, as I discuss in detail elsewhere, some investigators were misled by the term "Malabar" and "Siamese" gourds, in apparent ignorance of the fact that the Portuguese first occupied the Malabar coast immediately following 1500, and soon thereafter established a trading station in Siam, introducing certain Brazilian cultigens.

Curiously enough, the most important Portuguese period of expansion is almost universally ignored by botanists and others, although in the history of man-distributed plant species it is of the utmost importance. Two years after their first reaching India by sea in 1498, they accidentally discovered Brazil. For somewhat more than 160 years there was a direct and, for certain seasons at least, a very much travelled commercial route, actually initiated in 1500, from Lisbon to eastern Brazil and thence via the Cape of Good Hope *direct* to Goa, on the Malabar coast of India. Goa is still a Portuguese possession, although its glory has long since vanished. The Portuguese immediately established colonies in South Africa (and, here and there, on the east and west coasts of Africa) and explored a part of Madagascar. In a surprisingly few years they had established themselves at Cochin, Goa, and elsewhere in India, Ceylon, Malacca (1511), the Moluccas (1512-1514) and Siam, explored the Red Sea and the Gulf of Persia, reached Canton (1517), founded Macao (1557), which they still control, and, from this as a centre, they operated extensively in Formosa and Japan.

When one theorizes as to when a given American cultigen reached China, India, or Malaysia, one cannot afford to ignore: (1) the initial and most remarkable period of Portuguese colonial trade and missionary expansion in the Orient; (2) that they opened up the first direct route for the transmission of American economic species and weeds from the eastern coast of South America to the western coast of India, 65 years before the Spaniards initiated the colonization of the Philippines, operating from the *western* coast of Mexico; (3) that the Portuguese were thoroughly established in all the oriental places above mentioned, from one or two to five or six decades before Spain became active in Philippine colonization. One suspects that some of the biological and geographical theorists have been blinded by rash guesses of various anthropologists concerning early expeditions from India to North and South America, by which advanced cultures were brought to our backward American Indians, several thousand years ago, across the Pacific Ocean.

Were a really critical study to be made of the Portuguese *versus* Spanish operations in plant transfers between the two hemispheres, in these early colonial years, I should not be surprised if the Portuguese total might not be larger than the Spanish one. They operated for a shorter period (about 165 years), but the number of their ships was very great, and quickly developing a route, by way of Brazil, they covered a vast area in the Orient, on many of their outward voyages, extending from East Africa and Madagascar to the Red Sea and from the Gulf of Persia to India, Ceylon, Siam, Malacca, the Moluccas, Canton and Macao in China, Formosa and Japan. They reached, and were operating in all of these regions, before the Spanish began their colonization of the Philippines in 1565.

The Spaniards initiated the galleon route from Mexico to the Philippines and return, in 1565, both the eastward and westward trips being by way of Guam. Normally only one ship was dispatched in each direction, each year, sometimes two, rarely three. We know the approximate number of tropical American species (115) introduced into Guam, before the galleon line was discontinued in 1815, as well as the corresponding figures for the Philippines (200). This Spanish-sponsored shipping line lasted for 250 years. There has, however, been no intensive study of the Portuguese plant transfers, and it is now probably too late to make even an approximate estimate, at least as to the number of weeds of Brazilian origin, which were established in Indo-Malaysia, at early dates (after 1500). But that extensive introductions from Brazil were made in the Portuguese colonies in India, Ceylon, Malaysia and curiously even in Formosa and elsewhere, is manifest, to say nothing of South, East and West Africa.

Here is a little sidelight on local oriental history that likewise should not be forgotten. The Spaniards established their headquarters at Cebu in the Philippines in 1565. The Portuguese, already established in the Moluccas to the south of the Philippine group, some five decades earlier, also operated, on a limited scale, in the southern Philippines and naturally attempted to hamper the Spaniards in establishing their projected colony. This was the reason why the pioneer Spanish colonists soon abandoned Cebu and transferred their headquarters first to Panay and, in 1571, only six years after initiating their projected colonization at Cebu, centered all of their operations farther north, at Manila on the west coast of Luzon. But neither the earlier Portuguese incursions into the oriental tropics, beginning in 1498 and 1500, nor the Spanish occupation of the Philippines, six and a half decades later, can be neglected; both nations were pioneers in the actual distribution between the two hemispheres of the two groups of man's commensals, the cultigens and weeds. This process, initiated some four hundred and fifty years ago (*not earlier*, except on a very limited scale), is still active and will doubtless continue indefinitely, for modern man has long since become the greatest single agency in the distribution of plants throughout the world.

In my judgment, and on the basis of my long tropical experience,

I cannot correlate the strange trans-Pacific diffusion ideas with what can be definitely proven from the existing records of the non-transmission of man's plant and animal commensals from Asia to America, and *vice versa*, in pre-Magellan times. These ideas are based on three plants: the coconut, the sweet potato and the gourd.

Before 1520, the *coconut*, rather definitely of Old World origin and very largely man-distributed, had reached the west coast of America and was established on the west coast of Panama, and probably as far south as Ecuador, but only along the coast. When one quotes the word "Peru" from early records we may dismiss the modern idea of Peru, because the coconut palm will not thrive on dry coasts and, in early colonial times, the term "Peru" applied to most of the Pacific coastal area of South America (*cf.* p. 266).

The *sweet potato* had been distributed from South America all over the Polynesian triangle, as far south as New Zealand and even parts of Papuasia, by the twelfth or thirteenth century. Still quoted by the true believers in the fantastic diffusion theories is one of LAUFER's early papers, where, confusing a Chinese yam (*Dioscorea*) with it (*cf.* p. 307), he claimed that the sweet potato was in China long before MAGELLAN's time. But they cleverly disregard his general paper of a much later date, in which he reversed himself and definitely shows that there were no American cultigens in China until after the arrival of the Europeans. There may well have been some Portuguese introductions following 1517, after these pioneer explorers reached Canton, but most of them came by way of Manila.

And the third cultivated plant, the *gourd* (normally not a food plant) was from the earliest times in tropical and temperate America, Africa and Asia, being naturally taken up by primitive peoples as a cultivated plant because of the usefulness of its dried fruits as convenient containers (*cf.* p. 255 and 264).

These are the three plants on which the trans-Pacific migration idea is based, and these are the only ones of which we are certain. Only one of them made the grade of being more or less universally cultivated in both hemispheres in pre-Columbian times. I can only conclude that three species out of many hundreds, seems not enough on which to base such a revolutionary theory.

The records at the British Museum (Natural History), assembled by BANKS and SOLANDER on COOK's first voyage (1768-1771) and by the two FORSTERS on COOK's second voyage (1772-1775), tell us, indeed, a story of unexpected interest. Tahiti was discovered by Capt. WALLIS in 1767, two years before COOK visited it; BOUGAINVILLE visited it in 1768. The four competent botanists, on COOK's two voyages, spent a total of nearly five months in the Tahiti group, and they made, for the first time, a rather thorough botanical survey of a part of the coastal plain, river valley, and neighboring hills of Tahiti proper (except the higher mountains), particularly about Matavai Bay; they also investigated some of the neighboring islands (*cf.* p. 201).

Now, before I shock the true believers by discrediting their theories of the more or less universal distribution of economic plants and weeds of American origin in the Pacific Islands in pre-Magellan days, and

by showing that the early field work of four competent botanists proves it, I merely comment that, as Dr. BUCK has so convincingly shown, Tahiti was the centre of the Polynesian culture area,
and from this centre the Polynesians extended their explorations over
an area of at least 5,000 miles from north to south, and 4,000 miles
east to west, or, as is evident, to America about 7,000 miles. I agree
with him that the *Polynesians* may have introduced the sweet potato
from South America (?) and, to add another statement which may
seem shocking, it is most certain that the Polynesians introduced the
coconut on the west coast of America between Panama and Ecuador,
not too long before the Spaniards arrived (*cf.* p. 267).

There was, in Tahiti, in 1769, as I will discuss later in greater detail, one cultivated plant of possible American origin: the sweet potato.
There were, at that time, not more than two or three weeds of possible
American origin, no matter how many there may be now (*cf.* p. 219).
The only domestic animals — the pig, dog, and fowl — had
been introduced by the Polynesians themselves from the west. There
were a fair number of Indo-Malaysian weeds (at least twenty-five
species) thoroughly established, some of which have not as yet reached
tropical America. All of their cultivated food plants (except the
sweet potato) came from the Malaysian region, and they were peculi-
arly few — the taro (*Colocasia*), three species of yams (*Dioscorea*),
the elephant ear (*Alocasia*), probably the giant taro (*Cyrtosperma*)
(it is there now, but the four early botanists did not mention it), the
banana and plantain (many varieties), the fehi banana (several varieties), all undoubtedly introduced from the west. There was also one
species each in *Abelmoschus, Abrus, Aleurites, Amaranthus, Amorphophallus, Artocarpus, Broussonetia, Cocos, Dracaena, Hibiscus,
Inocarpus, Jambosa, Lagenaria, Sesbania, Spondias*, and perhaps representatives of a few other genera of economic importance, such as
Pueraria, all from the west. There is an increasing amount of evidence
(though no real proof as yet) that the sweet potato may have originated in Africa, reached tropical America perhaps a few centuries
before the arrival of COLUMBUS and, by way of Madagascar and the
islands of the Indian Ocean, reached southern Malaysia, Papuasia,
Polynesia and even Peru.

Having provided a considerable number of factual items bearing
on this general subject, I now turn to a consideration of a few fictional
ones in the long series of proposed explanations of the peopling and
acculturation of America. The recent *Men out of Asia(3)* fantasy is
one of the worst. According to this, all advanced culture in America
came with the sailors and carpenters that were left in the Gulf
of Persia, when ALEXANDER died in 323 B. C.! Having nothing to do
and nowhere to go, they sailed in their great ships (biremes to pen-
taremes) southward along the coast of India, across the Gulf of Burma,
through the Strait of Malacca, and eastward north of Java through
Malaysia. By that time, they and their descendants had miraculous-
ly transformed their great ships into double canoes (catamarans)

3) GLADWIN, H. S. Men out of Asia, i-xv. 1-390. illus. 1947.

and so they continued eastward, across the unknown Pacific, split
into two parts, one bringing "all culture" to South America, the other
"all culture" to Central America and Mexico! It seems almost better
to revive the Atlantis and Mu theories in which, curiously enough, a
great many still implicitly believe.

As a botanist, who, some forty years ago, acquired a wide working
knowledge of the contents of a large number of early reports on Pacific
exploration, which I have recently reread rather critically, I remain
utterly unimpressed.

After all, one has to assume that the teredo existed in 323 B. C.;
for it is no accident that the outrigger and other types of canoes in
Malaysia and Polynesia were and still are drawn up on the beach
when not in use. Captain COOK comments on what the "worms" did
to the bottom of his long boat after it had been in the water for three
months at Matavai Bay, Tahiti.

Let us return to consider the Atlantis idea, which is by no means
dead. In the summer of 1951, there were various reports in the London newspapers about an expedition that set out to discover this hypothetical sunken island or continent; but aside from publicity for the
originator of the idea, nothing else was heard of it. According to
Time (Sept. 8, 1952), the lost Atlantis has been "found" all over the
world from Ceylon to Sweden and a German clergyman reported, most
positively, that he had discovered the lost Atlantis near Helgoland,
of all places! One really prefers to accept PLATO's account "as a political pamphlet about an imaginary state", but the myth still thrives
and has even grown, begetting Mu (sunk in the Pacific) and Lemuria
(sunk in the Indian Ocean). Some specialists have also done some
sinking of individual Pacific Islands to bolster up beliefs they wish to
support.

Some twenty years ago I lectured to a group of school teachers at the American Museum of Natural History in New York City on the general subject of our
cultivated plants, where they originated, and when and how they became distributed between the two hemispheres. I happened to mention the very apparent
fact that the pre-Columbian non-distribution of the basic food plants and domesticated animals, between Europe and America, clearly indicated that the hypothetical continent of Atlantis never existed. The true believers in Atlantis, or at least
the extremists, claim that the Atlanteans were a very highly cultured people who
colonized both the Mediterranean region and the Americas. This being so, they
must have had a highly developed agriculture and, as they expanded, they naturally would have taken their cultivated food plants and their domesticated animals
with them, as did the Europeans when they colonized America, following 1492. At
the end of the lecture, one of the true believers in Atlantis took me to task for
what I had said. When I pointed out again that if the hypothetical Atlanteans
were a highly civilized race, they must have had a very highly developed agriculture, the answer was as simple as it was unconvincing: "Oh, the Atlanteans were
a very highly cultured ethereal people who needed no mere food!" Thus my efforts
failed, as they will presumably fail with those theorists I criticize in this memoir.

We may smile at these stories or legends which still persist and
in which many implicitly continue to believe. Yet, we must remember that, basically, the Atlantis fable is the predecessor of the extreme
diffusionist theories. That the fantastic CHURCHWARD Mu idea was
pure fiction makes no impression on those who have accepted the ac-

count as factual. One is impressed by the apparent fact that some may feel that if they come up with a sufficiently spectacular theory, that may create a sensation in newsmagazines, it hardly matters whether the basic tenets of the new theory be true or not. Why waste time in checking this or that detail, even if there be an inkling that an accepted premise be untrue?

To quote from WASHINGTON IRVING's *Knickerbocker History of New York*, I should like to refer to his fourth chapter, in which he treats in a very humorous manner the various theories proposed in Europe, following COLUMBUS's first voyage, to explain the populating of America. It is, as IRVING expresses it, hypothetical argumentation (as is much of that proposed by our modern diffusionists and some of their allies in anthropology, geography, a few theoretical geneticists, and occasional representatives of other disciplines) which involves the early civilized peoples of the Mediterranean basin, most of the peoples of Europe, not forgetting the Japanese, Chinese, and various peoples of Asia Minor, Mesopotamia, and India. One characterization that really intrigues me is the part that certain peoples of the Holy Land hypothetically took in this trans-Atlantic migration. IRVING says: "Some writers . . . insinuate that the Canaanites, being driven by the Jews from the land of promise, were seized with such a panic that they fled without looking behind them, until, stopping to take breath, they found themselves safe in America. As they brought neither their national language, manners, nor features with them, it is supposed they left them behind in the hurry of their flight. I cannot give my faith to this opinion". But after all, this idea is no more fantastic than are some of those expressed in very modern times as to when and how economic plants were transmitted from the eastern to the western hemisphere, and *vice versa*.

There will never be even an approximate agreement, among all investigators in various fields, as to when and by whom a very few cultigens, and perhaps fewer weed species, were first spread between the two hemispheres. We may safely assume that early man was a very limited factor, and that what he accomplished in this field was accidental and not deliberate. I can see little reason for even considering that there was such a transmission of selected species across the Pacific, either directly or indirectly, although there is perhaps some valid evidence that certain associations of the peoples of Africa with those of tropical America across the Atlantic did occur in pre-Columbian times. This is not merely a personal opinion but is based on existing records of one type or another. To me, it seems, that there is much more of a chance that some of the early navigators of the Mediterranean region coming through the Straits of Gibraltar and blown into the Atlantic by adverse winds, may have brought the advanced cultures to Mexico, Central America and parts of South America.

Here, I have been most conservative as to the number of different species involved. DE CANDOLLE, our best authority, considered only 247 cultivated species. One of our leading anti-DE CANDOLLE theorists, in 1952, published a most curiously constructed list, limited to about one hundred species and lacking a great many of the really important species, but including a number that never should have been mentioned. Examples are the marigold and the dahlia. True, the two latter are cultivated for ornamental purposes, but their histories and their places of origin are known. It would have been just as logical to have included the now pantropical species of *Euphorbia*, and representatives of some scores of other genera that man has distributed, from America to Eurasia or *vice versa*, within the past five hundred years. Both the marigold and the dahlia fall in that category; the latter, as a matter of fact, first reached Asia within the past century or, at most, a century and a half. Even ROXBURGH, as late as 1832, does not mention it, and there is little that was present in those parts of India, with which he was familiar, that he missed up to 1813.

Yet in 1933-1940, AKEMINE*(4)* published his summary of the total number of cultivated species and varieties in the world, bringing the total up to the rather astonishing figure of 1837 species and 2070 varieties. These figures include many species not cultivated for food, yet the author claims that 49.95 per cent of the total listed are food plants, including, I suspect, varieties (the text is in Japanese, with a short English summary). This is a striking contrast to the shorter lists prepared by other authors. There is no more indication of Eurasian-American, pre-Columbian or pre-Magellan distributions in AKEMINE's greatly amplified list, which is by no means complete, than there is in similar, but very much shorter, lists of other authors.

---

4) AKEMINE, M. Kinds of Crop Plants under Cultivation in the World. Agr. and Hort. (Japanese) 8: 19-75. 1933; 13: 65-81, 111-116. 1933; 14: 65-81, 111-116, 73-78. 1939; 15: 1-12. 1940. Japanese text. The periodical has not been seen, the pages indicated being those of the reprints. The paper appeared in Vol. 8, Nos. 8-10. 1933; Vol. 13, Nos. 11, 12, 1938; Vol. 14, Nos. 1-3. 1939; and Vol. 15, No. 6. 1940. The promised volume on the subject, announced in the English summary of the last part, has not appeared so far as is known.

TEXT FIGURE 3 (*opposite*). — A typical page from SOLANDER's unpublished manuscript flora of Tahiti. — The annotation in the left hand margin ("*V. articulatum* Burm.") is in the handwriting of JAMES BRITTEN.

340.

tibus parvis, ovalis, acutis, apice conniventibus Corolla nulla. Germen inferum, magnum, subrotun-
do-ovatum, basi calycis indutum Styli nulli Stigmata octo, divaricatissima, reflexa, supra canali-
culata Pericarpium (adhuc immaturum) carnosum,
carnosum glabrum, subrotundum, octoloculare
Semina solitaria.

opuntioides. VISCUM Linn. Sp. pl. 1452. 4.
Hab. in Otaheite arboribus parasitica

V. articulatum
Tourn.

HEXANDRIA.

pentaphylla DIOSCOREA Linn. Sp. pl. 1462: 1. Mscr p. 462
Katu-Nuren-Kelengu Rheed. Mal. 7 p. 63 t. 34
Ubium quinquefolium Rumph. amb p. 359. t. 127.
Paa-Ura Otaheitensibus
Hab. in Otaheite
Caules teretes in adultis spinosi, sæpe rubri
Folia alterna, petiolata, quinata, in ultimis ramis
interdum ternata vel quaterna; Foliola oblongo-
lanceolata, acuta, basi in petiolulum brevem atte-
nuata, integerrima, glabra, triuncialia raro qua-
driuncialia, venosa; venis inferioribus e basi exe-
untibus
Petioli longitudine foliorum, inermes.
Bulbi axillares, subglobosi.
Pedunculi axillares solitarii, filiformes, teretes spithæ-
mae
Flores a nobis examinati, subhermaphroditi sessiles,
per totum pedunculum sparsi
Bractea dua, ovata, concava, ad basin germinis sitæ;
exterior major vix tamen lineam longa
Calyx campanulatus, ad basin usque sexpartitus, La-
cinia ovata, concava, virides; tres exteriores pau-
lo minores acutiuscula, interiores obtusæ
Corolla nulla
Filamenta sex; una alterna altius in receptaculo
sita, subulata, brevia, erecta, sterilia, tria reliqua
brevissima, capillaria, inclinata: Antheræ reni-for-
mes parva incumbentes
Germen ovato-turbinatum, trigonum, villis ferru-
gineis pubescens Styli tres brevissimi Stigmata
bifida, parva
Forte sola Varietas Dioscorea pentaphylla Linn.
Sp. pl 1462: 1

alata. DIOSCOREA. Mscr. p. 1462. Linn. Sp. pl. 1462. 4
α. Ubium vulgare Rumph. Amb. 5. p. 346: t. 120.
β. Ubium digitatum Rumph. Amb. 5. p. 350. t. 121.
γ. Ubium anguinum Rumph. Amb. 5. p. 351. t. 122
δ. Ubium anniversarium Rumph. Amb. 5. p. 353
t. 123.
Euwhi Insulanibus Oceani Pacifici.
Hab. in Otaheite, Huaheine, Uliatea, Olaha
Caules volubiles, glabri, inermes, tetragoni: angu-
lis membranaceis.

F. Polkinghorne Pascoe.

CHARACTERES

GENERUM

PLANTARUM,

QUAS

IN ITINERE

AD INSULAS

MARIS AUSTRALIS,

Collegerunt, Defcripferunt, Delinearunt,

ANNIS   MDCCLXXII——MDCCLXXV.

JOANNES REINOLDUS FORSTER, LL.D.

Societ. Reg. Scient. ut & Antiq. ap. Lond. Sodalis.

ET

GEORGIUS FORSTER.

LONDINI,

Proftant apud B. WHITE, T. CADELL, & P. ELMSLY,

MDCCLXXVI.

TEXT FIGURE 4. — Title page of the FORSTERS' *Characteres generum Plantarum.... Maris Australis* (1776) which, as all of the FORSTERS' publications, contains much material taken, without proper acknowledgments, from SOLANDER's unpublished manuscripts and probably from PARKINSON's drawings (*cf.* p. 203, 359, etc.).

Chapter II

BANKS, SOLANDER AND THE TWO FORSTERS

It had been JOSEPH BANKS' plan to accompany Capt. COOK's second voyage (1772-75), at his own expense, with an even larger corps of assistants than he had financed on the first voyage, to prosecute further natural history work in the Pacific. COCKAYNE*(1)* has summarized what took place in London at the time, and I can do no better than quote his statement:—

"Sir JOSEPH BANKS's explorations in the vast unknown lands of the south spurred him on to fresh exertions. He accordingly made arrangements to join COOK's second voyage, which was to leave England in 1772, the Government accepting his services, as well it might. So extensive were the preparations he made that, his wealth notwithstanding, he was obliged to specially raise money to meet the expenses. He engaged, so we read, 'ZOFFANY the painter, three draughtsmen, two secretaries, and nine servants acquainted with the modes of preserving animals and plants.' The Comptroller of the Navy, however, succeeded in putting so many obstacles in BANKS's way that he withdrew in disgust from the project. Notwithstanding all this, BANKS to his everlasting credit, took great interest in the new adventure, and succeeded in getting Dr. JOHN REINHOLD FORSTER . . . . . and his son JOHN GEORGE appointed naturalists to the expedition."

In the summer of 1772 BANKS and SOLANDER left on a botanical trip to Iceland.

The elder FORSTER was required by the Admiralty, as were other officials, to sign an agreement not to publish an account of the voyage previous to the issuance of the official report, but the son, who was seventeen years old at the time, was above suspicion and was not required to sign such a document. In 1777, a few months before Captain COOK's official report was published, apparently all concerned were shocked when there unexpectedly appeared in London a two volume account of the voyage under the authorship of the younger FORSTER*(2)*. The reaction was naturally a violent one, particularly in the Admiralty, and this episode clearly wrecked the future botanical careers of both father and son.

The FORSTERs botanized at Tierra del Fuego, Tahiti, Friendly Islands, and New Zealand, all visited by BANKS and SOLANDER on COOK's first voyage, and a high percentage of the plants they there collected merely duplicated the collections made a few years earlier by BANKS and SOLANDER; they also collected specimens on various islands not

---

1) COCKAYNE, L. New Zealand Plants and Their Story, ed. 2, i-xvi. 1-248, illus. 1919.

2) FORSTER, J. G. A. A Voyage round the World in H.M.S. *Resolution*, commanded by Capt. COOK during . . . . . 1772-5. London. 1777. Reissued in J. H. MOORE's "Collection of Voyages and Travels." Volume 2 (1780?). Also translated into German and published in Berlin in 1778.

DISSERTATIO INAVGVRALIS

BOTANICO - MEDICA

DE

PLANTIS ESCVLENTIS

INSVLARVM OCEANI AVSTRALIS.

QVAM

EX DECRETO ORDINIS GRATIOSI

SPECIMINIS GRATIA

PRO ADIPISCENDIS SVMMIS

IN MEDICINA HONORIBVS

PRIVILEGIIS ET IMMVNITATIBVS

PVBLICAVIT

AVCTOR

GEORGIVS FORSTER

PHIL. D. ET LL. AA. M.

SERENISS. POLONIAR. REGI A CONSILIIS SANCTIORI-
BVS, HIST. NAT. IN ACAD. VILNENSI PROF. PVBL. ORD.
ACAD. CAES. NAT. CVRIOS. SQCC. REGG. SCIENT. LOND.
ET HAFNIENSIS, NEC NON ACAD. REG. MATRITENSIS
MEDICAE ET SCIENT. SOC. AGRARIAE CELLENSIS ET
CASSELLANAE, VT ET ANTIQVARIOR. QVAE CASSELLIS
FLORET, AC SOC. NATVRAE CVRIOSOR. BEROL. SOCIVS,
SOC. REG. SCIENT. GOETTINGENSI COMMERCIO
LITTER. CONIVNCTVS.

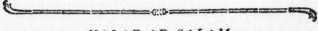

HALAE AD SALAM
TYPIS FRANCKIANIS, MDCCLXXXVI.

TEXT FIGURE 5. — Title page of GEORG FORSTER's *De Plantis
Esculentis* (1786) which was published a few months earlier
than his *Prodromus* (*cf.* p. 205).

visited on COOK's first voyage such as the Marquesas and Easter Islands, as well as in New Caledonia and in the New Hebrides.

On their return to London, in 1775, they apparently took their collections to Sir JOSEPH BANKS' residence where they commenced to study the material. At that time the very large private BANKS library on natural history was certainly more extensive than that of any government agency in London, and his private herbarium was an important one, particularly so for botanists interested in studying Pacific islands material. There was, in the 1770's, no herbarium at Kew worthy of the name. The British Museum, while possessing extensive collections and library facilities, had not yet become very active in the botanical field — it was to this institution that the great BANKS library and natural history collections eventually went by bequest. BANKS, most generously, made his collections and library available to competent workers; and the two FORSTERs were competent, even if it very soon became evident that they were unscrupulous. Their joint *Characteres generum plantarum(3)* with 75 plates and accompanying text appeared in London in 1776. (FIG. 4).

The younger FORSTER published what was supposed to be his journal of a voyage round the world, on H.M.S. *Resolution,* in London in 1777. This was his privilege as he had not been required to sign an agreement not to do so; but all indications are that he was inspired, aided and abetted by his father. This FORSTER f. Journal antedated COOK's official account by some months. This strange action created a crisis which one judges effectually blocked the access of both the FORSTERs to the BANKS treasure house, and also blocked any future measurably complete work on the collections made by them during COOK's second voyage, yet it seems clear as Mr. ALSTON notes *(in lit.)* that Sir JOSEPH BANKS tried to act as mediator between the wrathful Earl of SANDWICH, First Lord of the Admiralty, and the two FORSTERs. But between 1775 and 1777, when the inevitable break came, both of the FORSTERs had apparently free access to the BANKS and SOLANDER collections made on COOK's first voyage, the PARKINSON plates, and the SOLANDER manuscripts. Through Sir JOSEPH BANKS the British Museum eventually received two folio volumes of original pencil and water color sketches of plants made by the FORSTERs during Capt. COOK's second voyage, 1772-75 (*See* Cat. Libr. Brit. Mus. (Nat. Hist.) 2: 595. 1904; PL. 87). I suspected that possibly these data had been retained because BANKS had a financial stake in the matter as he provided the equipment needed for this natural history venture of

---

3) The note following entry No. 2981 in PRITZEL's *Thesaurus* is misleading. The data at Leningrad, plates only, no text, do not refer to the *Characteres generum plantarum,* but to an entirely new work, projected by the younger FORSTER which he never finished, entitled: *Icones plantarum in itinere ad insulas maris australis collectarum.* The prints are in two volumes, 131 plates. These were once in the possession of LAMBERT but in 1868 were acquired from FRIEDLÄNDER for the St. Petersburg Garden. The original copper plates were apparently destroyed, perhaps by fire, and these prints are the only known extant ones, except for copies of some of them inserted in the British Museum set of the original FORSTER drawings referred to below. For a full account *see* F. VON HERDER, Verzeichniss von G. FORSTER's Icones plantarum . . . . . Acta Horti Petropol. 9: 485-510. 1886.

FLORVLAE

INSVLARVM AVSTRALIVM

PRODROMVS

AVCTORE

GEORGIO FORSTER M. D.

SERENISSIMO REGI POLONIAE A CONSILIIS INTIMIS
HISTORIAE NATVRALIS ET BOTANICES IN ACADEMIA
VILNENSI P. P. O. ACADEMIAE CAESAREAE NATVRAE
CVRIOSORVM REGIAE MEDICAE MADRITENSIS
REGIAR. SOCIETATVM SCIENTIARVM LONDINENSIS
ET HAVNIENSIS SOCIETATVM ANTIQVITATVM ET REI
AGRARIAE QVAE CASSELLIS SVNT REI AGRARIAE
CELLENSIS ET NATVRAE SCRVTATOR. BEROLINENSIS
SODALI NEC NON REGIIS SOCIETATIB. GOTTINGENSI
SCIENTIARVM ET PARISINAE REI AGRARIAE
LITTERARVM COMMERCIO CONIVNCTO.

GOTTINGAE

TYPIS JOANN. CHRISTIAN. DIETERICH.

MDCCLXXXVI.

TEXT FIGURE 6. — Title page of GEORG FORSTER's *Florulae Insularum Australium Prodromus* (1786) discussed, in detail, on p. 206.

1772-75 that turned out so disastrously in the end for the two FOR-
STERS; yet, such an idea would be foreign to BANKS' well known gen-
erosity. Fortunately Mr. ALSTON found a record in the BANKS correspondence that the latter actually paid the elder FORSTER £420 for
the plates, dryly remarking that this impressed him as being a very
high price, as it most certainly was (*3a*). One cannot avoid the impression that the two men received what they figuratively asked for,
but did not expect — dismissal. Sir JOSEPH BANKS' generous action in paying such a large sum as £420 for the original sketches can
perhaps only be interpreted as a friendly attempt to alleviate the
financial stringency that suddenly descended upon the two FORSTERS.

Perhaps, after the lapse of the better part of two centuries, it
might be just as well to let sleeping dogs lie. However, in examining
the unpublished SOLANDER manuscript, I noted so many coincidences
in technical names proposed, but not published, by SOLANDER and
actually published by FORSTER f. as his own new species, a decade
or so after the final copy of the SOLANDER manuscript was finished,
that I felt compelled to consider certain implications. While it is admitted that no author is now required to give any attention to a new
but unpublished generic or specific name, here is a case where one
may reasonably assume that both the FORSTERS depended very heavily
on SOLANDER's knowledge, experience, manuscript descriptions, specimens, and the corresponding PARKINSON illustrations. When the
father and son published seventy-five new genera in 1776 based on
their South Sea collections, it is disconcerting to note that for fifteen
of their new Polynesian genera, in spite of the fact that they must
have known what SOLANDER had proposed for the same groups, they
ignored his names and published their own different generic ones for
the same groups; all this in London, with SOLANDER still active! If
other SOLANDER manuscripts were compared, particularly the one
appertaining to New Zealand, I am sure that the number of SOLANDER
new genera taken over by the FORSTERS would be considerably increased. This procedure must have had a strong effect when the final
break came in the next year, and may well have been the beginning
of the difficulties in which the two FORSTERS soon became involved.
When the younger FORSTER's *Prodromus* appeared in 1786, he not only
ignored the long and detailed technical descriptions of SOLANDER (who
had died in 1782) but published his own new binomials under absurdly
short diagnoses, except in the few cases where shortly before the
Prodromus was printed long descriptions appeared in his *De plantis*

3a) The following statement is quoted from a memorandum to BANKS from
J. R. FORSTER (*see* PLATE 86). "It must appear that no more than 235 £ were
left me at my return from the sum granted by Parliament for me and my Son.
I found myself soon under necessity to sell my drawings for which you gave me
£ 420 & besides that you have assisted me with £ 200: so that I have had in two
years time 835 £ to live upon in a very dear Metropolis." In a letter, dated
August 9, 1776, in London, FORSTER states: "I very readily agree to your kind
offer of four hundred Guineas for my Collection of drawings and am very well
content that the payment may take place whenever it will suit you best."

esculentis (1786) *(4)*. COCKAYNE, *op. cit.* 4, abruptly dismissed the *Prodromus* descriptions (rather diagnoses) of 170 New Zealand plants, and these mostly proposed as new species, because the "descriptions are altogether too short to be of any real use." This is true and applies also to the New Zealand species that the two FORSTERS published in 1776.

If one compares the index to the FORSTER f. *Prodromus* (1786) with that of the SOLANDER manuscript, with the PARKINSON plates, and with the BANKS and SOLANDER specimens, the only conclusion to be drawn is that the FORSTERS were very familiar with these documents. One suspects that, when the break came between the Earl of SANDWICH, the First Lord of the Admiralty, and the two FORSTERS in 1777, the relationship of the latter with Sir JOSEPH BANKS came to an abrupt end. In the *Prodromus* a considerable number of SOLANDER binomials appear as *nomina nuda*, all properly credited to him; and yet in the descriptive text of the *Prodromus* (such as it is) no less than twenty-three original SOLANDER binomials are published, with the younger FORSTER cited as the authority for the names, in each case the brief diagnosis being followed by the letter "F." One has reason to suspect that the excerpts from all the SOLANDER detailed descriptions had not been completed when the FORSTERS lost access to the BANKS library and herbarium. These SOLANDER *nomina nuda*, so casually published by the younger FORSTER in his *Prodromus*, approximate fifty, and they appear between Nos. 469 and 594 (p. 81-94) under "Plantae obscurae." There was really nothing obscure about them, because of the extant specimens, the PARKINSON drawings, and the greatly detailed SOLANDER descriptions to which the FORSTERS no longer had access.

In addition there are about fifteen Linnaean binomials misinterpreted and mis-applied to Tahitian species by SOLANDER; all of these were accepted without dissent by the younger FORSTER. But poor judgment was used when the new genus *Thespesia* Soland. was rejected and its type species *(Hibiscus populneus* L.) was redescribed as a new species, *Hibiscus bacciferus* Forst. f. Finally, the twenty-three binomials were all originated by SOLANDER for which in each he prepared greatly detailed descriptions, but the new names were appropriated by the younger FORSTER as his own and published, with the very brief diagnoses, referred to above, in the *Prodromus(5)*, each new name carefully followed by the letter "F". They are *Dorstenia lucida, Echites costata, Ficus prolixa, F. tinctoria, Glycine lucida, G. rosea, Hemionitis reticulata, Jasminum didymum, Lycopodium myrtifolium, L. squarrosum, Piper pallidum, P. tetraphyllum, Poa latifolia, Pteris comans, Ruellia fragrans, Spondias dulcis, Terminalia glabrata,*

---

4) For details on nomenclatural aspects of this work *see* MERRILL, E. D. Bibliographic notes on G. FORSTER's *De plantis esculentis insularum oceani australis* (1786). Pacif. Sci. 8: 35-40. 1954. This antedated the *Prodromus* publication by perhaps two or three months. The very brief *Prodromus* diagnoses are replaced by normally greatly detailed descriptions of those species included in *De plantis esculentis.*

5) FORSTER, G. Florulae insularum australium prodromus. 1-103. 1786.

Trichomanes demissum, T. elatum, T. gibberosum, Urtica argentea, U. virgata and *Weinmannia parviflora*. Under all rules of botanical nomenclature FORSTER f. is thus the actual author of these binomials, but not one was originated by him. If there were merely one or two cases where two botanists independently selected the same specific names for the same species from the same locality, one could take a more charitable attitude; but twenty-three SOLANDER names independently duplicated for the same species from the same island by the younger FORSTER strain one's imagination too much. It is true that unpublished manuscript names have no standing in our code of botanical nomenclature, which is logical and proper; but the wholesale appropriation of so many SOLANDER names and the publishing of them by the younger FORSTER as his own was not exactly ethical. In one case, among the binomials above listed, a greatly detailed description of *Spondias dulcis* was provided in *De plantis esculentis* 33. 1786, issued perhaps two or three months before the *Prodromus* was printed; but even here the binomial is followed by the letter "F" and SOLANDER, who originated the name and who prepared a much more detailed description, is not mentioned.

There is one strange oversight on the part of FORSTER f. In his treatment of the species of flowering plants he usually (not always) listed the island or island group whence his specimens came. But a change is noted when he came to consider approximately seventy-five species of vascular cryptogams. Of these (mostly diagnosed as new) about thirty-five of the new species lack any indication as to whence the specimens came. When it is considered that all the species that FORSTER f. described came from a vast area extending from Easter Island and the Marquesas Islands, Society, Friendly and Tonga Islands to New Zealand, New Caledonia, and New Hebrides, this placed an unnecessary burden on the shoulders of succeeding pteridologists to whom fell the task of associating these unlocalized and very inadequately described species with those described from the same vast region by other authors. Because of the very short diagnoses this could normally be accomplished only by those having access to holotypes or isotypes of the various species involved. Curiously the same statement applies to the nearly one hundred new binomials associated with the seventy-five genera described by the two FORSTERs in 1776. For the few genera, where more than one new species was involved, absurdly short diagnoses are provided, each consisting of two or three, or, in one case, as many as seven words. As I pointed out previously, were one to compare the other SOLANDER manuscripts with the FORSTER f. species from New Zealand, Tierra del Fuego, and elsewhere, I am sure many more cases of botanical piracy could be detected. In this memoir, I have considered only those genera and species in the single SOLANDER manuscript based on material from Tahiti and the Friendly Islands.

Chapter III

THE FORSTER HERBARIUM

Duplicates of the FORSTER collections are to be found in a number of the older European herbaria, although the University of Kiel and the Paris Museum are the only ones listed by DE CANDOLLE in 1880 as containing sets. There are two sets at the British Museum (Nat. Hist.), one of which came direct, a second through the Banksian herbarium; there are also specimens in the British Museum herbarium labelled "ex Herb. PALLAS", which indicates that PALLAS acquired a set of FORSTER duplicates. SPRENGEL certainly had a set at Halle, for he records FORSTER and SOLANDER species in his edition of the *Systema Vegetabilium* (1825-28), and in an earlier paper published in 1807 (appropriated from a still earlier thesis by BIEHLER) actually described certain new species based on FORSTER specimens (*see* p. 362 sub *Zizyphoides*). There are various "BÄCK" [FORSTER] specimens in the Linnaean herbarium and in that of the younger LINNAEUS; the latter herbarium, after it was acquired by Sir JAMES E. SMITH, was incorporated in his personal one, now at the Linnean Society of London.

Some of these specimens may bear the name of BÄCK as ABRAHAM BÄCK acquired a set and presented at least a part of the FORSTER specimens to LINNAEUS. It was customary at the time to credit such gifts to the donor, rather than to the collector. Though there was a botanical controversy, following 1781, between the younger FORSTER and the younger LINNAEUS, there is no reason to believe, so far as I know, that the younger LINNAEUS knew of any agreement between the FORSTERs and his father at the time the latter received the material from Mr. BÄCK. What remains of the BÄCK personal herbarium is now at the University of Uppsala(*1*).

Yet there is in the Sir JAMES E. SMITH herbarium a considerable number of FORSTER specimens, the labels in the handwriting of the younger FORSTER (information supplied by Mr. S. SAVAGE in December, 1952). Mr. SAVAGE also stated that some of the specimens, on which descriptions were based and published in the *Supplementum plantarum*, were incorporated in the original LINNAEUS herbarium. There is apparently a good set of the FORSTER specimens in the THUNBERG herbarium at Uppsala. Dr. JUEL has discussed these matters in considerable detail. In the United States, about 25 FORSTER speci-

---

1) JUEL, H. O. Notes on the Herbarium of ABRAHAM BÄCK. Svenska Linné-Sällsk. Arsskr. 7: 68-82. 1924.

mens are preserved in the herbarium of the Academy of Natural Sciences, Philadelphia. These, Mr. JOSEPH EWAN informs me, were presented by THOMAS NUTTALL. This small lot was first noted by PENNELL (Proc. Am. Philos. Soc. 94: 149. 1950).

Mr. A. H. G. ALSTON, who in November, 1952, confirmed the statement that there were two sets of FORSTER specimens in the British Museum herbarium, also mentioned other sets with which he was familiar or which had come to his attention. There is a large set in the WILLDENOW herbarium at Berlin, the specimens often marked SPRENGEL, as WILLDENOW apparently acquired his material from SPRENGEL. The general SPRENGEL herbarium, I am advised by Dr. WERDERMANN, went to Berlin where it was incorporated in the herbarium of the Botanical Garden and was thus destroyed in March, 1943, when the Museum building was burned in a bombing raid; fortunately the WILLDENOW herbarium was stored in an abandoned salt mine and thus saved. The SPRENGEL fern specimens were, however, purchased by KUNZE, I am informed by Mr. ALSTON, and were probably destroyed in Leipzig during World War II. SCHKUHR noted that a Count VON LEPEL had some FORSTER specimens, but what may have become of these is unknown. The British Museum was offered the FORSTER herbarium (by a grandson?) October 9, 1852; what disposition was made of this lot is unknown. The "Herbarium of GEORGE FORSTER", said to be his entire herbarium, was offered at the LAMBERT sale in 1842.

In December, 1952, Mr. ALSTON visited Liverpool to search for FORSTER types, but found very few for the reason that many specimens were transferred to Kew in 1885 (see Nature, Sept. 24, 1885 and infra) by the Liverpool Corporation before the Botanical Garden herbarium material was transferred to the Liverpool Museum.

It is perhaps a little quirk of fate that there are now so many specimens in England, as far as those at Liverpool escaped destruction by the ravages of insects and other causes; but after all, the collections made on COOK's second voyage were prepared under the auspices of the British government. It seems to be little known among taxonomists that after the death of the two FORSTERs, the son in 1794 in Paris, and the father in 1798 in Halle, that the herbarium, then at Halle, was purchased a few years later for the newly established Liverpool Botanic Garden, through the interest and zeal of JOHN SHEPHERD, its first curator(2). The garden had been established at the beginning of the nineteenth century, and opened to the public in 1803. In the garden report for 1808 it is recorded that its herbarium had been increased by the purchase of FORSTER's South Sea Islands plants which had been brought over from Halle(3). One suspects that the

---

2)   NUTTALL dedicated the genus *Shepherdia* to JOHN SHEPHERD in 1818 which is officially conserved against *Lepargyrea* Raf. (1818, 1819). A curious argument by RAFINESQUE against NUTTALL's selection of this name (Am. Monthly Mag. Crit. Rev. 4: 195. 1819) in his review of NUTTALL's work, is "the gardener SHEP[H]ERD does not deserve the dedication of a genus by all accounts." Both SHEPHERD and RAFINESQUE were then living in Philadelphia.

3)   STANSFIELD, H. Handbook and Guide to the Herbarium Collections in the Public Museums, Liverpool, 1-81. pl. 1-14. 1935 (p. 10, 50-51).

material may have been purchased from the FORSTER heirs rather than from the University of Halle. It seems to be clear that in their financial straits following the debacle in their personal affairs in London in 1777, which was clearly due to the unethical breaking of the signed agreement the older FORSTER had made with the Admiralty, they sold various sets of duplicates. Both father and son were apparently financially embarrassed between 1777 and 1780. In Mr. ALSTON's letter of November 12, 1952 is an excellent example of British understatement: "I am inclined to believe that the FORSTERs sold their herbarium several times over. This seems rather in character."

Mr. STANSFIELD records that, when the Botanic Garden herbarium was transferred to the Liverpool Museum, in 1909, it contained 40,000 specimens. About 16,000 were retained, as unfortunately the others had been so damaged by insects, mould and other agencies(4) as to be worthless. Yet a high percentage of the retained specimens are said to be scientifically and historically of great value.

Recently, Mr. H. STANSFIELD(5) has supplied some additional important information on the basis of an examination of the Liverpool records and the actual FORSTER botanical specimens still preserved there. The number of specimens transferred to Kew by action of the Liverpool Corporation in 1885 was 1359, of which 785 were FORSTER collections made during Captain COOK's second voyage. Of these only 227 were from the Pacific region. Among the flowering plants 187 were from the Polynesian Islands (including New Caledonia and the New Hebrides) and 119 from New Zealand. There were 21 from Tierra del Fuego. He indicates that the British Museum (Nat. Hist.) has the type specimens, but this would perhaps cover only those genera and species described by J. & G. FORSTER in 1776. He mentions also

---

4) One destructive agency, in the case of the BRADBURY Missouri River collection (1811), which applied to all other collections at Liverpool, was the gardeners' habit of making spills of the paper, on which the unmounted specimens were laid out, with which to light their pipes and keep the tobacco burning! This extended over many years during the period of decline of the Botanic Garden. To me, this was a new type of herbarium pest. It is, however, a good example of the vicissitudes to which often historically very important botanical collections may be subject over the course of a few generations. Another example was a small remnant of the historically very important LOUREIRO herbarium (China, Indo-China, East Africa), prepared before 1781, which escaped confiscation by the French army in Lisbon in 1807 under Marshal JUNOT. This being found to be in a bad state of preservation was deliberately destroyed shortly before 1880; well, burning insect infested specimens is an efficient method of killing the bugs! And a third case is what ELIAS DURAND did to the poorly prepared but historically important RAFINESQUE herbarium shortly after that erratic botanist's death in 1840 — cast into the trash heap, except for the nicely prepared specimens of COLLINS and others that it contained. The MUHLENBERG herbarium in Philadelphia and that of STEPHEN ELLIOTT in Charleston are other examples of what happened through mistreatment and neglect. I am frankly afraid that the pressure for space and funds on the part of "general biologists" now in power in certain of our academic institutions of high rank is perhaps the most serious threat of all.

5) STANSFIELD, H. A Botanist with Captain COOK in the South Pacific (1772-1775). Liverpool Libr. Mus. Bull. 2: 5-25. fig. 1-10. 1953.

the second set presented by FORSTER to Sir JOSEPH BANKS and the PALLAS material now also at the British Museum. Judging from the photographs of some of the FORSTER labels and specimens still at Liverpool, I judge that what the Liverpool Botanical Garden acquired about 1808 was a sort of run of the mill set of duplicates, not the actual holotypes.

It is of distinct interest to note in the quoted passage, p. 21-23, that Sir JOSEPH BANKS stated that in 1776 he paid £420 for the FORSTER drawings "in various degrees of finish, some being coloured and others in part, and others merely pencil sketches", and added the very significant statement "named by SOLANDER": not that the FORSTERs gave any credit to that botanist, on whose knowledge their work depended.

He also stated, on the authority of LASÈGUE, that there are FORSTER specimens in the Sir W. J. HOOKER herbarium, now at Kew, and records other sets as being at Leiden and at Vienna; about one fourth of the Vienna herbarium was burned toward the end of World War II. He confirmed the fact that the FORSTERs received £4,000 for their three years' work. Additional sets of FORSTER duplicates may show up from time to time in other older herbaria of Europe.

In searching for FORSTER holotypes it is possible that there may be a few in the general herbarium of the Liverpool Museum, although Kew is a much more likely place. The actual FORSTER holotypes may prove to be of distinct importance in view of the fact that the J. R. and G. FORSTER species associated with the seventy-five new genera which they published in 1776 were not only undescribed (except as descriptive data were included in the generalized generic descriptions), but mostly not even localized; and a very considerable number of the species so briefly diagnosed by the younger FORSTER in 1786 were also not localized. And the collections on which the many technical names were based came from a vast range, Easter and Marquesas Islands to the east, westward via the Society and Friendly Islands to New Zealand, New Caledonia and the New Hebrides group. Yet it seems rather risky to state positively that this or that specimen, now in this or that herbarium, is actually a holotype.

Chapter IV

THE REAL SIGNIFICANCE OF THE BANKS AND SOLANDER TAHITI COLLECTIONS OF 1769

This was the first large and critically studied collection of botanical material ever made in Tahiti or elsewhere in Polynesia and thus it has a very strong bearing on what plant species, native and introduced, were or were not present there, or in other Polynesian islands in 1769; and Tahiti was the very center of the Polynesian culture area, as Dr. BUCK has shown. The *Endeavour* was the fourth ship to reach Tahiti, that island having been discovered two years earlier by WALLIS (PLATE 80). Here was a flora that, as to its constituent species had not been very greatly altered, other than by the relatively few economic species and weeds that had been introduced by the Polynesians themselves. A critical analysis should be consoling to the large conservative (not orthodox) school of anthropologists who conclude from anthropological, philological, cultural and other data that the pre-Magellan inhabitants of the Pacific Islands came out of Asia via Malaysia. As I outlined on p. 195, thence came all of their few domestic animals, all but one of their cultivated food plants, and certain other cultivated economic and ornamental plant species, as well as most of their relatively few man-distributed weeds, previous to the arrival of the Europeans. The great influx of aggressive American weeds came after 1769, except for those introduced into Guam following the establishment of the Acapulco-Manila galleon route after 1565. It should be equally disconcerting to certain positive, but botanically ill-informed specialists in certain fields, some of whom may even accept the HEYERDAHL thesis that Polynesia was populated by the American Indians, who nonchalantly "prove" that this or that cultigen occurred in both hemispheres before the Europeans reached the Pacific. I merely repeat that there is still only one species, the common gourd (*Lagenaria*), for which we now have incontrovertible evidence that it was not only in tropical and temperate America but also in the corresponding parts of the Old World in pre-Columbian times. I realize that we are now threatened with "proofs" of the presence of maize and of cassava in Africa in pre-Columbian times, which, considering the relatively short distance between the bulge of Brazil and Africa, is of course possible; that the Arabs had discovered America before the time of COLUMBUS (the Portuguese seem clearly to have done so, as did the Norsemen) and had even transported negro slaves across the Atlantic, the latter immediately escaping and establishing themselves as independent settlers; and, perhaps the strangest of all, that the Negritos and Papuasians, wherever they occur in the islands south of Asia, and eastward to Fiji, are merely descendants of negro slaves brought from Africa by the Malays. These ideas, are, for the most part, side issues of the diffusionists' beliefs, and supposedly all of them are as possible as was the existence of Atlantis, the purely fictional Mu of CHURCHWARD and similar ideas which a surprisingly large number of modern educated people accept, as well as the purely imaginary regatta of the Greek sailors left in the Gulf of Persia when ALEXANDER died in 323 B.C. and who sailed from there through Malaysia and across the Pacific bringing civilization to Mexico, Central and South America.

It is indeed curious to note how many still accept certain strange ideas propounded by Dr. O. F. COOK*(1)* some fifty years ago. One extreme view expressed by him may be quoted in this chapter: "Botanical evidence makes it plain that most of the plants shared by people of the two continents originated in America . . . the use and cultivation of which are habits acquired by primitive man in America and carried in remote times westward across the Pacific, together with the social organization and constructive arts which appear only in settled communities supported by the tillage of the soil." The author, were he alive today, would doubtless repudiate these views. At the time he wrote the paper, he was intent on proving that agriculture in America antedated that of the Old World. There is not a word of truth in the opening sentence of the above quoted passage, and nothing that supports the idea, except what HEYERDAHL has incautiously published. When BANKS and SOLANDER and the two FORSTERs made the critical and intensive botanical surveys of the Matavai Bay coastal plain area in Tahiti in 1769 and 1773, covering a total time lapse of about five and a half months, there was very little in the way of plant species that they missed. Little did they think that, when the still extant collections were being made, roughly 175 years ago, that a study of their results would prove the utter falsity of certain theories proposed by imaginative, ill-informed and theory-bound writers in the first half of the twentieth century. Their collections were the first ones made in all of the Pacific Islands and they clearly indicate the lowland species which were and which were not present in the years 1769 to 1773. They even collected the now despised weeds and plants belonging to another category (equally despised by most modern collectors, and strange as it may seem, by most anthropologists who prosecute field work among more or less primitive peoples) : the cultivated plants!

It would be foolish to assert that there were no communications across the Pacific in pre-Magellan times, but there is no dependable biological evidence that there was any effective direct communication across the great ocean until after MAGELLAN's pioneer voyage in 1521. The very presence of the sweet potato in New Zealand, and all over Polynesia proper, before COOK's first voyage, offers positive evidence that this important food plant had been transmitted between Polynesia and South America, or Africa(?). HEYERDAHL and others

_1)_ COOK, O. F. Food Plants of Ancient America. Ann. Rept. Smithsonian Inst. 1903: 481-497. 1904.

believe that this basic food plant reached the Pacific islands via a balsa raft. Unless it were carried as a living plant, in soil, a method of transmission widely used by the Polynesians, no sweet potato tuber could possibly retain its viability in a humid atmosphere, at sea level, for longer than a month or at most six weeks, and the HEYERDAHL balsa raft took in excess of three months to make the passage. All the evidence I have examined indicates that the Polynesians themselves secured this plant and then distributed it all over their cultural area, even to distant New Zealand (*see* p. 349).

After this was written, I, fortunately, had an interview with Dr. THOMAS DAVIS who has a thorough mastery of various Polynesian dialects and wide experience in the Pacific Islands. Late in 1952 he sailed from New Zealand on a small ketch, the *Miru*, across the Pacific to Callao and then north to Boston to take up special work at the Harvard Medical School. He admits that this trip would have been much easier if made in summer, rather than in the fall and early winter. Lest those, who read HEYERDAHL, be misled into believing that it would be impossible for a Polynesian outrigger or double canoe to sail from the eastern Polynesian islands to South America (HEYERDAHL, I believe, does not claim this, but he infers that an ancient, much more clumsy, balsa raft must have made a return voyage): Dr. DAVIS sailed from Rapa to Callao in forty-five days, covering only the last two hundred miles under power; the distance was 4,500 miles.

He also gave me the outline of an almost forgotten Raiatean legend regarding the discovery of South America by MAUI MARUMAMAO, including the route, the time spent in South America where MAUI MARUMAMAO died, the return of his son to Easter Island, and eventually, with at least some of the party, to Raiatea. The route eastward was from Raiatea to Hikuveru (on maps, Hikueru), Marokakau (on some maps, Marokau) and Raroia, all in the Tuamotu group. From these islands he proceeded to Rapanui (Easter Island) and thence to "Te Au Tuaivi, the land of ridges (or backbones), namely South America." Most of the anthropologists and ethnologists who have worked in the Polynesian field apparently did not learn of this legend. It offers no real evidence, as PRAIN taught me, but supplies as valid an argument as the legends covering the discovery and populating of New Zealand, including the introduction of the sweet potato there. What is perhaps most important is that this legend covers the sailing directions and includes the names of the foods which they took with them on the eastward voyage. One judges that there is here a much more logical explanation of the HEYERDAHL evidence regarding the American influence on Polynesian organizations and cultures than what he claimed. Such influence, in all fields, is much more apt to have been due to returned Polynesians, who had lived in the Inca dominated parts of South America for a considerable period of time, than by a few stray Indians possibly cast ashore on a Polynesian island from a balsa raft!

It is sincerely to be hoped that Dr. DAVIS may be able to consummate his tentative plan of following the MAUI MARUMAMAO legendary route to South America in a Polynesian canoe, 40 to 50 feet long, using no navigating instruments, no canned foods, but only those items which the Polynesians could have taken with them on their long voyages; this, as he expresses it, "to bring the thinking which *Kon Tiki* has engendered back to normalcy." If one still doubts the possibility of small boats navigating the distance eastward from the Polynesian islands to South America, it is suggested that the account of the loss of the whaler *Essex* of Nantucket be considered. Her bow was stove by a whale, on Nov. 20, 1820, an episode which provided the basis of the last chapter in HERMAN MELVILLE's *Moby Dick*. The *Essex* was sunk at 0° 40′ south and 119° west. On very scant rations and little water, the three open boats proceeded south to Henderson Island, then took off for Easter Island which they missed. Two of the three boats were picked up not far from the Juan Fernandez Islands, the distance covered between 4500 and 4600 miles, the elapsed time about ninety-six days. Only eight of the twenty men, who started out, survived.

Whatever communication there may have been between the Polynesians and the Amerindians, it is clear that trips were so rare and infrequent that the residents of the western coast of South America failed to acquire, from these rare visitors from the west, the techniques appertaining to the building and navigation of outrigger and double canoes.

QUIROS, in 1606, records the fact that members of a party, which landed on one of the Tuamotu Islands, observed an elderly woman wearing a gold ring set with an emerald. There being neither gold nor emeralds in Polynesia, this item must have been introduced from either America or Asia. It proves nothing either for or against this or that origin, but it does indicate that occasionally there was casual and probably some direct or indirect intercourse with non-Polynesian peoples, both to the east and to the west, and that the early Pacific peoples were not entirely isolated once they had occupied the widely scattered islands in the great ocean. One really does not have to suggest that, like culture, this emerald ring reached the Tuamotu Islands before 1520 through the medium of a renegade or a fugitive from justice, even though some ethnologists dote on this method of extending new or advanced ideas from the cultured to the uncultured segments of humanity, several thousand years ago. These imaginary renegades, fugitives from justice, and even Buddhist priests, had to eat during their hypothetical wanderings, but they all, certainly, left their basic food plants and domestic animals at home. One can understand why orthodox vegetarian Buddhist priests would not bother with animals, but surely they must have taken with them a food supply of vegetable origin!

HEYERDAHL, the latest exponent of American origins of the Polynesian peoples and cultures, like his few predecessors, including Dr. O. F. COOK, grossly misinterpreted the agricultural and botanical evidence. While such misinterpretations may be manna to possibly a few ethnologists, non-botanical geographers of some new schools, and perhaps a few geneticists, it should be remembered that the often aggressive workers in these, too frequently misinformed, groups do not include a single experienced botanist. Yet, a thorough knowledge of the "outmoded" field of descriptive botany and wide botanical field experience is most important, as well as mastery of the very extensive, specialized botanical literature, a most essential basis on which reasonably accurate judgments may safely be based. Some of the "specialists" whom I criticize have accepted the grossest of gross errors at times, merely because certain unchecked items agree with what they believe and hope to prove.

The fact remains that for American species in Polynesia one scarcely needs to go farther back than the year 1769, except for one species of *Cucurbita* introduced into Tahiti by Capt. WALLIS who discovered the island in 1767. The definitely pre-Magellan sweet potato, and possibly a few other economic species and a very few weeds, perhaps introduced into the Marquesas Islands and into the New Hebrides by QUIROS some 350 years ago are possibilities. As I will discuss later (p. 239 and 249) he planted only maize on the Marquesas Islands, and maize and certain other cultigens which failed to persist on the New Hebrides. In making this positive statement as to the absence of American cultigens in the Pacific Islands, previous to 1769, I ignore the Mexican species introduced into the Marianas Islands, following 1565, via the Acapulco-Manila galleons. The botanical evidence is positive and cannot be controverted. One may take exceptions to my interpretations of Old World or New World origins of a few introduced and naturalized pre-Magellan weeds, but anyone going farther than this must prove that SEEMANN's and all other botanists' identifications of the BANKS, SOLANDER and FORSTER specimens are false, which would involve critical monographic work on a very large scale. Those who have erred in their conclusions will probably be satisfied merely to answer this challenge with vague, indirect generalities.

Of the 260 Tahitian species, collected in 1769 and critically described by SOLANDER, about 197 are manifestly indigenous and mostly endemic ones and the rest mostly man distributed. This last group breaks down into several categories, including those species reaching Tahiti by natural means long before man arrived on the scene, the purposely introduced and cultivated food and other economic plants, and the accidentally introduced weeds. I would stress the fact that a weed adapted to certain ecological conditions, once introduced and naturalized, will normally persist as long as there remains a vestige of agricultural activity in what was originally a forested region and, in many cases, after agricultural activity has ceased, as long as abandoned cleared areas do not revert to forest conditions.

Man-Introduced Economic Species:— Taking up the purposely introduced economic species (mostly food producing ones, but some, such as *Broussonetia, Hibiscus rosa-sinensis, Sesbania, Lagenaria* and *Abrus* for other purposes), about thirty species are involved, in the genera: *Aleurites, Dracaena, Cucumis, Benincasa, Inocarpus* (probably), *Tacca, Spondias, Eugenia (Syzygium), Abrus, Ipomoea* (one species, the sweet potato), *Abelmoschus, Sesbania, Colocasia* (sixteen varieties mentioned by SOLANDER), *Alocasia* (six varieties), *Amorphophallus, Amaranthus, Artocarpus(2)* (twenty-one varieties),

---

2) Many more varieties of both *Artocarpus* and *Musa, fide* ELLIS, Polynesian Researches (1822) occurred in Tahiti. G. P. WILDER (The Breadfruit in Tahiti, Bishop Mus. Bull. 50: 1-82, fig. 1-39. 1928) recognized thirty-two varieties of the former, most of them, including one occasionally seed-producing form, illustrated; he also obtained the names of twenty-seven other varieties from various sources. ELLIS in 1822 refers to about 50 varieties. All authors used only the native names for these "varieties," so fortunately no Latin trinomials are involved. They are all "sports," the better varieties being perpetuated by asexual propagation, as they appeared.

Broussonetia, Lagenaria, Dioscorea (at least three species), *Sacchar-um, Zingiber, Curcuma, Musa* (twenty-eight varieties), *Tacca* and *Cocos*. All of these were, with one exception, early introductions through the agency of man from Malaysia.

In addition PARKINSON enumerated several unclassified and un-named economic plants but unfortunately they were not described. From the brief non-descriptive data given by PARKINSON I have not been able to place these; important clues may be found in the local names cited by him. One I suspect might be a *Dioscorea*, another per-haps a *Pueraria* and possibly a third a *Cyrtosperma*. The above list includes all the cultivated food plants basic to the economy of the pre-Magellan Polynesians on which their civilization was based and by which it was maintained; there were of course their few domestic animals and plentiful sea food.

A *Pueraria* species very similar to *P. thunbergiana* Benth. (= *P. lobata* (Willd.) Ohwi) was apparently once rather widely distrib-uted in Polynesia, at least in semi-cultivation as an emergency food plant; it still persists here and there and several recent collections have been made in Fiji. It is a native of eastern Asia. This is a beau-tiful example of how easily a theory-ridden individual can be led astray. SEEMANN (Fl. Vit. 63. 1865) misidentified his Fiji material as representing the American *Pachyrrhizus trilobus* DC., and his specimens of the Fijian *yaka* or *wa-waka* are still extant. Dr. COOK in-cautiously accepted this identification as correct, apparently because he felt that he had to prove his theory that many American plant species had reached Polynesia in pre-Magellan times. If Dr. COOK really had known *Pachyrrhizus erosus* (L.) Urb. (*P. trilobus* DC.) in the field, which seems to me to be very doubtful, he would not have per-petuated SEEMANN's original error. But, assuming that he knew that it had white, turnip-shaped, firm, perpendicular roots a few inches long, normally eaten raw, then he never read SEEMANN's discussion. Some *Pueraria* species do have tough bast fibers as SEEMANN indicated but this is not true for any *Pachyrrhizus*; all one has to do is to test the bast fibers of the first available herbarium specimen. But more confounding is SEEMANN's description of *yaka* roots as being some-what starchy (those of *Pachyrrhizus* are essentially for water stor-age), *horizontal, sometimes 6 to 8 feet long and as thick as a man's thigh!* To overlook this was inexcusable.

In approximately 75,000 slips on which I had compiled the pub-lished binomials, native names, synonyms and bibliographical data from the botanical literature covering all the Pacific Islands, I find several records of the true *Pachyrrhizus* from Guam, the earliest re-corded collection being that of CHAMISSO (1817). It is there known as *hicamas*, this Mexican name coming in with the plant via one of the Acapulco-Manila galleons. There is no record that its range was ever extended to the neighboring Caroline Islands.

The erroneous SEEMANN Fiji, New Hebrides and New Caledonia records were not corrected until 1942 (A. C. SMITH, Sargentia 1:39). From certain sarcastic remarks made by a prominent neogeographer on the foolishness of descriptive botanical work, rather than the foolish botanists concentrating on strictly economic species in which many geographers are interested, one suspects that, in spite of gross errors made by botanists and geographers, he belongs to that great brotherhood who disparages the value of herbaria and of herbarium work; and yet it is these botanical records, not merely notes and descriptions, but rather actual historical specimens, that trip the incautious theorists!

For the record I cite *Degener 14942*, collected in Fiji in April 1941, which bears a note in part reading "Yaka . . . root elongated, edible when cooked". I have examined recently collected specimens from Fiji, Niue and the New Hebrides, all referable to *Pueraria lobata* (Willd.) Ohwi (*P. thunbergiana* Benth.). There is one record of *Pachyrrhizus* from Samoa and one from Hawaii but at least one of these may refer to the *Pueraria*. And there is no particular reason why this *Pachyrrhizus* species should not now be widely distributed in Polynesia, as it still is in the Philippines, yet that is not and never was the case. It certainly never reached any of the Pacific Islands before the Spaniards introduced it into Guam, probably in the 16th century. It still persists as a naturalized species there, as it does in the Philippines. Thus it is that a rather gross error once appearing in a standard work is selected by a rather blind blazer of new trails and perpetuated by his followers, not one of whom ever took the trouble to check the original record. This error, made by a thoroughly competent botanist, nearly a century ago, which still persists, is a good example of how a correction seldom catches up with the published error, or, as tersely stated by another author, "denial seldom catches up with allegation!"

It is interesting to note that in one strictly American genus, *Cucurbita*, *C. pepo* L. was listed for Tahiti, but not described, in the SOLANDER manuscript. I suspect, however, that what Captain WALLIS, who actually planted it in 1767, may have had were squash seeds (*C. maxima* Lam.), not those of the pumpkin. As a rule, we recognize two species here, *C. pepo* L. and *C. maxima* Lam., but as yet no taxonomist, geneticist or agriculturist has really succeeded in demonstrating the actual botanical characters by which the two species may constantly be distinguished. For most of us the pumpkin is *C. pepo* L. and the squash is *C. maxima* Lam. This is an interesting field for the geneticists, for clearly hybridization has ruled for some thousands of years, until now we cannot say that this or that wild species may be a potential ancestor to the swarms of cultigens now known.

The SOLANDER record is merely: "Hab. spontanea in Otaheite ubi Anno 1767 a Capitaneo WALLIS primum sata." Captain COOK mentions in the journal of his first voyage that the natives had accepted the species first planted by Captain WALLIS two years earlier. In any case, here is a positive date for the introduction of a representative of a strictly American genus, a species of which, on the basis of confusion of the large gourd *(Lagenaria siceraria)* with *Cucurbita maxima* Lam., is currently listed as having been in Polynesia by that too often overworked phrase "since time immemorial." This false record was based on a form of the true gourd *(Lagenaria)*, although *Cucurbita maxima* Lam. had been established in Hawaii certainly before 1840.

Incidentally, in 1606 QUIROS recorded having planted seeds of *calabaza de Peru* in the Santa Cruz islands, when he attempted to establish a permanent colony there. This would be a true *Cucurbita*, probably either *C. pepo* L. or *C. maxima* Lam., for he also recorded having seen growing plants of *calabaza de España* near the seashore on the Marquesas Islands; the latter would be the true gourd *(Lagenaria)* which was well known in Spain at that time. So much for the introduced economic species.

Weeds:— Perhaps no assemblage of plants has been as casually treated as the large group, including representatives of many families, which we recognize as weeds. Everywhere, in the settled areas of the tropics, these plants dominate, either as ruderals in densely settled areas, or, as aggressors in cultivated fallow and waste lands. It is perhaps not so strange that the weeds, like the definitely man-distributed cultivated ornamentals, to say nothing of the cultivated basic food plants, are now found in and about towns and cities, and in the settled areas generally, in both hemispheres. This was not always so. Turning to the weeds found by BANKS and SOLANDER in Tahiti in 1769 we find not a single species that, we may positively say, came from America although probably a few may have originated there. On the other hand, a surprisingly high percentage of the Tahiti weeds, at the time indicated, are clearly of Indo-Malaysian origin, some of which have not as yet reached America. The total number of species, no matter where they may have originated, is about 30, including one, rarely two, species in the following genera: *Kyllinga, Mariscus, Fimbristylis, Oplismenus, Eriochloa, Digitaria, Centotheca, Cenchrus, Eleusine, Paspalum, Plumbago, Physalis, Solanum, Achyranthes, Cyathula, Polygonum, Cardiospermum, Oxalis, Leucas, Ilysanthes (Vandellia), Urena, Mucuna, Desmodium, Adenostemma, Dichrocephala, Siegesbeckia, Phyllanthus, Fleurya,* and *Andropogon.* Of these it is suspected that *Adenostemma* may have originated in tropical America, as did *Physalis,* perhaps the *Siegesbeckia,* and possibly the form of *Solanum nigrum* L. *sensu lat.* (*S. nodiflorum* Jacq.) that now occurs in all tropical regions, and which is frequently eaten as greens.

When I noted the *Cenchrus echinatus* L. entry in the SOLANDER manuscript, my first thought was that we had an authentic pre-Magellan American weed from Tahiti. On examining the actual BANKS and SOLANDER specimen in 1951 I found it to represent a very different species, perhaps the Polynesian endemic, *Cenchrus calyculatus* Cav.; it is not at all the American *C. echinatus* L. As the rather numerous introduced food and other economic plants with one exception clearly came out of Malaysia and some of them, like the seedless breadfruit, had to be transported in earth as established young plants, it is rather clear how some of these Old World weeds reached Tahiti in early times. For that matter all of the basic food plants known to the Polynesians, other than a few fruit trees, had to be grown from underground parts (tubers, rhizomes and corms) which in turn were mostly carried from island to island in soil. It is surprising how many weed species were described in ROXBURGH's Flora Indica (1820-1832), the plants developing in the Calcutta Botanic Garden from seeds in soil scattered in the garden from containers in which a large number of living economic species had been transported from various parts of Malaysia (this for the benefit of the non-botanical theorizers).

One curious aspect of the early weed distribution between the two hemispheres is that there are, even now, no records for representatives of some of the species involved in the above list recorded from any part of America *(3)*. The only cultivated food plant which had reached Polynesia, from elsewhere, was the sweet potato. As its keeping qualities are limited it must have been introduced as a growing plant, in soil *(4)*.

One other very striking thing is that it is certain that many now ubiquitous pantropic weeds, clearly of American origin, were not present in Tahiti or elsewhere in Polynesia proper at the time the first explorations were made by Europeans. This involves very aggressive species of *Cassia, Hyptis, Mimosa, Argemone(5), Scoparia, Stachytarpheta* and numerous other herbaceous species in various other genera, to say nothing of the weedy shrubs and small trees such as *Lantana camara, Acacia farnesiana, Leucaena glauca, Psidium guajava* and other American species, all of which were conspicuous

---

3) I should still like to stress the evident fact that Old World economic species, ruderals and weeds reached America on the return voyages of such ships as those used on the Manila-Acapulco route. It was a two-way traffic. Elsewhere I discuss one case, *Dentella repens* J. R. & G. Forst., a very widely distributed ruderal plant (not an aggressive weed), extending from India and Ceylon through Malaysia to tropical Australia. The FORSTERs collected it in the New Hebrides. *See* p. 246.

4) OVIEDO, writing regarding this plant, about 1525, in Hispaniola (first published in 1535) noted: "Quando las batatas están bien curadas, se llevan hasta Espana muchas veçes, quando los navios açiertan á hacer pronto el viaje, y las mas veçes se pierden por la mar." (Hist. Gen. Nat. Ind. 1: 274. 1851). On returning from his first voyage COLUMBUS reached the Cape Verde Islands in a month, sailing from Hispaniola, so a month to six weeks, at most, would normally cover the time that well cured tubers would keep unless carried planted in soil. In very dry climates the tubers sometimes shrivel in drying and eventually produce buds. One can only infer from OVIEDO's statement (and by his own account, he carried sweet potato tubers from Hispaniola to Avila in Spain) that the tubers, unless planted in soil, could not have been transported on a balsa raft from Peru to the Tuamotu Islands, as this took HEYERDAHL three months. Almost of necessity the place of permanent introduction must have been one of the high islands for ecological reasons. I suspect that the vehicle by which the introduction was made — in fact it could scarcely have been otherwise — was on the faster Polynesian double canoe, either as cured tubers or tubers planted in soil; in this field of transportation of food plants these people, no matter from where they came, were very expert.

5) A recent morphological and cytogenetic study by Dr. G. B. OWNBEY shows that this Hawaiian form, *A. glauca* Nutt., is an endemic species not allied to *A. mexicana* L. nor even closely to *A. alba* Lestib. It has been confused with the latter two species for some scores of years. It is an American element in the Hawaiian flora, not a man-introduced taxon there, and is not identical with any known American representative of the genus. *See* p. 259.

by their absence at the time the first botanical explorations were made in the Pacific islands.

In 1941, when I published a basic paper on the significance of Polynesian weeds(6), depending rather largely on the SOLANDER lists of those species present there in 1769, I had to dissect SEEMANN's idea as expressed in his *Flora Vitiensis*, 1873. There were then sixty-four troublesome weeds in Fiji. He stated that forty-eight of these were common to America and Fiji and only sixteen were confined to Indo-Malaysia and Fiji. He thought that the Polynesian islands may have formed a bridge by which the New World species may have reached the Old World, and *vice versa*, but while he sagely observed that Fiji was to American weeds altogether virgin ground, he forgot to consider the historical aspects of plant introduction. His idea that the Pacific islands acted as stepping stones for the transmission of weeds in both directions is correct but he did not realize that the interposition of man as the real agent in transmission was essential. The real significance of this 1941 paper has been, most curiously, over-looked, but what is included in it cannot, for the most part, be challenged, no matter what others wish to prove. One reason why aggressive American weeds of tropical origin, once introduced and established in the Old World, develop "Napoleonic ambitions" (another way of stating, after SEEMANN, that "Viti is to American weeds altogether virgin ground") is that they were introduced without the insect, fungus and other enemies that kept them, more or less, in check in those parts of America whence they came.

With the impressive lists of weeds and of economic cultivated plants clearly of Indo-Malaysian origin, as well as the few domestic animals more or less generally distributed to the east as far as Fiji, the Marquesas and Hawaiian Islands, and the almost entire absence of plants and animals of American origin in all of the Pacific islands previous to the appearance of the Europeans in the early decades of the sixteenth century, one can see little or no basis for the HEYERDAHL claims that the Polynesians came from America, or that the "American Indians" ever peopled Polynesia proper; there seems to be no doubt that they did reach the Galapagos Islands but these islands are not Polynesian, and they may accidentally have reached certain Pacific Islands nearest to the west coast of America.

The biological evidence certainly favors the widely and generally accepted theory that the inhabitants of the Pacific islands came out of Malaysia. The fortunate preservation of the first botanical collections made by Messrs. BANKS, SOLANDER and the two FORSTERs gives us something very tangible on which to base this opinion, for actual specimens enable us to get away from speculation, and to me, a mere botanist, I can only repeat: the HEYERDAHL thesis is unproved and unprovable. If one could prove that a high percentage of the identifications of the actual collections made on Capt. COOK's three voyages are erroneous, or that the basic cultivated plants in the Polynesian

6) MERRILL, E. D. Man's Influence on the Vegetation of Polynesia, with Special Reference to Introduced Species. Proc. Sixth Pacific Sci. Congr. 4: 629-639. 1940 [1941]. Reprinted Chron. Bot. 10: 334-335. 1946. *(Merrilleana)*.

Islands in 1769 to 1779, as well as the weeds of Old World origin, were also in tropical America before these dates, that would perhaps alter the conclusion which I have reached; but there is no reason whatever to indicate that this was the case.

In addition to the manifestly man-introduced weeds in Polynesia there is another series described by SOLANDER from Tahiti which were apparently of pantropic distribution in 1769. I suspect, but cannot prove, that these are all natural "wides," many, perhaps all, having attained their extended ranges in earlier geologic times, long before man became a factor. Among these "wides" are certain species of sedges (*Kyllinga, Cyperus, Fimbristylis*), a few grasses, and a very few species in the dicotyledonous families. These are all worthy of individual, critical studies. They include *Ipomoea bona-nox* L., *Operculina turpethum* S. Manso, and a few others. I have, for the present, accepted the SEEMANN identification of SOLANDER's concept of each species as correct, rather than citing the original SOLANDER binomials, most of which were never published. Very likely the *Cardiospermum* which I have placed in the weed list belongs here.

It seems unnecessary to discuss the species of natural pantropic distribution such as *Thespesia populnea* Sol., *Hibiscus tiliaceus* L., *Dodonaea viscosa* Jacq., *Ipomoea pes-caprae* R. Br., *Canavalia rosea* (Sw.) DC., *Sophora tomentosa* L. and *Cassytha filiformis* L., although I judge that certain non-botanists see red when *Hibiscus tiliaceus* L. is included in this category. To them this "most valuable" plant must have been man-distributed between the two hemispheres because Dr. COOK said so! Now it is reported to be actually cultivated in Jamaica, not for its bast fibre (which was useful to primitive peoples) but to help maintain a normal supply of cricket bats in England. If any plant species attained universal distribution in the tropics via its floating seeds, this was it, whether Dr. CARTER likes it or not.

Then there were a few indigenous Pacific Islands species which the Polynesians themselves deliberately distributed from island to island, such as *Solanum uporo* Dun. (*S. anthropophagorum* Seem.) which was cooked for food (at cannibal feasts), and *Gardenia taitensis* DC. for its very fragrant large white flowers.

The term "science fiction" definitely applies to some of the conclusions of those whose foibles I have brought out into the light of day in Chapter VII. No matter what HEYERDAHL has so laboriously "proved", the pre-Magellan Pacific phytogeography fails to conform to this idea; I mean, of course, the cultivated plant species and weeds, dependent on man for their present distribution. As I will show, HEYERDAHL's phytogeographic views are not sound, simply because he did not know the subject and was hence incompetent to judge the actual value of the work of those on whom he depended for his evidence. In their special fields, others, for one reason or another, failed just as abjectly, chiefly because they were either ignorant of the early history of the routes by which plants were widely distributed between the two hemispheres through the agency of man; or if they were informed, they were blinded by the brilliance of their preconceived ideas.

Chapter V

EARLY TRADE ROUTES
IN RELATION TO PLANT DISTRIBUTION

A consideration of this phase of the subject of man-distributed economic plants and weeds is almost too elementary to warrant discussion. Yet, the historical aspects of early commercial routes are all too often ignored by some theorists, to say nothing of their general neglect of the published reports of early voyages of exploration. After all, man has travelled widely for a very long period of time. In early times, however, there were very distinct limitations to sea travel, particularly between the eastern and western hemispheres. This holds true for both the Atlantic and Pacific Oceans.

One may well understand why certain biologists would be unfamiliar with this situation, and, perhaps, why little attention has been given to the matter by anthropologists. But it is difficult to understand how and why some leading historical geographers have deviated from the strait and narrow way; after all, trade routes, ancient and modern, even if they have no direct connection with either biology or anthropology, do have a very direct connection with geographical studies.

It is doubtful if it is generally appreciated, even among many botanists, that, since the close of the fifteenth century, man, intentionally or inadvertently, has been the greatest single factor in extending the ranges of plants. This applies to plants characteristic of both the tropical and the temperate regions of the globe. Up to about 450 years ago, there were, with the well-known exception (*Lagenaria*), no cultivated economic species and, apparently, none of the aggressive weeds common to either the temperate or tropical parts of the two hemispheres. To these we must add the sweet potato and the coconut, both with limited distribution, in parts of the eastern and the western tropics.

A great change came with the expansion of European interests in the fifteenth century which I shall discuss, in some detail, in this chapter.

Introduced Plants in North America:— For the North Temperate Zone, FERNALD*(1)*, in 1950, recorded no less than 284 genera, from the northeastern United States and adjacent Canada, represented only by introduced and naturalized plants, as contrasted to 849 indigenous ones. As to species, 1098 are introduced and naturalized, as against 4425 indigenous ones. In minor categories (varieties, forms, and

---

1) FERNALD, M. L. GRAY's Manual of Botany. Eighth (Centennial) Edition — Illustrated. i-lxiv. 1-1692. Fig. 1-1806. 1950.

De TOMATL
MILTOMATL.

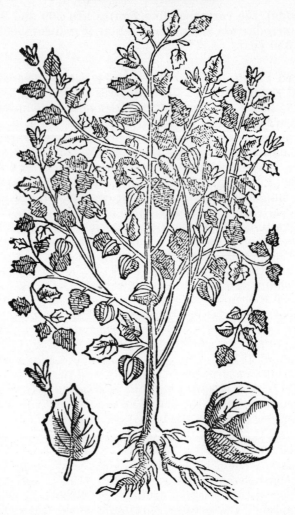

TEXT FIGURE 7. — *Physalis*, one of the ground cherries, a weed of American origin, now occurring throughout the world. — The Nahuatl name *Tomatl* is at present used for another, economically more important genus of the *Solanaceae*, the common tomato (*Lycopersicum*). This figure has been referred to *P. philadelphia* Lam. by I. OCHOTERENA in his *Historia de las Plantas de Nueva Espana, por* FRANCISCO HERNANDEZ (3 vols., Mexico, 1942-1946), the latest of the many editions of HERNANDEZ's writings. — The above and several following wood cuts have been reproduced (often slightly enlarged) from the RECCHI edition of HERNANDEZ's "Thesaurus", *Nova Plantarum. . . . Mexicanorum Historiae* (Romae, 1651). Most of the wood cuts from this Italian edition are supposedly based on drawings made, between 1571-1577, by HERNANDEZ's Aztec assistants. As it is important to ascertain which plants HERNANDEZ actually found in Mexico, in the 1570's, it may be mentioned that material from his original note books, burned in Spain, and not included in the RECCHI and other editions, was included in his PLINIUS edition (hitherto unpublished? ms. in the Madrid Biblioteca Nacional?). This was utilized by GERONIMO DE HUERTO in his well-known Spanish PLINIUS edition of 1629 (*cf.* MENÉNDEZ y PELAYO, *Ciencia Espanola*, vol. 3).

named hybrids) the corresponding figures are 209 and 2608. As to the time of introduction and naturalization, it reduces itself to a record of not over 350 years.

Introduced Plants in California:— The period covered is roughly two hundred years, although the Spaniards explored at least a part of the coast in 1542-43. No permanent settlements were made until much later. JEPSON(2), in 1925, taking a conservative view as to the limits of species, recognized a total of 4019 of which 292 were naturalized aliens. The naturalized species were mostly from those parts of the world with a Mediterranean type of climate. Regarding these aliens, all introduced within the past 200 years, his statement is very significant: "The number 292 gives no proper concept of these alien populations, since the species are often very aggressive, produce countless numbers of individuals and have an important significance in relation to the dominance or persistence of native species which in many cases they successfully dispossess." This statement applies to many aliens introduced into the eastern United States, a beautiful example being *Lonicera japonica* Thunb., unknown to CHAPMAN as late as 1897. *Setaria faberi* Herrm. was first recorded only two decades ago, yet within this short period it has become one of the most widely distributed and aggressive weeds (*see* p. 283). The case of *Trapa natans* L. is disconcerting but, at the same time, amusing. Its whole history with us dates from about 1877 (*see* p. 283). The numerous tropical American weed species, once naturalized in the Old World tropics, follow the same pattern in their new homes, but what is not understood by the non-botanical theorists is that the actual introductions do not antedate the period 1500-1565, as far as the Old World is concerned.

Introduced Plants in New Zealand:— Even more striking, for the South Temperate Zone, is the situation in New Zealand, where the influx of aliens had hardly started before 1790. Most of the influx has taken place within the past century. CHEESEMAN, in 1925, recognized 1763 species, the greater part indigenous. At the same time, he listed 528 species in 285 genera as introduced and naturalized. ALLAN(3), in 1940, was also conservative, his list of introduced and naturalized plants comprised 500 species, distributed over 261 genera in 63 families. In an appendix, he enumerated about 440 additional species, recorded as occurring in New Zealand, which, for one reason or another, he thought best not to include in his handbook. Yet, of these 440 species, he admitted that more than thirty had fairly good claims to naturalization. HEALY(4), in 1949, by including the hardy cultigens, trees, ornamentals, etc., raised the total to 1126 species, the

2) JEPSON, W. L. A Manual of the Flowering Plants of California. 1-1238. fig. 1-1023. 1923-25.

3) ALLAN, H. H. A Handbook of the Naturalized Flora of New Zealand. 1-344. Fig. 1-141b. 1940.

4) HEALY, A. J. Evolution of the Alien Flora of New Zealand. Trans. Roy. Soc. New Zeal. 77(5): 160-162, 1 graph, 1949.

TEXT FIGURE 8. — *Helianthus annuus* L., the common Sunflower. — One of the very few, North American cultivated plants which originated in the Central Plains region, not in Peru as one might gather from HERNANDEZ's account of the *Flos Solis* which begins with "De Chimalatl Pervina". In the 16th century the range of this hybrid sunflower extended southward at least as far as Mexico. — From F. HERNANDEZ's *Nova Plantarum . . . Mexicanorum Historiae* (Romae, 1651), probably drawn in Mexico, between 1571 and 1577.

rapidity of increase being indicated with a graph, by decades, from 1786 to 1946. *Phalaris canariensis* L., a Mediterranean species, was recorded by the FORSTERS on COOK's second voyage in 1773*(5)*; and, with the few cultigens which the Maoris introduced from Polynesia in the thirteenth to the fourteenth century, a very few weeds such as *Oxalis repens* L. and *Solanum nodiflorum* Jacq. (*S. nigrum* auct. plur.) may have arrived earlier. Following 1786, the increase was, at first, slow; but, when actual colonization commenced in 1840, the tempo increased. From 1850 on, the increase was very rapid; and it still continues, as in other parts of the world. If we accept HEALY's figures, the New Zealand flora has been vastly increased by deliberate and inadvertent man-introduced species within a little more than a century, for to the about 1760 recognized and mostly indigenous species may be added about 1125 introduced and more or less naturalized ones, bringing the present total flora up to about 2890 species. If this pace be maintained for a few decades more, very soon in this country, the native vegetation of which has been vastly augmented by a totally different alien flora, in less than one and a half centuries, the number of introduced species will exceed that of the indigenous ones. This great change, in but a little over a century, is due strictly to modern man and his activities.

Introduced Plants in the Tropics:— There has been little special study of the problem in tropical regions, but the number of exotic genera and species, already introduced and naturalized in Malaysia, Melanesia, Micronesia, and Polynesia, is very great and is increasing rapidly. This is also the case in Argentina, in Australia, and in the tropical parts of North, Central and South America, as well as in Asia and Africa. In California, there has been a very great influx of Mediterranean weeds which do not thrive in the eastern United States. It is very unwise for theorists in non-botanical fields to ignore this situation. When, how, and by which means a cultigen or a weed first found its way, across either the Pacific or the Atlantic, is most important. Whenever actual dates can be established, they always prove the weakness of preconceived theories of the extreme diffusionists.

BACKER *(5a)* has done pioneering work on Javanese weeds, while I have done some work on those of Guam and the Philippines.

---

5) There is a FORSTER specimen at Kew, apparently from the material received from the Liverpool Botanical Garden. This specimen was found by Mr. ALSTON, not in the *Phalaris canariensis* L. folder, but among the *P. minor* Retz. sheets. It must be studied critically, as it may represent some other species than either of the two above cited. Mr. ALSTON thinks that it may have been introduced into New Zealand by the *Endeavour* on COOK's first voyage. Captain COOK recorded the fact that he had planted many kinds of seeds on his first voyage, and that this garden site was visited again on the second voyage. Four species of *Phalaris* are recorded by Dr. ALLAN for New Zealand, all introduced.

5a) BACKER, C. A. Plantes exotiques naturalisées dans Java. Ann. Jard. Bot. Buitenzorg Suppl. 3: 393-420. 1909. Verwilderingscentra op Java van uitheemsche planten. De Tropische Natuur, Jubileum-Uitgave, p. 51-60. 1936. These references were provided by Dr. C. G. G. J. van STEENIS.

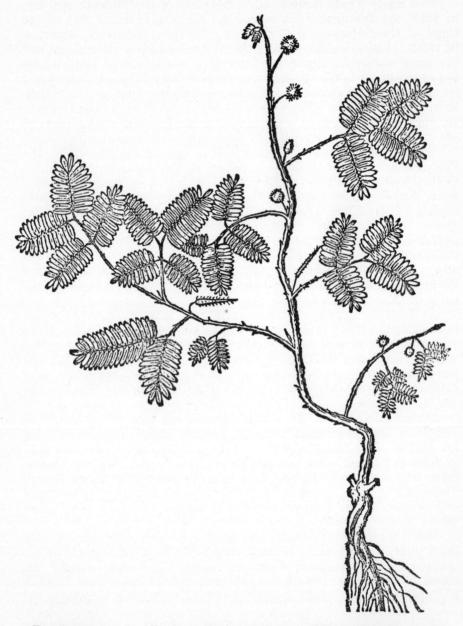

TEXT FIGURE 9. — *Mimosa pudica* L., the Sensitive Plant, originally a native of Brazil, now a weed, widely distributed throughout the tropics of the Old and New Worlds. It can be controlled by a 3% Na arsenate spray. — Reproduced from the *Historiae Naturalis Brasiliae* (1648) by PISO & MARCGRAVE.

Two Early Trade Routes:— At the close of the fifteenth century, in 1498, the Portuguese discovered the route to India, by way of the Cape of Good Hope, and COLUMBUS effectively discovered America, in 1492. It is no accident that tropical American economic plants and the more numerous aggressive American weeds almost immediately began to appear in the Orient. The former were purposely introduced by the early Portuguese and Spanish colonizers, later by the Dutch, British, and French. The weeds merely came along as commensals, for they are as definitely commensals, as far as man is concerned, as are rats, mice, the common cat, fleas, lice, and intestinal parasites.

Soon after establishing themselves at Goa in the year 1500, the Portuguese extended their control over various other parts of India, Ceylon, and limited parts of China and Malaysia, such as Macao, Malacca, Amboina, and Formosa(6). Why do we find certain weeds obviously of Brazilian origin (excellent examples are *Heliotropium indicum* L., *Malvastrum coromandelianum* (L.) Garcke, and *Mimosa pudica* L.) naturalized, at an early date, in the Orient, after the establishment of European colonies in Indo-Malaysia? There were others of Mexican origin, at first particularly in Guam and in the Philippines, but most of them soon became widely distributed in other parts of the oriental tropics.

At first, the Portuguese route went southward, more or less direct to the Cape of Good Hope. After Brazil had been discovered in 1500, a new and much used route was developed from Portugal to Goa, by way of Brazil and the Cape of Good Hope, for fresh food, wood and water were available in Brazil, and, at least at certain seasons, prevailing winds on this new route were more favorable than on the one directly south.

Incidentally, Mr. A. W. EXELL informs me that when, about the middle of the seventeenth century, Holland and Portugal struggled for control of Angola, many of the Portuguese soldiers, who took part in that campaign, were brought from Brazil; and then, of course, there was the long continued slave trade between Angola and Brazil. The route to India, via Brazil and the Cape of Good Hope, was a perfect setup for the transmission of Brazilian economic plants and weeds to the orient.

When Europeans initiated and later expanded their activities in the Pacific, with them, of course, came other despised and, too often, ignored tropical weeds of American origin. The route, usually followed by exploring expeditions and adventurers, was from Europe to Cape Horn. All ships stopped in Brazil to take on supplies. Up

---

6) A reminder of the Portuguese occupation of parts of Formosa, as they expanded their operations from Macao in the last half of the sixteenth century, is the presence there of the littoral species *Erythraea spicata* Pers. (of the Iberian Peninsula, the Mediterranean region, Asia Minor, Caspian Sea region). This is not a weed. It has extended its range southward to the Batan Islands between Formosa and Luzon. Thus, plants got about with the early European explorers. It seems scarcely necessary to mention the fact that Formosa (meaning "beautiful"), the widely used name for the island for which Taiwan has been substituted within the present century, is Portuguese in origin, as is the name Labrador for a large part of eastern Canada.

to the time of Captain COOK's first voyage (1768-1771), the route followed, once in the Pacific, was northward to the approximate latitude of Acapulco in Mexico, thence westward to Guam; this was a well defined route. It was followed rather strictly because fresh food and water could be obtained in Guam. When scurvy was a real menace, on all long voyages, fresh food was essential.

Thus all of the Pacific region, south of the equator, remained unknown to the Europeans, except for the voyages of MENDAÑA (1567) and QUIROS with TORRES (1595, 1606) from Peru to the Solomon Islands, Santa Cruz Islands and the New Hebrides, and a few Dutch ventures into the region from the west. This route, south of the line, was known only to the Spanish navigators. Unlike the Acapulco - Manila route, which became known to their competitors, the Spaniards did succeed in keeping the southern route a secret by forbidding early publication of MENDAÑA's report.

As pointed out, most of the European ships entering the Pacific from the west stopped in Brazil for supplies, and thus to the Mexican weeds transmitted to the Orient, by way of Guam and Manila, must be added the Brazilian ones. These same Brazilian weeds were also independent, early introductions into India, Ceylon and even Malaysia, by the older Portuguese trade route which antedated the Spanish one by six or seven decades.

The historical geographer, knowing little or no botany, and merely observing that in Indo-Malaysia and Polynesia strictly American weeds are now dominant, forgets (or never realized) that weeds are all heliophiles. Nor does he know that the vast open areas, in eastern Brazil and Mexico, were the centers of origin of a high percentage of the aggressive tropical weeds. Furthermore, he does not realize that these weeds, in foreign lands, are never found in the primary rain forests of the Orient. When the forests were cleared to provide space for the cultivation of food plants, these introduced aliens, once established, spread with great rapidity. Dr. C. A. BACKER's observation on the Napoleonic ambitions of American weeds in Java (cf. p. 238) is not only very expressive but is very true; it applies to all parts of the Orient, where these unwanted commensals of man have become established. The process, unwittingly initiated by the Portuguese about 1500, is still going on, for an appreciable number of these tropical American species became established, in and near Manila, immediately following World War II. They spread just as rapidly, once established, as did their predecessors of 400 years ago.

Thus it was that there were two totally different routes by which economic plants and weeds of Brazilian origin reached the Orient (1) *to the Cape of Good Hope direct by way of Brazil to India and Malaysia,* and (2) *by way of Brazil to Cape Horn, thence to Guam, and finally to the other parts of the Orient.* And the number of ships that followed the Cape Horn route from 1520 to well past the beginning of the nineteenth century was surprisingly large.

The Acapulco-Manila Galleon Line:— The third route by which many Mexican economic plants and, especially, aggressive weeds reached the Orient was the long-continued Acapulco-Manila galleon line(7). The first galleon crossed the Pacific in 1565, the last reached its final port in 1815, an interval of 250 years. This government-sponsored and government-controlled shipping line, monopolistic in character, holds the record of being the line with the longest continuous record of navigation, under the same auspices. Usually, one ship was dispatched each year from Acapulco (at first from Navidad) in Mexico, to Manila, and one from Manila to Mexico; but, sometimes, two or even three were sent each year. In addition, there were some clandestine, private enterprise interlopers at times, for successful ventures yielded what were veritable fortunes. Normally, about three months were needed for the westward voyage, but, occasionally, two and a half months sufficed, these being considered fast trips. Sometimes, however, five or six months or even more were needed. The eastward voyages were much more time-consuming, five or six to seven or eight months being required, and records exist of one trip which took an entire year.

SCHURZ quotes a striking statement, made by the much travelled G. F. GEMELLI CARERI, in the latter part of the seventeenth century, who made the round trip (Acapulco to Manila and return) : "The Voyage from the Philippine Islands to America may be called the longest and most dreadful of any in the World". In the early years of this long-lived enterprise, the size of the individual ships was limited to a few hundred tons, but restrictions were not enforced, and, finally, they were lifted. The number of individuals transported, east and west, was very great. In 1756, it is recorded that there were in excess of 600 passengers, crew, and soldiers, on the *Santisima Trinidad.* This ship, her capacity in excess of 2,000 tons, was taken by the British, who captured Manila, on Oct. 5, 1762. On her arrival in Plymouth the next year she created somewhat of a sensation. She was offered for sale, as one of the largest ships ever seen in England, and people came from all over southern England to see this "mightiest of galleons" which, incidentally, was constructed in the Philippines.

On these voyages, losses in life were great; scurvy and beriberi took their toll, and shortages in food and water were often serious. The greatest loss of lives on any one ship occurred in 1767, when an eastbound galleon (apparently the *San José*) was salvaged off Guatulco, south of Acapulco — all on board were dead! There were other total losses, when individual ships were burned or wrecked at sea, or cast on shore where hostile natives killed all or many of those who reached land. Added to normal risks, was the chance of interception by raiders and buccaneers, for the ships carried immensely valuable cargoes.

---

7) SCHURZ, W. L. The Manila Galleon. 1-453. 1939. This work is based largely on the great mass of documents preserved in the Archives of the Indies at Sevilla. Included in the Sevilla archives are Manila, Acapulco, Guadelajara and other Mexico documents appertaining to this old shipping line.

No matter what the faults of construction of these, at that time, great ships were, and no matter how faulty navigation may have been occasionally, the Spaniards had charts and sailing directions, and knew where they were going. One cannot say this of renegades, fugitives from justice, and Buddhist priests (Buddhism dates from 500 B.C.) whom a young anthropologist would have bring the advanced cultures to America from Asia (*without* any Asiatic food plants)! They had no charts, no sailing directions, and no knowledge whatever of the Pacific Ocean. With such boats as may have been available to them, there was little chance of any one of them reaching America, no matter how favorable climatic conditions may have been. To a botanist familiar with the Malaysian-Polynesian scene, but with only a passing knowledge of anthropology, this is one of the most fantastic "explanations" imaginable, even surpassing the HEYERDAHL Kon-Tiki theory as presented in his *American Indians in the Pacific*.

Further Notes on Early Voyages and Routes:— It seems needless to go into details about the important Cape Horn route to the Orient. If one wishes to follow it up, Dr. PETER BUCK*(8)* has provided a remarkably good bibliography (*also see* p. 230). To gain an excellent summary as to what happened in these early days, it is recommended that the recently published volume by PENROSE*(9)* be studied, not merely read.

I have not found the time to examine the original Portuguese records, but should one be really interested in gathering facts on just when eastern Brazil assumed a major importance in the old route from Lisbon to Goa, by way of the Cape of Good Hope, and other parts of the Orient, PENROSE provides an excellent bibliography.

I merely present brief data regarding some of the earlier Portuguese voyages. When BARTHOLOMEW DIAS left Lisbon in August, 1487, on an exploring expedition southward, he reached South Africa. On his return voyage, he discovered and named Cabo Tormentoso, a name which immediately, upon his return to Lisbon, was renamed Cabo de Boa Esperança (Cape of Good Hope). He had reached Algoa Bay, which, a decade later, became a point of departure for Goa. His trip from Portugal to Algoa Bay (east of the Cape of Good Hope), and back, took somewhat more than sixteen months. Failure to continue further was due to lack of food and the general condition and demands of the crew, but his accomplishment did show that the passage to India was possible, hence the name Cabo de Boa Esperança.

On July 8, 1497, VASCO DA GAMA, with four ships, left Portugal to capitalize on the DIAS discovery; he reached Calicut on the Malabar coast of India on May 20, 1498, making the outward passage in some-

8) BUCK P. (TE RANGI HIROA). An Introduction to Polynesian Anthropology. Bishop Mus. Bull. 187: 1-133. 1945; and also his Vikings of the Sunrise. xiii. 1-335. illus. 1938.

9) PENROSE, B. Travel and Discovery in the Renaissance, 1420-1620. i-xvi. 1-369. illus. 1952.

what more than nine months. On March 5, 1500, CABRAL, in charge of a fleet of thirteen ships, left Lisbon to exploit VASCO DA GAMA's discovery of the route to India, proceeding far to the west, possibly in the hope of finding more favorable sailing conditions or being driven there by unfavorable winds. In any case, on April 22, the Brazilian coast was sighted and the next day a landing was made at 17° S. He reached India six months after sailing from Lisbon.

Water, wood, certain food supplies, and, in due time, ports and settlements were available in Brazil. Thus from 1500 to about 1665, by this too-frequently forgotten trade route, the flora of the oriental tropics was enriched by various deliberately introduced economic species from South America and by a distinctly larger number of aggressive weeds of Brazilian origin. The Brazilian introductions, as we have seen, reached the oriental tropics by two entirely different routes, one around the Cape of Good Hope, the other around Cape Horn.

What certain ill-informed modern theorists overlook entirely is the Portuguese route to India via Brazil, which was initiated in 1500 and which antedated the permanent establishment of the Spanish route from Mexico to the Philippines by sixty-five years; and these sixty-five years were critical ones in the history of the introductions of American plant species into India, Ceylon, Siam, Malaysia, Kwang-tung, Formosa and even Japan.

Up to about 1600, the Spaniards had thorough control of the Pacific with MAGELLAN (1520-1521), LOYASA (1526), SAAVEDRA (1527), GAETANO (1542), LEGASPI (1565), as well as the MENDAÑA, QUIROS and TORRES expeditions, "south of the line," from Peru to the Solomon Islands, New Guinea, the Santa Cruz Islands and the New Hebrides. Their operations, otherwise, were largely confined to the long-con-tinued Acapulco-Manila galleon line (1565-1815) plus, of course, an unknown number of often unauthorized, speculative voyages. The Acapulco-Manila galleon line was actually a government monopoly, partly for the benefit of the Spanish government itself (at least for New Spain or Mexico and the Philippines) and partly for the benefit of private traders.

Even before 1600 the picture had changed, as DRAKE entered the Pacific in 1578, followed by CAVENDISH in 1587. Then for legitimate, and in some cases illegitimate, reasons other Britons came by way of the Cape Horn route; the Dutch, French, Spanish, German, Danish, Swedish, Austrian, and Russian expeditions followed, and finally, be-fore the middle of the last century, American. In the days of sailing ships, about sixty-five "official" expeditions traversed the Pacific, with from one to three ships each. By the beginning of the nineteenth century, trading and whaling ships rapidly increased in number, while missions were established in Tahiti (1797) (the Spanish attempt in 1774 was short lived), and in Hawaii (1820).

Long before the time of steamships, the Pacific ocean had become a more or less well travelled "lake". As to the total number of ships involved, the figure ran into many thousands before sailing ships were largely replaced by steam. WILLIAM ELLIS records, in his *Narrative of a Tour through Hawaii*, that, when he was in the Hawaiian Islands (1823-24), there were at certain seasons as many as forty ships at anchor in Honolulu at one time. Very seldom, at any time of the year, were there less than three or four. Weeds, of course, were not distributed by all ships, but one should consider that, at least from the time of QUIROS, it was customary to carry some livestock (as sheep, goats, pigs, often domestic fowl, including the American Muscovy duck and the turkey). By the time of Captain COOK also cattle and horses were taken aboard. All this provided a natural setup for the accidental dissemination of weeds, as the ruminants had to be supplied with forage. Thus it was that when a stop was made for more than a day or so, such live animals as were being carried were taken on shore; when the ship departed, the forage supply was renewed.

By the time LINNAEUS had established the binomial system in 1753, some two hundred and fifty years of European control had existed in Ceylon, India, Malacca, Amboina, the Philippines, Macao, etc., and an extensive commerce had been developed. Here, as with the Acapulco-Manila galleon line, our plant commensals merely followed the trade routes, first the Portuguese (for 165 years) and the Spanish (for 250 years), then the Dutch, English and French, as well as various expeditions and missions sponsored and supported by other nations.

The Time Element in Trans-Pacific Voyages:— One suspects that some of our modern theorists, especially those with no personal knowledge of the Pacific region nor of phytogeography, think of sea voyages in terms of time-lapse more appropriate for travel on modern liners or by air, and do not give proper consideration to the situation that prevailed in earlier times. As I pointed out before, there was a period when man had to depend on rafts for water transport, then simple canoes, then outrigger canoes, and, by the time the more distant Pacific islands were occupied, double canoes or catamarans. Apparently, some theorists also give just as little attention to the conditions that prevailed in the early days of sailing ships. One need not go back beyond the period of European expansion, from the late fifteenth to the close of the eighteenth century to realize what some of the limitations were.

Is it possible that youthful reading of *Robinson Crusoe* or *The Swiss Family Robinson* has left the impression on some mature minds that all one had to do, on reaching an uninhabited tropical isle, to provide oneself with food, was to reach out with one hand and grab a banana, and with the other hand twist off a coconut — as simply as that! Some do not seem to understand that, on such islands, and in undeveloped tropical areas on the larger land masses, one could just as easily starve to death (except for sea food, birds, etc.) as on a barren desert. The fact is that, in all the Pacific islands, including New Zealand, which were among the latest parts of the world to be occupied by man, there were no important native basic food plants, with the exception of the few which were already established when the Europeans arrived. These had been introduced by earlier colonists from the west. Later, they secured one, the sweet potato, from South America. Originally, the natives had no taro, giant taro, sugar cane, elephant's ear, breadfruit, and no domestic animals. The very few native species in the islands, parts of which could be eaten, have been listed on p. 195. The pioneers who occupied the widely spaced Pacific islands were at first, necessarily, almost wholly dependent on sea food, birds and birds' eggs.

And, if we think that the variety of food was limited in Polynesia, even after the Polynesians had brought in a small number of plant and animal species, how infinitely more limited were the resources of New Zealand, when first explored by Captain COOK in 1769. There were then established the sweet potato, taro, and gourd, and the Maoris had introduced the dog. In the months when no tubers or corms were available, a basic food consisted of the rhizomes of the local form of bracken, *Pteridium aquilinum* (L.) Kuhn var. *esculentum* (Forst. f.) Kuhn, of which vast quantities were consumed.

Importance of the Marianas Islands:— When MAGELLAN entered the Pacific, in 1520, three months elapsed before he, most providentially, discovered Guam; other than a few small and mostly desert islands, his first real landfall. By that time he was destitute of supplies, his crew lived on the very verge of starvation and scurvy was rampant. He still had about a thousand miles to go before reaching the Philippines. Thus, for more than three centuries, one of the Marianas Islands (usually Guam) was a "must" for all expeditions entering the Pacific by way of Cape Horn route and for all galleons in the Acapulco-Manila service (on both their eastward and westward trips), for there the much needed fresh food and water could be secured. Up to the time of Captain COOK's first expedition (1768-1771), with the exception of the voyages of MENDAÑA, QUIROS, and TORRES (1567, 1595, 1606) from Peru to the Solomon Islands, Santa Cruz, New Hebrides and New Guinea, "south of the line," the Marianas Islands were always the objective on the western trip.

Two years before Captain COOK spent three months at Tahiti, Captain WALLIS, after passing Cape Horn, had proceeded far enough to the west to discover the island. His discovery of Tahiti was, in effect, accidental, as the Marianas Islands were really his objective.

The Floras of Guam and the Philippines:— It is obvious that the long-continued Acapulco - Manila route (over a period of 250 years) did serve as a medium for the enrichment of the floras of Guam and the Philippines. For the most part, the weed-species then introduced from Mexico, sooner or later, appeared in other parts of the oriental tropics. Yet, strange as it may seem, certain aliens then established in Guam, and others in the Philippines, still exist there, but have not, as yet, been found elsewhere in the Orient. These alien weeds will never die out so long as man is a factor in controlling the native vegetation for agricultural purposes. As soon as the primary, or in many places merely the secondary forest, replaces the open agricultural lands, the exotic weeds will, for the most part, disappear, except in regions where special climatic conditions exist which permit the persistence of non-forested areas or forests of the very open type.

As we have seen, there are certain American weeds and economic species which were originally described in European literature on the basis of specimens first collected in the Old World. This is exactly what one might expect, for certain economic plants and a great many more species of weeds, once introduced, spread very rapidly. Very few of the early botanical explorers in the Orient went far into the interior, before about 1750, being obliged to confine their collecting efforts to the settled areas where alien species of cultivated plants and weeds, once introduced, always abound. It is no accident that the ruderal tropical floras about the larger ports and the settled areas generally in both hemispheres are to a high degree made up of the same species of cultivated plants, weeds and ornamental plants.

The fact that certain weed species, clearly of American origin, were first named and described in European botanical literature, on the basis of specimens collected in India, Ceylon, or Malaysia, has been cited by Dr. CARTER as proof that these species were widely distributed in the tropics of both hemispheres, long before the discovery of America. In view of the historical aspects of the situation, as briefly sketched above, I think no more need be said about this matter. As a rule, even weeds, much less the cultigens, do not extend their ranges from one hemisphere to another without the intervention and aid of man. This situation should be realized even by those who do not understand the elements of botany, and who publish superficially impressive papers proving what they want to believe.

Beginning about 2,000 years ago (perhaps a few hundred years earlier), the advanced peoples of India reached Malaysia and gradually extended their control over the archipelago(10). For a long period before this, there had obviously been waves of migration of less advanced peoples, from southern Asia into Malaysia by way of the Malay Peninsula. Almost coincident with the expansion of the more advanced Indian peoples southward, or somewhat later, the Chinese extended their commercial enterprises into Malaysia, reaching the Philippines, Borneo, Sumatra, and Java, and eventually extending their activities to the southeast as far as New Guinea, long before the arrival of the Europeans in Malaysia.

It is an interesting fact that in this period many species of economic plants (and with them various weeds), particularly from India, were introduced into Malaysia, and, even today, current native names, designating many of these exotic species in Malaysia and in the Philippines, are of Sanskrit or Chinese origin. The names came into the archipelago with the introduced plants — a perfectly natural process.

Thus, as far as the Philippine plant names for certain early introduced species are concerned, we find a third very impressive list mostly of scarcely modified or only slightly changed Nahuatl (Mexican)

10) VLEKKE, B. H. M. Nusantara, A History of the East Indian Archipelago. i-xv. 1-439. illus. 1943.

names which were introduced into the islands between about 1570 and 1812 by way of the Acapulco-Manila galleons. And these names of Sanskrit, Chinese, and Mexican origin have persisted unchanged, or only slightly changed, century after century, some of them for at least 2,000 years! But the Mexican ones came after 1565.

It is, however, desirable to call further attention to some of the problems involved in the long continued Acapulco-Manila galleon route (cf. p. 231). In the entire recorded history of navigation, no other single line continued so long in operation, covering as it did a period of about 250 years. The effect of this on the dissemination of certain Chinese trade goods, the Mexican silver dollar, certain aspects of Spanish culture, and, for the purposes of this paper, economic plant species and weeds, was very great. In previous papers(11) I considered some of the economic plants which were purposely and the weeds which were accidentally distributed over this long continued trade route. In the small area covered by the Flora of Manila (40 square miles) there were, in 1912, about 1,000 known species, of which 175 were from Mexico and Brazil. In Guam, 212 square miles, there were, in 1914, 550 known species, of which 113 were from Mexico and Brazil. These figures include purposely introduced cultivated species, as well as inadvertently introduced weeds; they stress the floral influence of the old Acapulco-Manila galleon line on special areas remote from tropical America which too many tend to forget some hundred and forty years after it ceased operations.

Critical Notes on Authors who disregarded the early Trade Routes:— The STONOR-ANDERSON theory of maize in Assam in pre-Magellan times shows that these authors were ignorant of or forgot about the *direct* route from eastern Brazil to Goa on the Malabar coast of India by way of the Cape of Good Hope following 1500, for eastern Brazil is certainly where the strains of maize (popcorn) now cultivated in Assam originated. They, apparently, forgot even to look up what WILLIAM ROXBURGH wrote about maize in India before 1800. He said: "Cultivated in various parts of India in gardens, and only as a delicacy; but not anywhere on the continent of India, so far as I can learn, as an extensive crop." This indicates to me that what ROXBURGH knew was a popcorn and not a field corn ("only as a delicacy"); it apparently was not sweet corn.

COGNIAUX who, in 1881, concluded correctly that all the wild species of *Cucurbita* were native of America, but erroneously that all the cultivated species were Asiatic in origin, failed, just as STONOR and ANDERSON did, to consider the old trade route. He set the stage for the curious ideas, which still persist in uninformed circles, that the region to the west of western Pakistan represents a great centre of diversity in forms of *Cucurbita*; of course it is, for a very variable form introduced from the bulge of Brazil to Goa on the Malabar

11) MERRILL, E. D. Notes on the Flora of Manila with Special Reference to the Introduced Element. Philip. Jour. Sci. Bot. 7: 145-208. 1912; An Enumeration of the Plants of Guam. Op. Cit. 9: 17-155. 1914. See also: An Enumeration of Philippine Flowering Plants, 4 vol. (1923-26), 2135 pages.

coast simply continued to vary and, naturally, spread northward and westward (*cf.* p. 280). After all, much can happen to a variable culti- gen in a few hundred years, as is shown by the sweet potato in Poly- nesia and New Zealand. This old commercial route also explains the presence of the Malabar or Siamese gourd in India: look to eastern Brazil! And to those who speak of a certain type of peanut as resem- bling "narrow little shoestrings," with at least the inference that these (*cf.* p. 295) might have reached China from Peru: look to Brazil and remember the old Portuguese trade route which, by 1516, ex- tended from Goa to Canton! Brazil should never be overlooked as the source region of American plants established in the Orient at an early date following 1500 A.D.

A leading geographer, closing a letter in response to an inquiry stated: "I hope you will be able to concede that we, who have been following trails of far communication also, to the best of our several and unequal abilities, are trying to find closer approach to the truth." Conceded; but I would suggest that before getting lost in the maze of imaginary trails, some attention be given to the plainly marked ones that too many trail blazers of the present generation overlook.

The Distribution of American Weeds:— The aggressive American weeds, all heliophiles and principally from Mexico and eastern Brazil, once established in a new home where climatic conditions are favor- able, simply do not die out. And cultivated food plants, once estab- lished, with few exceptions normally persist only as long as man is present to care for them. In all of the settled areas of the Malaysian, Micronesian, and the Polynesian regions, Dr. C. A. BACKER's apt ob- servation that in Java these American weeds "display Napoleonic ambitions" applies.

In general, these American weeds are now dominant everywhere in the Old World tropics. Yet in 1769, perhaps not a single weed of unquestionable American origin (with the possible exception of two or three which might have originated in America) was found by BANKS and SOLANDER in densely populated Tahiti. Only a few years later (COOK's second voyage), one clearly American weed (*Waltheria*) was found there by the two FORSTERS, this apparently introduced on the *Endeavour* in 1769 (*cf.* p. 245).

The four very active botanists concerned spent a total of about five months engaged in what actually amounted to an intensive botan- ical survey of the densely populated area about Matavai Bay, on the coastal plain. Few low altitude species were overlooked. In such a densely populated area, the soil is annually disturbed for agricultural purposes, and introduced and naturalized weeds, as well as ruderals, always occur in abundance. *The significance of the absence or the practical absence of American weeds in Tahiti, the Friendly Islands, Hawaii, New Zealand, and the other Pacific Islands visited on COOK's three voyages, 1769 to 1779, at the time these islands were discovered or first explored, is most important and has been very generally ignored or misinterpreted.* This phase of the problem is worthy of an intensive study, for the records, *i.e.*, the botanical collections then made, are still available. And yet, as MARY CORMACK (*see* Taxon 1: 123, 1952) has expressed it: "How sweet our errant fancies to which we fondly cling! You may write a thousand papers but it will not mean a thing!"

One awaits, without undue anxiety, any possible refutation of the fact that, with one exception, all of the basic food and certain other economic plants utilized by the early Polynesians and all of their weeds (with a very few possible exceptions) came from Malaysia. As we have seen, the recorded attempt of QUIROS in 1595 to establish maize in the Marquesas Islands, and a decade later maize and other American species in the Santa Cruz Islands, failed, as did the later attempt of the Spaniards to establish an American species of *Phaseolus* (this was recorded as *pallares* and probably represented *Phaseolus pallar* Molina, a species still not well understood, *cf.* p. 249) in Tahiti, in the last third of the eighteenth century.

A sage remark made by my friend, I. H. BURKILL, in December 1952, while reading the proofs on his HOOKER lecture given before the Linnean Society in 1951(*12*), sums up the situation admirably: "Its ethnology will be beyond the ready knowledge of most botanists and its botany Greek to most ethnologists"; and I might add "to others who *will* theorize without a proper background". This BURKILL paper can be highly recommended to all those who are prone to use guess-work as to when man reached certain isolated or remote parts of the world and as to what he took with him on his travels.

---

12) BURKILL, I. H. Habits of Man and the Origins of the Cultivated Plants of the Old World. Proc. Linn. Soc. 164: 12-42. fig. 1-9. 1953.

Chapter VI

DISAGREEMENTS BETWEEN BOTANICAL FACTS
AND PRE-CONCEIVED THEORIES
IN VARIOUS FIELDS

It is to be regretted that the beautifully prepared SOLANDER manuscripts, with their greatly detailed plant descriptions, were not published soon after the return of the *Endeavour* to England in 1771. The manuscripts of special value to those interested in the Pacific and Malaysian problems are the descriptive texts appertaining to the floras of Tierra del Fuego, Tahiti and the Society Islands, New Zealand, eastern Australia and Java. BANKS and SOLANDER made the first botanical collections in the regions listed above, with the exception of Java, and a very few Australian plants brought home by earlier explorers, particularly Captain DAMPIER (1). Had early publication been effected, some minor, strictly taxonomic problems, which are still bothersome, would never have developed. Further, there is a very remote possibility that actual publication might have had a beneficial effect on certain theoretical ethnologists, some of the neogeographers and now, strangely, a very few geneticists, and might have caused them to be more cautious in supporting the idea that Asiatic cultures (curiously, *minus* all Old World cultivated food plants) reached America via the Pacific Islands or, as some still more curiously insist, via *direct* connection between India and America, after a highly developed civilization had become established in India; or perhaps the most fantastic of all theories, that the Polynesians were derived from the American Indians (*minus* all pre-Columbian cultivated food plants, other than the sweet potato). Some even insist that the distribution of economic plants and weeds, through the aid of man, was more or less universal, as far as the Pacific Islands are concerned, long before the Europeans reached the great ocean.

The evidence in the SOLANDER document, in the extensive BANKS and SOLANDER collections and journals, and in the journals of Captain COOK, supports only the idea that the Polynesians themselves came into the Pacific via Malaysia, bringing their culture with them, losing certain features of it (pottery, the art of spinning thread and of weaving cloth, and any knowledge of metals that they may have acquired in Indo-Malaysia), and in agriculture all cereals, *en route*. Those who argue so freely on the art of weaving, and the artifacts used therein, having been introduced into America via the Pacific

---

1) COMMERSON visited Tahiti in 1768, a year before the arrival of the *Endeavour*, where he made botanical collections some of which have not been studied as yet!

route overlook the simple fact that, all over Polynesia, weaving was an unknown art, tapa cloth everywhere taking the place of woven fabrics until the latter were introduced by the Europeans. PARKINSON in Tahiti, in 1773, noted that he once observed a native reinforcing bark cloth by inserting transverse strings by the use of a bodkin, but that isn't weaving! Their few species of cultivated food plants (other than the sweet potato?) and their domestic animals (three species only) came out of Malaysia. Not one of the plant species, except the coconut, and none of the domestic animals reached America (other than the dog via the Behring Strait route) until after its discovery by COLUMBUS. One does not have to argue that the primitive Polynesians themselves necessarily obtained their stock from Malaysia proper; they may have gotten many items from the Papuasians.

The theorists concerned know little or no botany, and apparently never for a moment doubt the truthfulness of the assumptions on which their theories are based, nor do they check them against the known biological background. But this is scarcely the place in which to expand on the strictly biological aspects of the situation. It is, however, manifest from an examination of the unpublished SOLANDER manuscripts, the still unpublished illustrations prepared by PARKINSON, and actual specimens on which the descriptions were based, supplemented by merely reading the published accounts of early Pacific voyages from the time of MAGELLAN (1521), MENDAÑA (1567), and QUIROS (1595 and 1606) to the end of the eighteenth century, that there is no evidence that any cultivated plant of American origin (except the sweet potato?), and *perhaps not more than possibly two or three weeds of American origin had become established on the Pacific Islands until after the period of European exploration commenced.* This also applies to Malaysia, as the sweet potato may eventually be proved to have originated in Africa.

There are three economic plant species which were definitely of trans-Pacific distribution, certainly man-distributed, as far as the Pacific Islands are concerned, two doubtful as to man's part. These were: (1) the sweet potato, of American origin (?), which the Polynesians somehow acquired and carried all the way to New Zealand (and incidentally transmitted to at least parts of Papuasia, and even to Malaysia proper): (2) the coconut of oriental origin, unquestionably transmitted by man to most of the Pacific islands, and actually established on the west coast of Panama, perhaps only a few centuries before the Spaniards reached that region; and (3) the very useful common gourd *(Lagenaria)* which is not primarily a food plant. It was clearly man-distributed in Malaysia and in Polynesia, but the strains there cultivated seem definitely to have come through India. I am unable to accept the *Gossypium* miscegenation theory propounded by certain geneticists, at least as interpreted by certain diffusionists, to make the count four.

Three species of man-distributed or partly man-distributed plants is indeed a very narrow basis on which to build a theory of early more or less universal distribution of cultivated economic plants between the two hemispheres; when at least fifteen hundred species are involved. It is, however, a better theory than the utterly fantastic concept, seriously proposed within our times, as the reason why agriculture, and then culture based on this agriculture, commenced in the Valley of the Nile — the famous floating barley seeds. The non-academic farming fraternity, even the most primitive tillers of the soil in all barley growing regions, could have assured the able but obviously too prejudiced academic proponent of this strange theory and his ardent but equally non-biological disciples that barley seeds (like those of all cereals) simply will not float; nor will they withstand immersion in water or in mud for more than about two weeks without losing their viability. But why ask any questions, the correct answers to which would destroy the basis of a pretty little theory? The latest development of the "Children of the Sun" idea that I have noted in anthropological literature has been very recently expressed (1950) by a true believer in unlimited diffusion. In a paper on "Negro Agricultural Origins", this theorist naïvely admits that the negroes in Africa were originally food gatherers (as if this does not apply to all the pre-agricultural primitive peoples!), and with even greater naïveté included, in his own abstract, the statement: "until taught agriculture by the Sky-Beings or usually called Children of the Sun." Botanists will not waste much time in pondering on this one, nor will most anthropologists, unless perchance they believe in flying saucers, for even the "Sky Beings" must have had some means of getting about.

We all admit pre-historical and historical diffusion of agriculture and of civilizations based on the cultivation of plants and on the domestication of animals, but any fair-minded individual must admit that there were limits to diffusion in ancient times. As yet, nobody has provided any worth-while evidence that refutes DE CANDOLLE's general conclusion of 1883, that, in his critical studies of the origin of cultivated plants, he had found no evidence of communications between the peoples of the Old and the New Worlds before the discovery of America by COLUMBUS. There were the Norsemen who reached eastern North America 1,000 A.D. and who actually attempted to establish a permanent settlement somewhere on our eastern seaboard a few years later, but their influence was nil in the field of plant introduction. We may admit that on rare occasions castaways from Africa may have reached America; that some Polynesians in their explorations for new lands, as the pressure of population became too great on this or that developed Pacific island, reached the west coast of America and that at least an occasional canoe made a successful return voyage perhaps with the sweet potato; and that natives of South America may have reached some of the Pacific islands on balsa rafts. But the chances of survival on the long voyages involved were slight, and even slighter on reaching an inhabited region. For the possible balsa raft travellers, who may have reached some one of the Pacific Islands, the "port of no return" would apply, as it must have applied to most of the small number of early Polynesian explorers who may, by accident or intent, have reached the west coast of America. Strangers attempting to land, at least in Polynesia, were much more apt to be met with force rather than with open arms. There were exceptions, as Captain COOK's narrative attests.

It is also a manifest fact that the high cultures developed in certain parts of South America, Central America, and Mexico were based on an agriculture, in turn based absolutely and entirely on cultivated plants and domesticated animals of strictly American origin. A high percentage of these selected and improved cultigens belong in genera having no native representatives in Eurasia and Africa. There is no reliable evidence (with one exception) that a single one of these selected and improved American cultigens was known in Europe, Africa, or even in Asia or Malaysia until after the European expansion, following the late fifteenth century voyages of the Portuguese and the Spanish or Spanish-sponsored navigators, who opened up the sea routes to the Orient and to America. The sweet potato had possibly been carried from South America to the high Pacific islands, and has been distributed by the Polynesians via the high islands (not the low ones) over all their culture area, as far to the southwest as New Zealand. It had also been transmitted to the adjacent Papuasian regions, to New Guinea, Guam, the Philippines and the Moluccas before the Spaniards discovered the Philippines. One cultivated food plant, out of several hundred pre-Columbian cultivated species of American origin, is indeed very thin evidence on which to base a theory of extensive pre-Magellan trans-Pacific associations; and looking at the other side of the picture only, two or perhaps three species of Old World origin in America in pre-Spanish times is no more comforting for those who would bring all advanced American cultures out of Asia via the Pacific route. As a matter of fact, all of the cultivated food plants in all the Pacific islands were, with one exception, derived from Malaysia, as were their only domesticated animals — the pig, the dog, and the common fowl; and like the plants, not one of these three domesticated animals (other than the dog which independently was brought to America over the northern route) reached America via the Pacific route. The Eurasian and American cultures were based on an utterly different series of plants and animals. When all is said and done, all advanced civilizations were based on an ample and assured food supply, just as all modern civilizations are equally dependent on this factor for their very existence. As a corollary, most cultigens (improved strains of plants and animals) are, in turn, absolutely dependent on man for their very existence.

I am not an anthropologist nor an ethnologist, having only a fair reading knowledge of the subjects, but I am convinced, merely from a consideration of the absolute bases of pre-Columbian American cultures, that the limited time permitted by certain anthropologists for the presence of man in America (6,000 to 10,000 years), is perhaps too short(1a). There must have been a period of thousands of years involved. There was the period of expansion of the invaders from

1a) This estimate was held particularly by HRDLICKA, but is no longer accepted by most anthropologists. See, e. g., WORMINGTON, H. M. Ancient Man in North America. Denver Mus. Nat. Hist. Pop. Ser. 4. 1949.

northeastern Asia, over all of North and South America, when all involved were simple food gatherers; other thousands of years in selecting the few out of scores of thousands of native American species worthy of and adaptable to cultivation; other thousands of years in developing simple agricultural processes and the more critical selection of better strains of both plants and, to a less degree, animals for improvement and perpetuation; and still others in the final development of the high civilizations that the early Spanish explorers found thoroughly established from Mexico to South America. The development of these high cultures was manifestly dependent on an established and dependable food supply which only a highly developed agriculture could provide. Were these pre-Columbian American civilizations based on the cultivated plants and domesticated animals of Eurasia (which they were not), rather than on strictly native American ones, all totally different from those known to the Eurasian agriculturists, I might be more inclined to listen to some of the theorists. There is a great deal of truth and common sense in a statement made to me, years ago, by Sir DAVID PRAIN, a very eminent botanist with long experience in India. He told me that he refused to listen to the theories proposed by the new school of diffusionists of the PERRY — G. ELLIOT SMITH group simply because, in reference to primitive peoples, what they ate and wore was infinitely more important than what they may have thought, or in some crude manner recorded. Merely because a very few anthropologists, within the past half century or so, repeatedly declared that man could not possibly have been in America longer than 5,000 to 10,000 years, is no reason why other equally misinformed individuals in other fields should feel that they must prove certain basic anthropological assumptions to be false, and pontificate on subject matter regarding which they are manifestly grossly ignorant, to prove what they most ardently believe to be the case.

Sometimes, I also wonder about my numerous colleagues who deliberately select one of the many subdivisions of plant science as proper for a life career, and who never get out of the grooves they prepare for themselves. One thing is certain, most of them never bother with taxonomy (and some would like to eliminate the subject entirely), anthropology, ethnology, archeology, comparative philology, geography, geologic history, palaeobotany, hydrography, or any other branch of science which borders on botanical research.

My own taxonomic work (as compared with field work which was mostly limited to the Philippines and China over a period of twenty-one years) took me all the way from the western Himalayan region, through much of India, Burma, Siam, Indochina, all of China and Manchuria, southern and eastern Siberia to Korea, Japan and all of the Sunda Islands (including British Malaya), the Moluccas, Solomon Islands, New Guinea, and many of the Pacific islands eastward to Tahiti and the Marquesas, with minor excursions outside of this vast area. In this very wide experience, I picked up a great deal of information not only in botany, but also in extraneous fields, and undoubtedly some misinformation. I could only wish that the closet theorists whom

I frankly criticize, especially those of the "romantic school" in botany, anthropology, neogeography and in genetics might have had a small fraction of the field experience that has fallen to my lot.

The fact that pre-Columbian American civilizations were based wholly on different cultivated plants and domestic animals as were the civilizations of the Old World would seem to be an incontrovertible argument in favor of parallel independent development of agriculture in the two hemispheres. One can only infer from it that a parallel development of civilizations naturally occurred in the two hemispheres with a minimum of intercommunications across either the Pacific or the Atlantic oceans. I say "minimum" because, unlike our own European ancestors, the pioneer primitive settlers of North and South America brought with them none of the food plants or domestic animals with which they were familiar in the lands whence they came.

Those who may not be prepared to accept reasonable and supportable conclusions on the almost absolute non-transmission of tropical American economic plants and weeds to the Pacific Islands in pre-Magellan times, on the basis of the evidence supplied by BANKS and SOLANDER collections in Tahiti and in the Society Islands in 1769, I refer to the collections made by the two FORSTERS (1b), on COOK's second voyage, on the same islands in 1773. The published data are available and these tell the same story. Here 594 species are listed, based on material collected by the two FORSTERs, botanists on COOK's second voyage (1772-1775), the first voyage having been made in 1768-1771. But because of the very short one, two or three line, rarely four or five line diagnoses the FORSTER results are sufficiently difficult to interpret even for trained and experienced taxonomists; yet most of the specimens on which the diagnoses were based are still available. The result is quite the same as with SOLANDER's unpublished manuscript. It merely enables me to add a solitary American weed to the Society Islands list from the FORSTER paper, *Waltheria indica* L. *(W. americana* L.). BANKS and SOLANDER failed to find it in 1769, although the FORSTERs found it at Matavai Bay, Tahiti, on COOK's second voyage; yet to complete the record one has to go to the actual FORSTER specimens, for no locality was cited. This is one of the now ubiquitous pantropic weeds, and one that spreads with very great rapidity, once introduced into a new region. It is suspected that actual introduction was via the *Endeavour* (COOK's first voyage) in 1769, but this cannot be proved. The only other chance was when WALLIS discovered the island in 1767, or when BOUGAINVILLE visited it in 1768. The Spanish attempt at colonization in 1774 was too late for consideration, in this connection. A very graphic statement as to how rapidly *Waltheria indica* will spread, once introduced into a region where the soil is subject to disturbance by man, has been made by JOHNSTON(2). Before the early part of 1944 the species was very local and not at all

---

1b) FORSTER, G. Florulae insularum australium Prodromus. 1-8, 1-103. 1786.

2) JOHNSTON, I. M. The Botany of San Jose Island (Gulf of Panama). Sargentia 8: 203. 1949.

common on San Jose Island. Extensive road building operations commenced in that year. A small colony appeared on a recent fill near the main camp in October. By March, 1945, it was common along many roads, and, less than a year later, it was dominant along all roads. Dr. F. G. MEYER of the Missouri Botanical Garden informed me, at the end of October 1953, that a specimen of this now ubiquitous weed was collected by DAVID NELSON in Hawaii on COOK's third voyage in 1779. This was not unexpected. It is interesting to compare this record with that of the distribution of *Sphacele hastata* A. Gray, originally described from Maui in 1862 and still known only from Maui, Revillagigedo Islands, and the mountains near the tip of Lower California (*see* I. M. JOHNSTON, Proc. Calif. Acad. Sci. IV. 20: 90. 1931).

Yet, the FORSTERS on COOK's second voyage found in the Friendly Islands and on Tongatabu *Cassia sophora* L., a weed of American origin, *Sida rhombifolia* L., and *Bidens pilosa* L., the last two also of pantropic distribution, but their places of origin are not yet proved; as well as *Sonchus oleraceus* L., and *Coix lachryma-jobi* L., both of Old World origin. I have accepted FORSTER's indentifications, some of which may be erroneous (*Cassia,* however, is definitely an American weed). If some theorists will not read and digest the simple, published annals of Pacific exploration which are all readily available, are they to be expected to examine and analyze early, published technical botanical works? One might reasonably expect that they would address some questions to experienced colleagues; but, perhaps, this simple expedient is too much to expect of those whose minds seem to have been made up in advance.

In dealing with these, almost the first botanical collections made in the Polynesian islands (the specimens are still preserved and available for study), we have something tangible, and these vouchers tell their own story. Interpretations may vary, but we are not restricted to merely personal preferences, preconceived ideas, or wishful thinking. Those who disagree with my interpretation of the significance of these old dried specimens of plants will have much explaining to do. The great period of introduction of American weeds into Polynesia proper commenced with COOK's three voyages, with possibly a few contributions from the earlier voyages of MENDAÑA and QUIROS to the Marquesas, Solomon, New Hebrides, and Santa Cruz groups (1567-1606); others were, following 1565, introduced by the Spanish galleons into the Marianas Islands.

Doubtless there are those who may not be impressed by the effect of old, long continued, and in various quarters long forgotten trade routes on the distribution of plants between the two hemispheres. Few of the theorists, I am sure, would bother to work out the case of *Dentella repens* J. R. & G. Forst. which was characterized and illustrated in 1776 from a New Caledonia specimen. The FORSTERS' binomial was not based on *Oldenlandia repens* L. which was first characterized in 1767; DE CANDOLLE seems to have been the first author who associated the two binomials (Prodr. 4: 419. 1830), and he was apparently correct.

Now it develops, that two different species are involved in what has usually been considered to represent a single one: *see* AIRY-SHAW (Kew Bull. 1932: 289. 1932) for *Dentella serpyllifolia* Wall., there first characterized, which extends from Orissa to Bengal and Assam, Burma, Siam, Lombok, Mauritius, Luzon (B.S. 1906 RAMOS), and which has glabrous fruits, and AIRY-SHAW (*op. cit.* 1934: 290-301. 1934), where he critically considered the Australian species. True, *D. repens* J. R. & G. Forst. has hispid fruits; there seem to be no intermediates. Both forms occur in the Philippines and Dr. FOSBERG found both in Guam. The point of this *Dentella* discussion is merely to record the fact that at least one of these forms established itself at Acapulco, Mexico, the terminus of the Manila-Acapulco galleon line, sometime before 1815, all ships stopping at Guam in transit; the other got as far as Guam on its way across the Pacific. There is one collection recorded from the Marquesas Islands. This is the entire record for the Pacific Islands to date and to me is a beautiful example of how a weed travels. I suspect the original India-Australia-New Caledonia distribution was due to the agency of migratory birds, but the West-East distribution (to Guam, Acapulco and the Marquesas Islands) was surely due to the commercial activities of man. I cannot quite see some of our non-botanical theorists bothering with a little thing like this — and yet this lowly *Dentella* case provides some corroborative evidence much more convincing than certain broad hints about a type of peanut in China and an absurd claim that *Tagetes* was an ancient sacred flower to the Hindoos in India.

Chapter VII

A CONSIDERATION OF CERTAIN "AUTHORITIES"

In this chapter, I will not give too much attention to the late Dr. O. F. COOK's writings (*cf.* p. 253), as I have more or less effectively dealt with some of his strange concepts elsewhere*(1)*. I still have no reason to change my opinion of the irresponsible conclusions of this author and of the erratic Dr. F. B. H. BROWN (*cf.* second item in the footnote and *infra*). If what I previously published stirs the ire of certain of my colleagues whose work I discuss below (several of whom are botanically untrained and inexperienced and hence have no inhibitions as to expressing their opinions on matters of which they are, unfortunately, profoundly ignorant), I can conclude only that the offenders merely "asked for it". This applies to all individuals discussed below no matter what their special fields may be, where they are located, or with what institution they may be associated.

Some of the ideas which well-meaning and sometimes unquestionably able individuals have tried to prove merely indicate their own ignorance of certain details. Nevertheless, there is no reason why they should continue to grasp at imaginary straws with the hope of securing some support for the cases which they want to prove.

Were HEYERDAHL's theory that the Polynesian islands were populated from America correct, the pioneers would have had to travel by raft, not only as far as the easternmost of the Pacific islands, but also, as far west, at least, as Fiji, or more probably even to Malaysia proper. All this travel would have to be done before they could possibly have acquired any of the basic cultivated food plants (other than the sweet potato?), as well as certain other oil and fibre and ornamental plants, and the three domestic animals upon which their economy and their civilization, by no means primitive, was founded and maintained.

Sea food, of course, was available, but there were only a few native land plants which had edible parts. Before the relatively few species of basic food plants were introduced (all but one from the west), there may have been coconut palms on some islands, *nono* (*Morinda*), the very inferior fruit of which can be (and was) eaten, and possibly *Inocarpus* seeds. We might also mention parts of certain other indigenous plants which could be used in an emergency: the caudices of some species of ferns; the tender shoots of *Hibiscus tili-*

---

1) MERRILL, E. D. Comments on COOK's Theory as to the American Origin and Prehistoric Polynesian Distribution of certain Economic Plants, especially *Hibiscus tiliaceus* L. Philip. Jour. Sci. 17: 377-384. 1920. Reprinted Chron. Bot. 10: 193-207. 1946 (*Merrilleana*); On the Significance of certain Oriental Plant Names in Relation to Introduced Species. Proc. Am. Philos. Soc. 78: 112-146. 1937. Reprinted *op. cit.* 295-315.

aceus L.; the very inferior *Ximenia* fruits; small seeds of *Cordia sub-cordata* Lam., and of one or two species of *Terminalia*; the small seeds and scanty pulp of the fruits and even the tender terminal leaf buds deeply buried among the leaves at the tip of each ultimate branch of *Pandanus tectorius* (Soland. ex) Parkins.; tender parts of *Boerhavia* plants; growing tips of *Ipomoea pes-caprae* R. Br., plus *Portulaca lutea* Soland. and *Sesuvium portulacastrum* L., both very widely used as greens; and perhaps a few others, as well as various marine algae. The coconut may have existed here and there, but, for the most part, it was surely man-distributed in the Polynesian islands. Such a meager list of food plants is a very sorry one for even hungry, primitive man to contemplate. In the beginnings of the occupation of Polynesia, there would hardly have been such a thing as a satisfying meal of vegetable origin in the entire Pacific islands area (*cf.* p. 195).

In the whole list, as above given, there is little real nutriment, but, of course, vitamins are present. One should never forget that the basic Polynesian diet in 1769, as far as plants are concerned, consisted of a few species of fruits, particularly the breadfruit and the plantain, and the starch from a fair number of species that produce corms or tubers. As already indicated, all but one were of later introduction from the Malaysian-Papuasian region, the one exception being American(?) in origin. No cereals were known. Even when maize was first introduced by QUIROS into the Marquesas (1595) and New Hebrides (1606) Islands and *Phaseolus pallar* Molina (supposed to be a form of *Phaseolus coccineus* L.) was planted in Tahiti by the Spanish missionaries from Peru, following COOK's first visit, they were not accepted by the natives. We presume that this was because the Polynesians were not a seed- or grain-eating people. One marvels at the entire absence of other species of *Phaseolus* and species of *Cucurbita, Capsicum, Lycopersicum* and other American plants always propagated by seeds. QUIROS enumerates still other American plants whose seeds were sown in the Santa Cruz islands in 1606. He mentioned only maize for the Marquesas Islands, but he may well have planted other economic species there. The maize did not persist in the Marquesas, nor is there any evidence that it persisted in the Santa Cruz Islands (*cf.* p. 216). Until the theorists wake up to the fact that Polynesian agriculture was based wholly upon plants and animals introduced from outside the Pacific islands (just as that of the vastly more extensive Malaysian-Papuasian region was based chiefly upon man-introduced plants and animals from tropical Asia), there will be no common meeting ground for botanists, theoretical anthropologists, near-anthropologists, archeologists, certain historical geographers and some geneticists.

I unquestionably have made some mistakes as to the place of origin and the time and method of distribution of some species of cultivated plants and weeds, but I think that I have abstained from mixing facts with fiction, and that I have successfully avoided most of the shoals of wishful thinking and preconceived ideas which are strewn with the wrecks of ideas of certain ill-informed and insufficiently experienced individuals.

The field is too vast for any one man to cover authoritatively all details. I, accordingly, restrict my attention to the plants which I know reasonably well and leave non-botanical problems to specialists in other fields. If, however, the numerous problems discussed in the latest impressive HEYERDAHL volume of 1952 are as weakly covered as are those in his 7th chapter which deals with the botanical evidence (p. 425-498), science would have benefited had this volume never been published. It will be interesting eventually to have the opinion of well-informed specialists in philology, archeology, anthropology and other fields.

F. B. H. Brown:— This writer was hailed by HEYERDAHL as an authority on the flora of the Marquesas Islands, and some of his strange illusions and conclusions were accepted without checking. I note so many extraordinary conclusions in his Flora of Southeastern Polynesia(2) that I think it is regrettable that no critical review of his work has ever appeared. It is further to be regretted that my adverse comments on it in 1941 (3) were entirely overlooked by HEY-ERDAHL. Yet, the latter lists this paper in his extensive bibliography, but apparently he never understood it. The only conclusion that we may draw from our knowledge of the introduced and established Polynesian plants as of 1769 is diametrically opposed to HEYERDAHL's theory as to the American origin of the Polynesians themselves.

At present, I confine my attention to some of the lists of species considered under various categories on pages 7 and 8 of BROWN's treatment of the dicotyledons. What he claims is, in general, most acceptable to those who argue for American origins; but, unfortunately, his claims are almost all without foundation. In the list of 35 "weeds", one finds such halophytes (of natural pantropical distribution) as *Vigna lutea* A. Gray=*V. marina* (Burm.) Merr. (if the Old World strand form really be identical with the American one), *Sesuvium portulacastrum* L., *Caesalpinia bonduc* Roxb., *C. bonducella* Flem. and *Bacopa monnieria* Wettst. From the very nature of their halophytic habitats, these plans are never "weeds." They were hardly man-distributed, for certainly most of them had a pantropical distribution millennia before man appeared upon the scene. One wonders if the author understood the subject-matter when he compiled this list of halophytes, for his listing of these species indicates that his knowledge of elementary ecology was extremely superficial. To list the two very spiny, rampant woody species of *Caesalpinia* as "weeds" will come as a surprise to all collectors who have ever attempted to force their way through the tangles they form bordering salt or brackish swamps and margins of the lower reaches of tidal streams. *Wedelia biflora* DC. is an Indo-Malaysian-Polynesian strand plant (it occurs

2) BROWN, F. B. H. Flora of Southeastern Polynesia III. Dicotyledons. Bishop Mus. Bull. 130: 1-386, illus. 1935 (The monocotyledons are treated *op. cit.* 84: 1-194. 1931).
3) MERRILL, E. D. Man's Influence on the Vegetation of Polynesia with Special Reference to Introduced Species. Proc. Sixth Pacif. Sci. Congr. 4: 629-639. [1940]. 1941. Reprinted Chron. Bot. 10: 334-345. 1946 *(Merrilleana).*

just back of the strand) and man has never bothered with it. At least sixteen species are listed which are clearly "recent introductions", *i.e.*, those introduced since the discovery of the islands in 1595 by MENDAÑA and QUIROS. Without distinguishing between aboriginal introductions and recent ones, BROWN says that the former outnumber the latter by nearly three to one. This is a very sad error.

The second list of twelve "recent" introductions approaches nearer to the truth. I exclude only two: *Amaranthus gangeticus* L., and *Cardiospermum halicacabum* L., simply because BANKS and SOLANDER found both in Tahiti in 1769, proving a pre-European introduction for both in the southeastern Pacific region, unless the *Cardiospermum* may have been a natural "wide", before man appeared an the scene.

The list of thirty-one species, introduced for cultivation by the Polynesians, in pre-European times, is very poor. To be excluded immediately are the strand species: *Colubrina asiatica* Brongn., *Hibiscus tiliaceus* L., *Erythrina indica* Lam., *Cordia subcordata* Lam., *Thespesia populnea* Soland., and perhaps the species of *Casuarina*, *Tephrosia*, *Calophyllum*, *Terminalia*, *Barringtonia*, and *Morinda*. It is conceivable that the early Polynesians may have assisted in the distributions of these last six Old World strand plants, because they all served various useful purposes; yet clearly the seeds or fruits of all of them should theoretically have been able to reach Tahiti by the sea route. Most certainly, however, there was no species of the Asiatic *Ocimum*, the European *Mentha arvensis* L., the American *Carica papaya* L., nor the pineapple in the region previous to the arrival of Europeans. Captain COOK planted pineapple seeds in Tahiti in 1769. I found no earlier Polynesian records. QUIROS, of course, may have introduced a form of the pineapple and even the papaya into the Marquesas, but if so, he did not record it (*cf.* p. 216, etc.).

For some reason Dr. BROWN did not attempt to compile corresponding lists of the Monocotyledons. It is perhaps just as well. Nevertheless, HEYERDAHL cites him as an "authority" for claiming a pre-European occurrence of the pineapple in the Marquesas, in Tahiti and elsewhere.

There are authorities and authorities — good, bad, and indifferent; and all make mistakes. There are those who never admit a mistake; there are others who realize that they do sometimes draw erroneous conclusions. I have myself corrected many of my own errors and know of many more minor ones that should be corrected. As I pointed out before, when Dr. BROWN embarked upon his Marquesas venture, it was clear that he was not equipped by training or experience to undertake this task, and he subsequently demonstrated his inability properly to prepare his memoir. These words may be harsh, but they are true. I was then on the staff of the Bishop Museum and it was as consulting botanist that I protested. The non-botanical specialists labor under a very great disadvantage, particularly those who are so convinced of their own wisdom that they do not seek advice from European and American colleagues who are trained in the discipline.

Since I have been engaged in my BANKS and SOLANDER studies, I have often regretted that the long-promised new Tahitian flora mentioned in the Annual Reports of the Bishop Museum, for the past twenty-five years or so, as "being in preparation" is not available to replace DRAKE DEL CASTILLO's flora of 1893. It may be just as well that this new text never be completed, unless it be produced on a much higher plane than the very inadequate and misleading Marquesan one which I have here so briefly discussed. From a strictly taxonomic standpoint, Tahiti remains the one strategic group of high islands of all Polynesia for which a comprehensive modern descriptive flora is sorely needed. The preparation of such a text, on the basis of collections now available, covering the endemic and introduced species of this limited flora, might take an active botanist, at most, a couple of years of not too intensive work. Fiji is being taken care of Dr. A. C. SMITH.

It is distinctly worth while in this connection to read CARL SKOTTSBERG's "Juan Fernandez and Hawaii. A Phytogeographical Discussion." Bishop Mus. Bull. 16: 1-47. 1925. The footnote comments by both SKOTTSBERG (a master of the subject matter) and by F. B. H. BROWN (who naturally disagrees in interpretive details) are entertaining, informative and sometimes rather pointed.

G. F. Carter:— An extraordinary paper appeared in 1950 under the authorship of Dr. G. F. CARTER(4). I use the word *extraordinary* for the simple reason that in my entire botanical experience I have never seen, in one botanical paper, so many gross and inexcusable errors. HEYERDAHL accepts CARTER as a botanical authority, notwithstanding the fact that CARTER does not know the elements of phytogeography or of taxonomy. This is clearly indicated by his conclusions. These conclusions also show that he, likewise, has no understanding of the differences between an endemic, an indigenous, a natural "wide", and an introduced and naturalized species.

For this study, he took, in part, a list of plants compiled from HILLEBRAND's Flora of Hawaii (1888) and then permitted his imagination to run wild. Apparently he did not realize that HILLEBRAND's excellent work was long out of date and that our botanical knowledge of the Pacific Islands has vastly increased since the beginning of this century. It is axiomatic that descriptive botanical accounts, covering inadequately explored regions, may become out of date within a very few years after publication. Yet, here is a case where a non-specialist, untrained either in botany or in taxonomy, went back seventy years for most of his basic information. There is no evidence whatsoever that he consulted any botanist familiar with the situation, despite the fact that there were two excellent authorities in Washington at the time whom he could have reached within an hour. Both of these had had wide field experience in Tropical America and in the Pacific Islands: one in Fiji, the other in Hawaii and many other islands. Either one could have warned him competently of the errors into which he fell; there was a third unusually well informed botanist in Hawaii. Dr. HILLEBRAND would, indeed, have been shocked at CARTER's misinterpretation of his list.

In his discussion of the evidence from cultivated plants, CARTER is partly correct in his statement regarding the sweet potato. But,

4) CARTER, G. F. Plant Evidence of Early Contacts with America. Southwest. Journ. Anthrop. 6: 161-182. 1950.

there is no reason whatever to assume that any considerable range of varieties was imported into the Pacific Islands. Nor, is there any reason to believe that variation of the sweet potato would be "quite slow". CHEESEMAN stated in 1900 that the Maoris of New Zealand recognized more than fifty varieties (the period covered amounts to less than about 700 years). There were numerous other varieties in all of the larger Pacific Islands (about twenty in Hawaii, according to HILLEBRAND). Nor does anything indicate any very great antiquity for this crop in the Pacific Basin. The Polynesians took it to New Zealand in the twelfth or thirteenth century.

It is really inexcusable for a geographer to admit, in print, his inability to explain the discontinuous distribution of the sweet potato in Polynesia. It is simply due to the differences between the relatively few and widely scattered high islands, whether of volcanic origin or of the raised coral type, and the infinitely more numerous low sandy ones. On the latter, where the rainfall may be more or less evenly distributed throughout the year, sweet potato cultivation is possible. In the very much more numerous low ones subject to alternating wet and dry seasons, however, its successful cultivation is practically impossible. On all the high islands, there seems to be little difficulty in growing this basic food plant. This is merely an example of the simplest and most elementary ecology.

I judge that, because he has taken exceptions to some of the conclusions I reached in 1920 when I challenged Dr. O. F. COOK's theories, Dr. CARTER assumes that I am strongly prejudiced against Dr. COOK and others. I am not prejudiced against COOK or any other author mentioned in this memoir, but I am opposed to certain unfounded and misleading conclusions. Whereas Dr. COOK never visited the Old World tropics, I have had twenty-one years botanical experience in that part of the world. I never was quite blind on my very numerous field trips.

The manuscript of my challenge to COOK's theories was actually finished about the middle of 1919, and published in October 1920. When it was typed, I immediately sent a carbon copy to Dr. COOK in Washington asking for his criticisms, suggestions or corrections, indicating that I would give careful consideration to his remarks. The original manuscript was placed in a drawer in my desk and was forgotten until after about nine months had elapsed. Dr. COOK never acknowledged receipt of the copy and when the text for Number 4 of the *Philippine Journal of Science* was being assembled, a year after the paper was written, I included the article in that number. I then wrote another letter to Dr. COOK, with whom I was rather well acquainted, having known him since 1899. I stated that I assumed he had no comments to make on the manuscript, in view of the fact that he had never acknowledged receipt of my earlier letter, and that I was sending the manuscript, in its original form, to the printer. Some two and a half months later, I received a note from him, in which he made no suggestions but explained that he had not acknowledged my earlier letter since he had heard that I was shortly to visit Washington, at which time we might discuss the problem personally. My conclusion, then, as now, was that Dr. COOK realized that he had made some rather serious errors and that he had read too much into the evidence he had so laboriously assembled.

Dr. CARTER admits that COOK was incautious and that he was even unwise in using a pantropic halophytic plant such as *Hibiscus tiliaceus* L. in an endeavor to prove that man may have carried this species from America to the Old World tropics. But he states that I was "so incensed by COOK's special pleading or so allergic to trans-

Pacific contacts (or both) that the violence of his [my] reaction blinded him [me] to the virtues of COOK's arguments". I do not recall that I was incensed, but I do have a recollection of wondering how anyone could read so much into so little evidence.

It is a recognized fact that the early Polynesians unquestionably distributed this plant over the Pacific islands, for they could not afford to take a chance of locating on an uninhabited island where this fiber plant, very important to the Polynesians, did not naturally occur.

I will now prove from extant specimens collected in the Polynesian islands during the decade following 1768-69 that my so-called allergy against the idea of early trans-Pacific interchange of cultigens (and weeds as well) between Indo-Malaysia and tropical America was well founded, although I would not personally have selected the word *allergy*. We may let the word stand, however, even though I do not have to invoke it to prove my point. There is no guesswork when dated specimens from a known island are available for study.

There is an ecological factor involved; and I suspect that, if we had reasonably complete palaeobotanic records, *Hibiscus tiliaceus* L. (as well as *Thespesia populnea* Sol., *Suriana maritima* L., *Ipomoea pes-caprae* R. Br., *Ximenia americana* L., *Cassytha filiformis* L., *Bacopa monnieria* Wettst.), and a few other widely distributed strand or near-strand species were actually growing, for ages, in both hemispheres, before man appeared on the scene!

The yam (*Dioscorea alata* L.) came from southern Asia, not from Java; and there is no evidence whatsoever that this species existed in tropical America prior to about 1550. Here the weight of authority intervenes — ASA GRAY made a very serious mistake when he followed HUMBOLDT and referred the *ajes* of Hispaniola to *Dioscorea*. There is not a word in OVIEDO's account of 1535 (which GRAY and TRUMBULL, as well as HUMBOLDT, misinterpreted) that could apply to *Dioscorea*, except that a tuber-bearing vine was involved. OVIEDO clearly stated that the *ajes* vine was prostrate and that the plant was propagated by planting its terminal shoots. This is still a standard method of propagating the sweet potato. All species of *Dioscorea* are twiners, and all the cultivated forms of this large genus are propagated by planting those parts of the tuber which bear buds. No true yam (*Dioscorea*) can be propagated by planting terminal shoots. *Ajes* is the starchy form of the sweet potato with nearly white flesh, rather large tubers, their external and internal colors varying (which is scarcely true of the true yams).

Incidentally, it is strange that ASA GRAY made this error in identification, because he recorded the fact that the word *ajes* was used by the Choctaw Indians in the southern United States to designate the sweet potato. GRAY, however, never had any tropical experience. It is true that the name *ajes* was later applied in the West Indies to certain introduced species of true yams (*Dioscorea*). Here we have two totally unrelated genera in two totally unrelated families of plants. Yet, all over the United States in grocery-store parlance, the yellow-fleshed form of the sweet potato which is very sweet and distinctly glutinous when cooked is usually now known as "yam", and the more starchy, more nearly white-fleshed tuber, which is dry when cooked, as the "sweet potato." In one of the emergency food manuals issued in Washington during the war years, tubers of both forms are figured, one as *Dioscorea*, one as *Ipomoea*, an indication of the deep-rooted misapplication of their names. We should, therefore, not be too critical of the confusion of names in Hispaniola some four hundred years ago, but it does often pay to scan original descriptions, such as those of OVIEDO, critically before taking too much for granted. This *ajes*, incidentally, is the tuber to which COLUMBUS applied the name *niames* (= yam) when he first observed the species in Cuba and Hispaniola in 1492 *(5)*. All he did was to search for a name for this new tuber-bearing plant and he thus made an erroneous guess that *ajes* was a kind of yam.

The common gourd (*Lagenaria siceraria* Standl.) was common to the tropics and temperate parts of both hemispheres from a very early date. One can take no exception to Dr. CARTER's conclusions in this case. It probably reached America from Africa by floating. This tremendously variable cultigen occurred in the temperate and tropical parts of both hemispheres long before the period of European expansion.

CARTER himself, in 1952, almost proved by a poorly planned and executed experiment that the gourds might have floated from Africa to America. And this seems to be an appropriate place to give further consideration to the single cultivated plant that was definitely found, as proved by archeological data, all over the world, in tropical and temperate regions, some thousands of years before the European expansion, as exemplified by the pioneer voyages of COLUMBUS, VASCO DA GAMA and MAGELLAN, in the last decade of the fifteenth century and the beginning of the third decade of the succeeding one.

The common gourd (*Lagenaria*) is generally interpreted as a monotypic genus. We do not know, with certainty, where it originated, but, from such evidence as is available to me, I favor Africa. Man was obviously responsible for its distribution within Africa, Europe, Asia, Malaysia, as well as within America and Polynesia. How, when, and by what means it reached America is another problem.

---

5) Dr. JUAN TOMAS ROIG Y MESA, in his *Diccionario botánico de nombres vulgares cubanos*, p. 110 (1928), sub *Boniato*, has beautifully and concisely stated the case thus: "Esta planta existía en Cuba cuando el Descubrimiento y los indios la cultivaban casi del mismo modo que se hace hoy. Aunque PICHARDO y otros autores dicen que los *ajes* o *ages*, de que habla COLÓN y los cronistas de la conquista y colonización, eran *names*, de la misma descripción que de ellos hace COLÓN en su Diario, se deduce claramente que eran los boniatos, pues dice que eran unas raíces largas y delgadas *de sabor a castanas*, que los indios plantaban fácilmente por medio de estaquitas o bejucos." He also mentions that, in Cuba, there is an infinite number of forms, differing in leaf and tuber characters, and lists thirty named ones, classified under the tuber colors (yellow, white, red, and brown). It is curious that the early Spanish explorers of both America and the Pacific spoke of the flavor of the sweet potato as suggestive of chestnuts. Yet, one of our ill-informed theorists deliberately went out of his way by stating that sweet potatoes cannot be eaten raw! They are, at times, eaten raw in all the major sweet potato growing areas of the world. The crisp flesh of the raw sweet potato actually has the taste which suggested the comparison with the chestnut!

Tab. CXI.

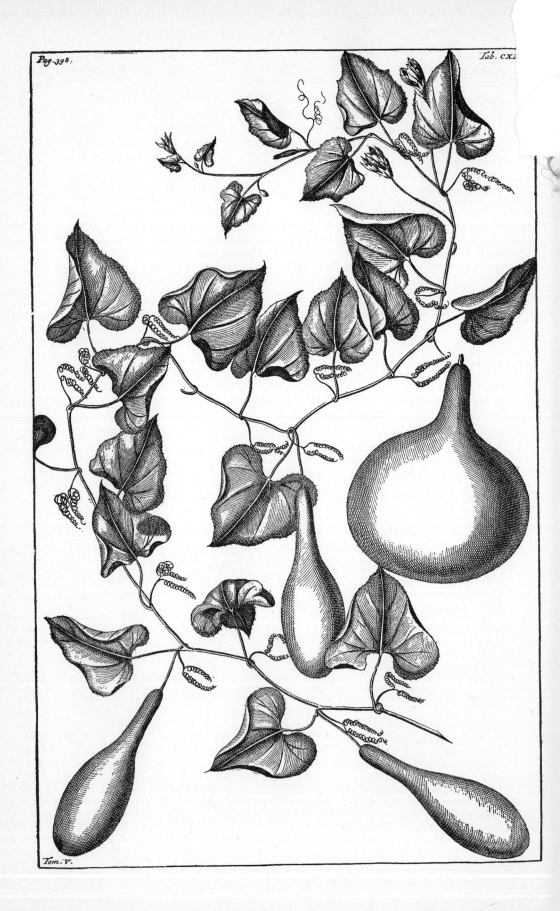

As far as I know, it hardly ever occurs as a wild plant. As a cultigen, it is enormously variable, particularly in the size and shape of the fruit. The gourds, as containers and utensils, were most useful to all primitive peoples, and we may safely assume that this explains why such a tropical cultigen appeared at a relatively early date in the tropical and temperate regions of Europe, Asia, North and South America, and was taken even to New Zealand, in perhaps the twelfth century, by invading Polynesians.

GUPPY's floating experiments, in 1896-1899, were inconclusive (but most certainly not those in very definite but overlooked results of 1902). One may now, on the basis of data available, doubt the need of questioning the "cultural transfer of plants across the Pacific again attaining prominence." This quotation is from a mimeographed pamphlet by CARTER(6), issued by the Isaiah Bowman School of Geography, Johns Hopkins University (Dec. 17, 1952). The floating experiments were very poorly planned and executed, for the project should never have been initiated in the brackish waters of Chesapeake Bay, nor even in any part of the temperate zone, but should have been done in the tropics. Dr. CARTER admits that it was merely a trial run (two lots of seven and eight gourds, July 8 to December 10), the period of floating varying from a minimum of twenty-two to a maximum of one hundred fifty-five days. In one lot, three out of eight gourds remained afloat after one hundred forty-nine days, in the other, three out of seven were still floating after one hundred fifty-five days. It is significant that one gourd sank and remained completely submerged for a period of about thirty-eight days, yet 40 per cent of its seeds germinated.

Unfortunately, no germination data are given for the seeds of the six gourds that remained afloat for the extreme periods of one hundred forty-nine and one hundred fifty-five days. Only seven days elapsed between the date of termination of the trial run and publication of the report, so such basic data as seed germination could scarcely be expected. The urge for publication must have been extraordinarily strong!

Dr. CARTER, whom one judges to be thoroughly convinced that there was a very early transmission of useful cultivated food plants between the two hemispheres, concludes: "The present tentative opinion, however, is that it appears possible that Lagenaria gourds could survive a drift voyage from Africa to America." If we keep in mind that desiccated gourds, the seeds not removed, were widely used by primitive peoples as floats for nets, one can readily understand why they would normally be carried on fishing expeditions. Thus, a journey across a part of the Atlantic might very readily have been made in a castaway canoe. CARTER has more than amply demonstrated transport by sea to be more than a mere possibility. After all, the distance between Sierra Leone in Africa and Natal in Brazil is only about 1,800 miles. Let us wait for the results from a better planned and better executed, tropical, strictly salt water experiment. Only one or a few successful transmissions of the gourd, across the narrowest part of the Atlantic, was needed. At one time in its history, it must have been an autochthonous species, no matter where it originated.

Infinitely more realistic is Mrs. TOWLE's account of GUPPY's results (Bot. Mus. Leafl. Harvard Univ. 15: 183. 1952). She observed that in Ecuador the gourds will float for many months and that then the seeds will germinate when

TEXT FIGURE 10 (opposite). — Lagenaria siceraria (Mol.) Standl., the true gourd, a very variable cultigen, common to the tropics and temperate parts of both hemispheres from a very early date. — As outlined on p. 255, it probably reached America from Africa by floating. This is the only species of cultivated plants which is positively known, from archeological remains, to have been common and widely distributed in the tropical and temperate zones of both hemispheres, prior to 1492. Normally it occurs as a cultivated plant only. — From RUMPHIUS's Herbarium Amboinense, Vol. 5 (1747).

planted, and she quoted GUPPY that "the gourds themselves will probably float for a year or more". Dr. MANGELSDORF tells me that according to Dr. THOMAS WHITAKER, who initiated gourd floating experiments in California two years ago, some of his gourds had in September 1953 been floating for nearly two years and still contain viable seeds. The time element conforms entirely to what might be expected.

The case of *Gossypium* is discussed in some detail on p. 335. For those who are willing to accept the theory of J. B. HUTCHINSON, SILOW and STEPHENS that man was a factor in introducing an Asiatic cotton into America, two or three thousand years ago, well and good. In that case, one will have to accept also the views of the extreme diffusionists among the anthropologists, including perhaps those about the fanciful "Sky Beings, generally called the Children of the Sun" who taught the primitive food gatherers of Africa the art of agriculture (*cf.* p. 242). But even these highly imaginary beings of the romanticists failed to transport any basic cultivated food plant from one hemisphere to the other. This remained a task for the early European navigators and colonists, beginning in the last decade of the fifteenth century — not so long ago, as we measure time.

The now more or less universal distribution of the basic cultivated food plants and of the domestic animals, as we have seen, dates only from the time of European expansion, beginning with the discovery of a route to India, by the Portuguese, and the effective discovery of America, by COLUMBUS, at the end of the fifteenth century.

I may be a maverick, but, until someone can prove that other food plants than the common gourd (not a basic food plant) were of universal distribution in cultivation in North and South America, Africa, Asia and the Pacific Islands in pre-historic times, I remain unconvinced.

The non-botanical "true believers" cite only the gourd, the coconut, the sweet potato; and some erroneously add the yam for good measure. Dr. COOK, in gross error, added "and many other American species." Yet, not even in the tropics, much less in temperate or subtemperate regions, has a single one of the few species, so confidently accepted as proof of early intercommunications across the Pacific (but most curiously not across the Atlantic), shown a universal distribution, in both hemispheres, until after the close of the fifteenth century. The coconut must be eliminated. Notwithstanding Dr. O. F. COOK's elaborate thesis as to its American origin, this palm was not of early universal distribution in the tropics. It was entirely absent from the Atlantic basin until after the Portuguese introduced it from the Indian Ocean after 1500. The Spaniards introduced it into southern Mexico and the West Indies from the west coast of Panama. It is really worth while to read BRUMAN's proofs of these introductions to which I have referred elsewhere. In his 1953 paper (*see* p. 367), CARTER categorically states that I apparently did not know what BRUMAN had discovered and published. I had, however, previously sent Dr. CARTER a typed copy of BRUMAN's last paper on the subject!

6) SEITZ, C. H. A. and CARTER, G. F. Oceanic Drifts of Gourds. 1-5. 1 chart. 1952.

CARTER's chapter on man and cosmopolitan weeds shows a striking ignorance of botanical details. *Argemone mexicana* L. is a good example of his misinterpretations. The entire genus *Argemone* (except for one endemic Hawaiian species) is strictly American. The Linnaean species was introduced into Europe, apparently, in the early sixteenth century; and from the European botanical gardens it was distributed to other parts of the world, partly because of its value as an ornamental and partly because of its supposed medicinal qualities. From certain entries in the literature of early medicinal botany, one might infer that the species was a panacea for all human ailments, beginning with house-maid's knee. In Hawaii, the juice of *A. glauca* Nutt. is still used to treat toothache.

In the tropics, wherever conditions were favorable, once introduced, *Argemone mexicana* L. quickly became naturalized. Thereafter, it soon lost its reputed medicinal appeal and persists as an ordinary weed. Often it is abundant, as in parts of India, where its seeds are utilized as a source of oil. It has no Sanscrit name. As to the white-flowered Hawaiian form, a critical, but as yet unpublished, cyto-taxonomic study by Dr. G. B. OWNBEY clearly shows that this species, *Argemone glauca* Nutt., a Hawaiian endemic, is not even closely allied to *A. alba* Lestib., of North America, with which it has been associated even by such an able taxonomist as Sir DAVID PRAIN. But such relationships as are evident show alliances with South American species. How long a period of isolation is required to develop specific differentiation within this genus we do not know. What is obvious, however, is that the American progenitor of this Hawaiian species reached Hawaii, by natural means, long before man appeared on the scene. Thus, a taxonomic error is perpetuated and the evidence in this *Argemone* case is completely misinterpreted in an attempt to support a theory (*cf.* also p. 220).

Then follows the strange list of binomials compiled from HILLE-BRAND's Flora of Hawaii (1888) of species indicated "to be related to American plants but are not designated as introduced after COOK's discovery of the islands" (*cf.* p. 252). This is where HILLEBRAND showed his wisdom, for he *knew* the difference between an indigenous, an endemic, a natural "wide" and an introduced and naturalized species. So did FOSBERG, whom CARTER quotes as saying of the American element in the Hawaiian flora (which is high) that "a far greater part of the species are only slightly distinct from their American relatives (probably indicating geologically recent arrival) than is true for the other elements." Now "geologically recent" may be anywhere from a few hundred thousand to a few million years or so. FOSBERG was correct, but he was not thinking of *identical* species. One may agree with the statement that "the entire list of 'cosmopolitan' weeds deserves to be studied"; but I would add "from a botanical point of view"! I have done a little work on the "botanical" aspects of CARTER's studies and can only hope that the "ethnobotanical" aspects are more satisfactory. Let us now take up the nine "Hawaiian" species listed by CARTER:

1) Portulaca oleracea L. — This is a post-Cookian introduced European or Eurasian weed. The indigenous halophyte, *P. lutea* Soland., was unknown to HILLEBRAND. It is never a weed, but strictly a halophyte of wide Polynesian distribution. It occurs in the Hawaiian group on rocky peninsulas and off-shore islands on or near Oahu, Lanai, Molokini, Hawaii, Nihoa, Necker, French Frigates, Gardner, Laysan, Lisiansky and Midway (according to information supplied by Dr. ST. JOHN). For a successful revival of the species from synonymy *see:* SETCHELL, Carnegie Inst. Publ. 341: 250. 1924; and CHRISTOPHERSEN, Bishop Mus. Bull. 96(13): 12. 1931.

2) Hibiscus youngianus Gaudich. = *H. furcellatus* Lam., var. *youngianus* (Gaudich.) Hochr. — *H. bifurcus* Cav., to which HILLEBRAND compared the Hawaiian form, is known only from tropical America; *see* HOCHREUTINER, Ann. Conserv. Jard. Bot. Genève 4: 108. 1900. The LAMARCK type was from tropical America. There *are* actual differences between "allied" and "identical" species, even though some historical geographers do not seem to realize the differences. This is probably worthy of a critical re-study, for perhaps it was introduced in Hawaii from America.

3) Erigeron albidus (Willd.) A. Gray = *E. bonariensis* L. *(E. linifolius* Willd.; *Conyza albida* Willd.) = *Conyza bonariensis* (L.) Cronq. (1943). — This is a widely man-distributed pantropical weed extending into the temperate zones. The type came from Buenos Aires. The species was introduced into the Old World in the sixteenth century. There is no reason whatever to believe that it had reached Hawaii before COOK's third voyage. It is believed that the type of the Linnaean species was a native of eastern North America, an early introduction in Buenos Aires. A critical study of the types involved may result in the acceptance of another specific name.

4) Physalis peruviana L. — Of South American origin, this plant has been man-distributed in the Old World since the sixteenth century. It has been introduced into Hawaii since COOK's third voyage. All that we can say, in full confidence, is that it was there in 1825, or a few years earlier.

5) Ipomoea acetosaefolia R. and S. = *I. stolonifera* (Cyr.) Poir. — This, a pantropical halophytic species of sandy seashores of "West India Islands, Guiana and Brazil," was distributed in the same way as *I. pes-caprae* (L.) Poir., by its floating seeds. The range in both hemispheres is vastly greater than HILLEBRAND indicated in 1888. In the Old World, this may well be a man-introduced strand plant.

6) Amaranthus paniculatus L. = *A. cruentus* L. — This species certainly occurs in Hawaii, but it was man-introduced after COOK's third voyage.

7) Chenopodium "sandwichensis" = *C. sandwicheum* Moq. — This is an endemic, not identical with any known American species. Again, one must differentiate between an endemic species and an allied species from outside the region in question.

8) Potamogeton pauciflorus Pursh (non Lam.) = *P. foliosus* Raf. var. *macellus* Fernald. — This is not accounted for, as to its Hawaiian record, by BUCHENAU (Monog. 1907). FERNALD (Mem. Gray Herb. 3: 46. pl. 4, 1932) has very critically considered this case. The species is very widely distributed in North America, and the first Hawaiian record dates from 1842. Dr. ST. JOHN is convinced that it is not a native Hawaiian plant.

9) Eragrostis mexicana Link. — "From Mexico, Venezuela and Cuba." This is not LINK's species. It is *Eragrostis mauiensis* Hitchc. (1922), a Hawaiian endemic.

Following these amazing entries, more than four pages are devoted to the case for maize. ANDERSON has surmised that maize, a strictly American plant, may have originated in Upper Burma and was an early introduction into America, but this idea (fortunately only casually mentioned in print) is utterly erroneous. Even the STONOR-ANDERSON "proofs" that maize was in Assam long before the Portuguese reached India in 1500 had been completely discredited by the time CARTER and HEYERDAHL compiled their data.

The explanation is due to the ignorance of all theorists of the long continued trade route from Lisbon to Goa via eastern Brazil and the Cape of Good Hope which was used for one hundred and sixty-five years following 1500 (cf. p. 192 & 229). The type or types of popcorn in Assam reached India by way of this old trade route, and there is no question but that the same forms will still be found, in cultivation, in eastern Brazil today. The case is so clear that to clarify the situation further by additional field work would be a waste of time, effort and money.

There are differences of opinion between teams of geneticists and anthropologists as well as between taxonomists, as can be seen by the discussion between STONOR-ANDERSON ("Maize Among the Hill Peoples of Assam", Ann. Missouri Bot. Gard. 36: 355-404. 1949) and MANGELSDORF-OLIVER ("Whence came Maize to Asia?", Bot. Mus. Leafl. Harvard Univ. 14: 263-291. 1951). There is absolutely no reason why any attempt should be made to revive the Asiatic origin idea. It comes up, from time to time, and immediately dies. We may, I suppose, charge the last resurgence of this hypothesis to the influence of Dr. O. F. COOK on his assistant G. N. COLLINS(7), who in 1909 and 1920 gained fleeting fame by discovering a new type of maize in China and a waxy type in Burma (cf. also p. 237 & 253).

When ANDERSON had abandoned the untenable and extreme idea of an Asiatic origin, in collaboration with a similar-minded anthropologist, he tried to show that certain types of maize had existed in Assam long before the Europeans reached India. But in his latest, most readable and interesting book *Plants, Man and Life* (1952), one notes that he had to bow to the storm and merely mentioned his continued faith in the STONOR-ANDERSON idea in a short mild statement. I deliberately use the term "abandoned", which I know the author will not accept, for the simple reason that, were his faith unshattered, here was an opportunity for preparing what might well have been the most interesting chapter in his book, for in the world as a whole maize is one of the most important of food plants. The claim in 1952 that maize "might have crossed the Pacific in very early pre-Columbian times" perhaps should have been left out entirely. *It first crossed the Atlantic from Brazil to Goa in India via the Cape of Good Hope.* After it was introduced, it travelled as far as northern India; had it been introduced some 2,000 years ago, it would have been very widely distributed

---

7) COLLINS, G. N. A New Type of Indian Corn from China. U. S. Dept. Agr. Bur. Pl. Ind. Bull. 161: 1-28. 1 pl. 1909; Waxy Maize from Upper Burma. Science 52: 48-51. 1920.

in the Old World by the time of the Portuguese expansion in 1500 (*cf.* p. 366).

As my memoir was in part predicated on the influence that various explorers, especially Captain COOK, had had on the plant life of the Pacific Islands, I again call attention to at least two recorded maize plantings, both apparently failures, by QUIROS in the Marquesas Islands (1595) and in the Santa Cruz Islands (1606) (*cf.* p. 249). The theorists should keep in mind that insular peoples long accustomed to securing their carbohydrates from certain fruits, tubers and corms (as were the early Polynesians), and starch (sago) from certain palm trunks (as were the Papuasians), would not accept a cereal substitute simply because they were not seed-eating peoples. After long association, yes; but merely after a ceremonial planting at the Marquesas Islands and a colonization scheme on Santa Cruz Islands that failed, after a few weeks, no!

Dr. CARTER's last four pages are devoted to surmise. Perhaps the most surprising statement in this collection of *horribilia botanica* is his assertion that the *Lonchocarpus* of tropical America appears to be "botanically the same plant" as *Derris* of tropical Asia. Now, all taxonomists will admit that the numerous American species of *Lonchocarpus* (some 200 described species) are botanically allied to the scandent Indo-Malaysian genus *Derris* (perhaps 100 species), but it is indeed spectacular taxonomic "news" that the numerous species of both genera are "botanically the same plant"! Can it be that, since 1823, when *Lonchocarpus* of HUMBOLDT, BONPLAND and KUNTH was described, all taxonomists have missed the boat? Such an unwarranted and unqualified statement by a botanically uninformed anthropologist-geographer may be anthropology or historical geography, but it is neither botany nor science.

Clearly the paper never should have been written, much less published, for it discredits all who were associated with it as well as North American science in general. It is fictional, not factual. My main reason for dissecting it is that HEYERDAHL uncritically accepted CARTER as a botanical authority. GEORGE BORROW in *The Zincali* beautifully stigmatized the type of "scientific" work exemplified by CARTER's paper when he wrote: "I see no reason whatever why anyone in pursuance of simple details of a science should have resource to conjecture and guesswork."

A year or so ago, I very mildly criticized a list of now widely distributed species of cultivated American plants which was published by a non-botanical correspondent. The reason for my criticism was that he included, *as a food*, *Chenopodium ambrosioides* L. This plant is an effective vermifuge, and its seeds are still used, in small quantities, for flavoring foods (a few of them will go a long way). But it is not a food plant; and, wherever it grows, it is definitely a weed. The list had merely been copied from VAVILOV. In my letter, I casually mentioned the aquatic and strictly American *Nelumbo lutea* Pers. as an excellent example of a native American food plant that had been deliberately and widely distributed by the American Indians, if a really good example be needed. It is, however, not a "cultivated" species in the strict sense of that term. The "range" of the American *Nelumbo lutea* Pers. now covers an area from Minnesota to

Ontario southward; it occurs in Mexico, Honduras (Lake Yojoa), and Cuba; and is reported from the Magdalena River in Colombia.

If the truth were known about the spread of its Old World counterpart, *N. nucifera* Gaertn. (*cf.* p. 248), it would probably be found to have originated in eastern Asia, and to have been distributed by man *as a food plant* westward to India and Egypt, and southward to the Philippines and Malaysia. And even if it were sacred in ancient Egypt, where controls were lessened in intervals between powerful dynasties, what would prevent hungry common people from exterminating it in the Nile Valley? After all, a dual-purpose food plant (very large edible rhizomes and large edible seeds) was a very important asset, in early times, as it still is in China. It does not help anyone's reputation to argue that there are two identical species, but after all what can one expect from a non-botanical geographer?

The real importance of the plant lies in its edible rhizomes and its large edible seeds. This is why the benighted North American Indians distributed it where favorable conditions existed, *i.e.*, in shallow protected fresh water with a muddy bottom, in lakes, slow streams, etc. And it is, incidentally, about the only American food plant native of the United States (other than the sunflower) that, through the activities of man, extended its range south of the Mexican border. The only other species known is the pink flowered sacred lotus of Asia to which I have referred above.

The idea, expressed by my correspondent, was that this "needs looking into," simply because the American lotus flowers were occasionally used in decorative designs (I know of two records; there may be others), as were those of its Asiatic counterpart on a very much larger scale. The inference was, I gather, that the idea of the *use* of the lotus flower in America, and perhaps even the plant itself, may somehow have been transmitted across the Pacific by man.

Let us consider a very important aspect of the situation that some historical geographers overlook or ignore. *Nelumbo* is one of the oldest and most primitive genera of flowering plants among the phanerogams. There is one species in Asia and one in America. It would take no one very long to "monograph" this small genus. But geologically one would have to go back to the Eocene, millions of years ago, to find a clue to the present discontinuous generic distribution. One would have to consider what happened in the North Temperate Zone, during the great epochs of glaciation, near the end of this long period of time. So far as discontinuous distribution is concerned, this *Nelumbo* situation parallels that of very many other genera now characteristic of and limited to eastern Asia and eastern North America. There is a partial list of eastern American - eastern Asiatic genera on p. 340. Not even a well-informed geographer would claim that these numerous genera were man-distributed, for man was not a factor when the geographic continuity was broken in the north, leaving two great "islands" of similar types of vegetation and representatives of many genera permanently separated half way around the world from each other; there are no identical species involved.

T. Heyerdahl:— When HEYERDAHL published the fascinating adventure story of his balsa raft expedition from Callao, Peru, to the Tuamotu Archipelago, he stated, at the very end of the volume on the *Kon-Tiki* expedition, that the success of the trip did not necessarily prove his theory that American Indians populated the Polynesian Islands, but that it did prove that a trip of some 3,000 miles on a balsa raft, within a period of three months, was possible. Apparently, in spite of rather severe criticisms by certain anthropologists, he felt that this theory must be proved*(7a)*. It must be admitted that he has

7a) HEYERDAHL, T. The Voyage of the Raft *Kon-Tiki*. An Argument for American-Polynesian Diffusion. Geogr. Jour. 115: 20-41. 4 pl. 1950; American Indians in the Pacific. The Theory Behind the *Kon-Tiki* Expedition. i-xv. 1-821. illus. 1952.

"proved" to his own satisfaction what he wanted to believe. Yet, at the same time, he amply showed that what he accepted as proven facts does not conform to what we actually know in various fields. This is most unfortunate. As I pointed out before, one can but hope that his proofs drawn from various fields, such as anthropology, archeology, ethnology, philology, etc., are based on more soundly established facts than are those extraordinary ones which he has drawn from the field of plant distribution.

His 1952 bibliography of more than a thousand titles is impressive. It is also obvious that articles and volumes, covering a vast range of subject matter, were not only read but that they were intensively studied in a search for statements which would help "prove" what this courageous explorer believed and wished to prove. Whatever he thought supported his theory was too quickly accepted as true evidence. I leave the various unproven generalities in philology (these are, indeed, manifestly very weak), similarities in artifacts, etc., to other specialists and confine my remarks to the plant evidence.

In his chapter on "Botanical Evidence of Polynesian Routes" (p. 428-498), HEYERDAHL naturally had to depend on the papers of relatively few botanists who have published on the Polynesian field. However, he was not in a position to discount the opinions of incompetent authors who made many serious mistakes. He also failed to realize that the strange conclusions of a few recent workers represent merely personal opinions which are not based on anything but very limited field experience and much less still on an actual knowledge of what has transpired in the past few hundred years in plant distribution.

Everyone recognizes the botanical abilities of such nineteenth century workers as HILLEBRAND (cf. p. 252) on the Hawaiian flora and of SEEMANN on the flora of Fiji. Yet one should appreciate the fact that both were pioneers. They did the best that they could with what was available to them; but, like all of us, they made errors which have been perpetuated in the literature. Modern botanists have detected and corrected many of the early errors, but their scattered comments are all too frequently overlooked.

Among all the species involved in the HEYERDAHL discussions, only one is possibly of American origin: the sweet potato. And this plant was distributed to all or nearly all of the widely scattered high islands of Polynesia some centuries before the Europeans entered the Pacific. The sweet potato may be found occasionally growing on a low island, but normally only on those where the annual rainfall is rather high and is distributed over most months of the year (cf. p. 213, 322, etc.).

To distinguish, as HEYERDAHL does, between the bottle gourd and the giant gourd is but a quibble. Both are forms of the monotypic Lagenaria siceraria (Molina) Standl. These very large gourds occur in the Philippines and have been reported from America; they also occur in Africa. EAMES and ST. JOHN definitely determined the botanical status of the Hawaiian giant gourd in 1943. Yet SEEMANN, in 1865, who was in Hawaii, about 1848, as botanist on the Herald, confused this large fruited form of Lagenaria siceraria (Molina) Standl. with Cucurbita maxima L., stating that the latter (which then had been introduced) had been cultivated in Hawaii "from time immemorial." HILLEBRAND accepted this conclusion. The first true *Cucurbita* introduced into Polynesia was the form that Captain WALLIS (*cf.* p. 216) actually planted in Tahiti in 1767, with seeds from Brazil, which is very far from "time immemorial". This is how errors persist indefinitely.

The tetraploid cotton theory of HUTCHINSON, SILOW and STEPHENS (1947), based on the *direct* introduction by man of an Indian cotton into South America two or three thousand years ago where it is supposed to have hybridized with a native American cotton, has never been and scarcely can be proved. Nevertheless, HEYERDAHL makes much of it (*see* also p. 279, 291, 335 & 370).

I can only place maize and the variable species of *Cucurbita* (including *C. ficifolia* Bouché) among those American cultigens originally introduced into India along the Malabar coast by the early Portuguese colonizers via the Lisbon-Brazil-Cape of Good Hope-Goa route*(8)*. The grain amaranths also belong to this list of American species which followed the trade route from Brazil to India, after 1500. Their distribution seems a mystery to those theorizers who disregard or are not familiar with this Portuguese route! In this same category is the famous peanut of southeastern China which is neither primitive nor shaped like a shoestring. It safely reached Asia by the same roundabout route, not across the Pacific, direct from Peru to China, but from Brazil to Goa and China. One form of the *Cucurbita* later became known as the Malabar gourd.

For these introductions we certainly do not have to go back beyond 1500 A.D. to explain their presence in India, yet, investigators continue to cite the Pakistan-Persia region as one of the great centers of variability in *Cucurbita*. It is true that much variability occurs there, but only since the sixteenth century. There is no reason whatever to go back of the beginning of the Portuguese period of expansion to explain the presence of this strictly American genus in Asia. A variable cultivated species, once introduced into a new region and subject to the manipulation of man, will continue, more or less, to vary. This we know to be the case with the breadfruit, taro, the greater yam and other species in Polynesia, after their introduction from Malaysia, and with the sweet potato which possibly came from America.

One suspects that HEYERDAHL failed to appreciate the significance of the MANGELSDORF-OLIVER interpretation, in which the real significance of the supposed origin of Asiatic maize or its presence in Assam long before the arrival of Europeans, is settled. MANGELSDORF and OLIVER's criticism (*cf.* p. 179 & 261) is caustic, and in the same paper is an equally strong criticism of the J. B. HUTCHINSON *Gossypium* theory.

HEYERDAHL's long account adds nothing to what we already know. For the confirmed Americanists, a most important SEEMANN reference was overlooked. The coconut, an Old World species (at least as I and

---

8) MERRILL, E. D. Observations on Cultivated Plants with Reference to Certain American Problems. Ceiba 1: 3-36. 1950.

others believe it to be) apparently appeared on the west coast of tropical America (from Panama to Guyaquil), *i.e.*, on the Pacific side only, a few hundred years before the Spaniards reached Panama.

Perhaps of all the unwise theories that Dr. COOK originated but failed to prove, his worst was that of 1901 and 1910 when he assumed that the coconut was a native of tropical America (*cf.* p. 253). His ideas have been ably refuted by Drs. BECCARI (1917) and CHIOVENDA (1921-23). I can find no evidence that this conspicuous and very useful palm even occurred in the Americas, except along the seashore from Panama to Ecuador (as far as the northern part of the Gulf of Guayaquil), until it was distributed by the Spaniards northward into Mexico, eastward into the West Indies, and to northern South America. There is a lot of simple ecology involved here. The introduction into eastern Brazil was an independent Portuguese one, undoubtedly over that route so fatal to non-botanical theorists, Goa (or East Africa in this case) to Brazil. I can further find no evidence that would lead me to believe that it even occurred on the coast of tropical West Africa until after the Portuguese took it around the Cape of Good Hope following 1500*(9)*.

OVIEDO certainly saw it on the Pacific coast of Panama prior to about 1525, but his cursory description includes data about other palms and the illustration (added long after the author's death) represents a species of *Bactris* and must be dismissed as being as unreliable as the illustrations of the seed of *Mangifera indica* L. and of the Australian kangaroo. When OVIEDO wrote his text, about 1525, Australia and its kangaroo were entirely unknown and the mango was not introduced into Mexico until sometime after 1565.

In partial support of COOK's theory, as to the American origin of the coconut palm, is the fact that the tribe to which *Cocos* belongs is basically American. Yet, it is also significant that a fossil *Cocos* fruit has been found in New Zealand and described as a new species which is at least an indication of a probable generic distribution through Antarctica in Tertiary times.

If one wishes more "proof" of the American "origin" of *Cocos nucifera*, I refer to SEEMANN's neglected entry based on personal observations made at Solano on the west coast of Colombia, a short distance south of the Panama boundary in January, 1848*(10)*. He states that here there was a great quantity of wild coconut palms, and that these occurred in places along the entire coast of Darien even "in places where no human beings or any signs of them were to be seen". Dr. I. M. JOHNSTON reports self sown coconuts in the masses of drift here and there on the coast of San José Island, in the Gulf of Panama. Certain Polynesian islands such as Palmerston, as reported by Captain COOK, Bikini, as recently reported by Dr. TAYLOR*(11)*, and Palmyra as reported by ROCK, should also be mentioned. Captain COOK's ac-

9) This conforms to BRUMAN's conclusions which, at the time this paragraph was drafted, I had overlooked even as had CARTER (*cf.* p. 258).

10) SEEMANN, B. Narrative of the Voyage of *H. M. S. Herald* 1: 227. 1853.

11) TAYLOR, W. R. Plants of Bikini and Other Northern Marshall Islands. i-xv. 1-227. illus. 1950.

count of the Palmerston Island situation states definitely that the coconuts were not only self-sown, but that they were clearly introduced by floating, not by man.

In most of Malaysia, the coconut apparently has become dependent on man, because of the presence of certain destructive agencies as the wild hog, rodents, and crabs that destroy the germinating nuts, when they are not thoroughly protected. In twenty-one years experience in the Philippines, I do not remember ever having observed a coconut palm which originated with certainty from a self-sown nut. In many, perhaps most, Polynesian islands, the coconut was undoubtedly man-introduced by the Polynesians themselves. It will not thrive on the dry islands, including the high islands, such as Easter, and some of the low ones. Controlling factors are the amount of rainfall and its seasonal distribution.

The last word has not been yet said as to where the species originated nor as to when and how it attained its present wide distribution. One thing is certain: the coconut palm was thoroughly established along the wet Pacific coast of Panama and adjacent Colombia before the arrival of the Spaniards. Two very interesting contributions have been made to the voluminous literature, on this subject, within the past decade, by BRUMAN(12). The second one of BRUMAN's papers is most significant, for it includes part of a letter from ALVARO DE GUIJO, dated at Panama, April 18, 1539, and addressed to HERNAN CORTÉS. This letter notified CORTÉS that GUIJO was sending him two dozen fruits from a palm there known as cocos. The shipment went apparently to Colima. As Dr. BRUMAN notes, the indications are that coconuts were unknown on the Pacific coast of Mexico before that date.

The BRUMAN papers are significant for those who have perhaps "guessed" when and how the Filipino practices of extracting the sap from coconut inflorescences and the distillation of the fermented product known as tuba to produce vino de coco started. The industry was established by Filipino sailors arriving at Acapulco after the palm had been established on the coast. One may well interpret this as strong evidence against Dr. O. F. COOK's ideas as to the American origin of the coconut and as equally good evidence that this palm was established on the Pacific coast of Panama and Ecuador, either through natural means (floating), or by the Polynesians themselves. There is good reason for believing that the palm had actually extended over a limited stretch of the American Pacific coast, only a few centuries before the Spaniards arrived. Even though COOK's hypothesis has been rather thoroughly discredited by competent botanists, some workers will continue to bring it up whenever it helps to prove what they wish to believe.

The idea that the pineapple (cf. p. 268) and the papaya were of pre-European introduction into the Marquesas Islands rests solely on the personal opinion of F. B. H. BROWN, who made so many erroneous

---

12) BRUMAN, H. J. Early Coconut Culture in Western Mexico. Hisp. Am. Hist. Rev. 25: 212-223. 1945; A Further Note on Coconuts in Colima. Op. cit. 27: 572-573. 1947.

Tab. LXXXI.

A

claims (*cf.* p. 251) that his judgment cannot be trusted. The first published record that I have found about the pineapple in Polynesia is Captain COOK's report of having planted the seeds in Tahiti in 1769; he mentions having planted it again on his third voyage. It is, apparently, no accident that in Hawaii its local name is *hala kahiki* (*hala* = *Pandanus*), a name which indicates its introduction into Hawaii from Tahiti ("Kahiki"), not long after missionary activities commenced. I suspect that the introduction of the pineapple into Hawaii occurred during the first or second decade of the nineteenth century. If this be so, I doubt very much if the word *Kahiki* should be interpreted to mean "foreign"; it seems rather to refer to "Tahiti".

The very few "other American elements in Marquesan flora" may be dismissed as of no significance. The species listed are allied to American ones, indeed, but there are no possibly identical species introduced by man. The South American element formed a part of the Hawaiian flora long before man was present. In this connection we may point out again that HEYERDAHL did not appreciate the difference between *identical* and *allied* species; neither did CARTER.

I am certain that Dr. SKOTTSBERG must have been upset by HEYERDAHL's false interpretation of his studies of the South American element in the Easter Island flora. This false interpretation parallels CARTER's erroneous one as to the Hawaiian *Argemone*. A local endemic, in such an isolated place as Easter Island or Hawaii, proves only one thing: that, no matter what its botanical alliances may be, a species has been present for a long time, certainly long before man appeared on the scene. At least four of the taxa mentioned by HEYERDAHL as "South American" elements for Easter Island are endemic species, i.e., *known only from Easter Island!* Their botanical alliances happen to be with South American species, which is understandable and logical. Some of the other species mentioned are "wides", more apt to be of natural distribution than man-introduced. SKOTTSBERG lists thirty-two species in the very poor total flora of the island as having been *unintentionally* introduced by man's activity after the discovery of the island by ROGGEVEEN in 1722.

TEXT FIGURE 11 (opposite). — *Ananas comosus* (L.) Merr. (*A. sativus* Schult. f.; *Ananana sativa* Lindl.), the pineapple. This unusually beautiful drawing made ca. 1680 together with the detailed description by RUMPHIUS in Latin and in Dutch form the type and sole basis of the Linnean species *Bromelia comosa* L. Of American origin, like all but one of the representatives of the family, though an easily transported and transplanted cultigen, the pineapple does not seem to have reached Tahiti until 1769 when Captain COOK planted seeds which he brought from Brazil. — About the pineapple supposedly shown on a Pompeii mural, *vide* p. 367. There exists no record whatsoever about an introduction of this plant, before 1500, into any part of Africa or Asia. — Dr. J. L. COLLINS of the Pineapple Research Institute, at Honolulu, has recently published a series of interesting papers on the history of the pineapple (Pineapples in Ancient America. Sci. Mo. 67: 372-377. 1948; History, Taxonomy and Culture of the Pineapple. Ec. Bot. 3: 335-359. 1949; Antiquity of the Pineapple in America. Southw. Jour. Anthropol. 7: 145-155. 1951). — From RUMPHIUS's *Herbarium Amboinense*, Vol. 5 (1747).

It is clear that there is no botanical evidence to support the claims made by HEYERDAHL in 1952. In his entire list there is only one species probably or possibly of American origin that was present in the Polynesian Islands before the Europeans arrived, thoroughly upsetting the balance of nature as it existed before the time of MENDAÑA, QUIROS, and other early explorers. The real impetus in the introduction of new economic plants and weeds came with COOK's three voyages, effectuated between 1768 and 1779.

We must always remember that it was a practice of many early explorers (from the time of QUIROS and also carried on by Captain COOK and later explorers on a large scale) of taking with them sheep, goats and, in COOK's later voyages, even cattle and horses, which were judiciously placed here and there for the benefit of the Polynesians. Whenever more or less extended stops were made, these animals, as well as pigs, turkeys, muscovy ducks, etc., were taken ashore. A supply of forage was always taken on board just before the departure of the ship and at the next stop, this practice was repeated. A more ideal method of disseminating weeds could scarcely be devised.

Dr. F. VERDOORN tells me that there are several accounts of gardens aboard ships in the early, particularly Dutch, travelogues. Unfortunately, their importance seems to have been studied from a medico-historical rather than from a biogeographical point of view.

I will be charged with being prejudiced, but, in Manila, some fifty-odd years ago, when I became interested in the problem of man-distributed plants, including weeds, I read with open eyes and, I hope, with an open mind, a vast number of the early accounts appertaining to Indo-Malaysian and Polynesian exploration, from the time of PIGAFETTA and QUIROS to well into the nineteenth century. During the past year, I have re-read a great many of these travel accounts, as well as many additional ones. I know the botanical aspects of this type of literature well and in questions of zoology, geology, hydrography, paleobotany, comparative philology, history, etc., I have always sought the advice of competent authorities. If my conclusions differ from those of some theorists, I am sorry; but I have no apologies to make. Only occasionally and in minor details (the occurrence of the coconut in America and the presence of the sweet potato in Polynesia in pre-Magellan times) did I need to change my earlier published views.

My only desire is that the authors, whose opinions I criticize in this chapter, procure reliable data from specialists in the future. For, as we have seen as a sad example, the "botanical evidence" which HEYERDAHL cites is wholly untrue. His case seems, to me, to show beautifully how the human mind, once decided, can practice self-deception.

For a review of HEYERDAHL's philological belief, which in no respect demonstrates his contentions, see the admirable 44-line review by A. S. C. ROSS, "Comparative Philology and the 'Kon-Tiki' Theory" (Nature 172: 365. Aug. 22, 1953). It is rarely that such a short review can be so devastating. The reviewer declares that: "comparative philology affords an absolutely decisive disproof of Mr. HEYERDAHL's theory." — An interesting, general review of HEYERDAHL's *American Indians*, by R. FIRTH, will be found in Nature 171: 713-714 (April 25, 1953).

This reviewer concludes: "In his anxiety to leave no loose ends, the author brushes negatives aside. The Polynesians had no pre-European cereals. Yet maize was a characteristic food-plant in the Peruvian area from which the author supposes them to have come. How did it escape them? By having been lost during the landing of the Amerindian craft through the surf on Polynesian reefs, or by having failed to give a successful crop after having been sown, he answers. But the question does not really interest him. The absence of pottery from Polynesia, too, attracts discussion only to demonstrate the lack of relation with South-East Asia, whereas no very cogent reasons are given to explain why pottery should not have been brought from Peru, where it had reached a high state of development by the time that the ancestors of the Polynesians are said to have left. Finally, the author rather overdoes his argument about the virtual impossibility of the ancient Polynesians making headway against the trade winds and the prevailing currents — the 'one-way ocean escalator from Peru westwards'. ELSDON BEST and S. PERCY SMITH have pointed out three factors which are relevant for voyages in the opposite direction. First, the prevailing winds do not prevail always. Winds, often of considerable strength, blow for significant periods from west-north-west or even south-west. Secondly, Polynesian canoes could beat to some extent against a contrary wind, helped by the long steering-oar. Thirdly, in a contrary wind that was not too strong the Polynesian often paddled his craft. Moreover, the effects of the equatorial counter-current, variable and weak as it often is, are not to be dismissed. Without decrying the author's magnificent achievement on his raft, it may be fairly said to have involved seamanship rather than sailing skill, and one receives the impression that he consistently undervalues what an oceanic sailing canoe can do".

C. Sauer:— As one reads the records, one gets the impression that, to a very considerable degree, certain modern geographers try to improve upon the work of specialists in archeology, ethnology, anthropology, etc., while some seem to infer that certain of these disciplines are as obsolete as straight botanical and zoological taxonomy are, in some circles, thought to be. SAUER is not trained in systematic botany or zoology, yet, without consultation with specialists, he uses taxonomic data, often with an absolute abandon, to prove what he believes and has set out to demonstrate. We find in SAUER to some extent the O. F. COOK method of developing a theory or hypothesis, and then "proving" it without checking on the facts.

Dr. SAUER is reported to have claimed, for years, in his lectures, that certain cultivated food plants were more or less widely distributed in both hemispheres long before the European expansion in the sixteenth century. This is contrary to A. DE CANDOLLE's conclusions of 1883 in his very critically prepared *Origin of Cultivated Plants*. Yet, as of today, the score still stands as one species only — the common gourd (*Lagenaria*) — known with certainty to have been widely distributed in the temperate and tropical parts of both hemispheres. *And this one species stands against 1800 or more cultivated species which were never common to nor widely distributed in both hemispheres, until after 1492! (12a)* The other two species which obtained a wide, yet limited, distribution are discussed on p. 194.

12a) AKEMINE in 1933-1940 made the total 1837, DE CANDOLLE who mastered the field, in 1883, limited his attention to 247 species, and ANDERSON's selected list of 1952 contains only about 100 species (*cf.* p. 294).

No one questions Dr. SAUER's ability. But, as in the case of others discussed here, one regrets that he lacks training, experience and appreciation in biogeography. He, apparently, fell under Dr. O. F. COOK's influence, sometime during the latter's productive career, and was carried away by some of his erroneous theories.

Insofar as I can judge from SAUER's published papers, his attitude until 1952 was mostly conservative. In that year, however, and for the first time as far as I know, he very definitely expressed super-diffusionistic ideas. In a small volume, recently issued (13), he has made some unqualified statements that are so manifestly untrue that I cannot permit the challenge to pass. His large paper on the cultivated plants of Central and South America is an excellent compilation(14), though its author might be disturbed by certain marginal notes, made in a library copy, by one of our most widely experienced and productive specialists in tropical American botany. In this 1950 paper, all species discussed are mostly of American origin and were unknown in the Old World, until after 1492; many have *still* never been introduced there. This supports the idea, whether its author realizes it or not, that agriculture originated independently in America on the basis of strictly indigenous American plant and animal species. Nothing but the same conclusion can be drawn from the very critical archeological excavations now being made in our own southwest, in Mexico and in South America. As to food plant remains, the record is 100 per cent strictly American species.

In the remarkable excavations made by Dr. JUNIUS BIRD, of the American Museum of Natural History, at Huaca Prieta on the coast of Peru, first reported upon in 1948(15), we who are inquisitive as to what plant species were or were not in cultivation in Peru in pre-Spanish times will be interested in seeing the final list of identifiable plant material. Here we have something really tangible. The site was continually occupied by man who practised some type of agriculture continuously from pre-ceramic and pre-maize days up to the time of the Spanish occupation. The oldest radio-carbon date determination worked out as about 2500 years B.C.; some have estimated 4000 years from the time of the first occupancy by primitive agriculturists. I have had nothing to do with the identifications of any of the plant remains from what actually is a very large midden, but I have been mildly amused by wild guesses made by some individuals (but not by Dr. BIRD or by any experienced taxonomist), who have seen some of the material, that certain specimens, which actually proved to be a *Canna,* were (or might be) a plantain (*Musa*). In verification of the *Canna* identification, Dr. BIRD informs me that skins of *Canna* rhizomes

13) SAUER, C. O. Agricultural Origins and Dispersals. i-iv 1-110. pl. 1-4 (maps). 1952.

14) SAUER, C. O. Cultivated Plants of South and Central America. *In*: STEWARD, J. H. (editor) Physical Anthropology, Linguistics and Cultural Geography of South American Indians. Handbook of South American Indians. Vol. 6 (Smithsonian Inst.) Bur. Am. Ethnol. Bull. 143: 487-543. 1950.

15) BIRD, J. America's Oldest Farmers. Nat. Hist. 57: 296-303, 334-335. illus. 1948. This Huaca Prieta site was constantly occupied by fishermen-farmers for at least 4000 years, from pre-ceramic and pre-maize times.

occur at all levels throughout this great midden, but nowhere were there any traces of the skins of plantain fruits. So we may conclude that no *Musa* species occurred at Huaca Prieta, but what they did have was the indigenous American *Canna edulis* (*cf.* p. 278). Here I should point out that Dr. R. SCHULTES informs me of the discovery recently in Colombia of fossilized banana-like remains (*15a*) but I do not think that this very recent paper by HUERTAS and VAN DER HAMMEN has any bearing on the problem of the edible banana (or plantain) in America in pre-Columbian times; certainly the earlier BERRY report of a fossil *Musa* (seeds only) of a species of the *M. ensete* group has nothing to do with the edible *Musa* species (*cf.* p. 345).

I am not at all concerned with the list of species included in the second work referred to above, for they are all American ones, but I am concerned with certain very unequivocal and positive statements, included in Dr. SAUER's 1952 booklet, which will be accepted by many readers as correct.

On p. 54 of *Agricultural Origins and Dispersals* one finds the apparent basis of the author's belief in a certain amount of trans-Pacific or trans-Atlantic distribution of cultivated plant species, long before the period of European expansion. Unfortunately, he cited no species, presumably because he could not safely do so. Dr. SAUER says: "We geographers find it easier to think of the earth as a continuous surface, for certain conveniences in map making represented by an eastern and a western hemisphere" and precedes this with reference to geographers "from HUMBOLDT and RATZEL to SAPPER [who] have thought that there was diffusive culture from the Old World to the New."

No matter who the theorist may be, he *must constantly keep in mind the profound biogeographical differences between the Old and the New Worlds*. Merely citing HUMBOLDT, RATZEL and SAPPER proves nothing, for these scientists were not taxonomic specialists. As stated elsewhere, we *must* admit a very limited number of cultivated plant species that actually did get across the Atlantic or the Pacific Oceans, or both, in pre-Columbian times, but that does not change the fact that the great distribution between the hemispheres (including most or all of the weeds) came after the year 1500 A.D. Man was not an important factor until the expansion of the Spaniards and the Portuguese in both America and the Orient.

There was unquestionably diffusion of culture along the northern coasts of Asia to America, thence east and south in America. But the early peoples were surely not agriculturists, and even if they were they could not have brought Asiatic plant species with them over the northern route. They did bring the dog and the knowledge of making weapons of offense and defense, fishing and hunting techniques, basketry, pottery, ornamental designs, etc. What is more important, they brought with them the mental ability to develop further, once they became settled in their new homes, learned what could be useful to them in various fields, and then, largely on their own initiative,

---

15a) HUERTAS G., G. and Th. VAN DER HAMMEN: Un posible banano (*Musa*) fósil del Cretáceo de Colombia. Rev. Acad. Col. Cienc. Exact. Fis. y Nat. 9 (33-34): 115-116. 1 pl. 1953.

developed from simple food gatherers and nomadic hunters and fisher-
men into primitive agriculturists, thereafter they advanced to agriculturists, and finally reached the high civilizations that so surprised the
Spaniards, at the time of the conquest, in the early decades of the
sixteenth century.

There was no east to west distribution of important or even secondary species of cultivated food plants that exceeded the limits of
the eastern or the western hemispheres, except for one (?) American
cultigen (cf. p. 322) ; and, by the time the Europeans had reached
the Pacific, this had been carried by man as far as New Zealand and
parts of Papuasia, Guam and the Philippines and even parts of Malaysia (the Moluccas).   There were also a relatively few Malaysian
species that the Polynesians had carried to the easternmost islands of
the Pacific which they discovered and occupied, but not to America
except for possibly two or three species.

I can see no reason why the Polynesians could not have occasionally
reached the American coast, and hence no reason why they could not
have brought with them a few of their cultivated food plants of Indo-
Malaysian origin, such as the taro (*Colocasia*), the plantain, sugar
cane, the yam, and others.   But there is no tangible proof as yet that
they did so.   I would not hesitate to add the coconut to the above
list.   Dr. COOK was so positive that sugar cane and taro were pre-
Columbian introductions into tropical America, that he did not hesitate to extrapolate on the basis of taro, that its presence actually inspired the tropical American Indians to develop certain native American species of the allied *Xanthosoma* as food plants!   This impresses
me as the height of absurdity, in view of the fact that these same
American Indians, independently discovered the edible qualities of
some thousands of native American species and actually domesticated,
as cultigens, some scores of them.   YANOVSKI, in 1936*(16)*, actually
listed no less than eleven hundred species from the United States
alone which were eaten by the Indians, and there is no reason for
believing that the list is complete; very few of these northern species
were ever cultivated.

In contrast to this lack of orbital east-west distribution, there was,
within the limits of the eastern and the western hemispheres, a very
striking north and south distribution of cultivated species.   This can
be illustrated by citing maize, several species of beans and of *Cucurbita* and tobacco in America, which were spread to the very limits of
possible cultivation, northward and southward, from the more tropical
regions where they originated.

There was a similar, but distinctly less spectacular, north and south
distribution in the Old World, in such genera as *Sorghum* (Africa to
northeastern China).   One striking difference is that a high percentage of the basic Old World food plants were of northern origin, whereas most of those of America were developed as food plants in tropical
or subtropical regions.   The separating oceans were a factor that

---

16) YANOVSKI, E.   Food Plants of the North American Indians.   U. S. Dept.
Agr. Miscel. Publ. 237: 1-83.   1936.

must be considered in the distribution of both agriculture and the culture that was based on the permanent and dependable food supply that the former provided, whether an erratic historical geographer likes it or not.

After this little digression we now return to the work of CARL SAUER. Taking up his 1952 volume *Agricultural Origins and Dispersals* again, one notes some very curious, dogmatic and unequivocal statements. The many millions of rice farmers, for example, will, indeed, be surprised to learn that: "Rice is the only cereal which is still a perennial, though in cultivation it is treated like an annual" (p. 27). Maybe I am blind, but in the thousands of acres of rice I have seen in Malaysia, the Philippines, China, California, and parts of tropical America (both upland and paddy types), I have never seen a perennial rice plant in cultivation. The most that could legitimately be admitted is that perhaps there was a perennial species in the ancestry of the unbelievably variable *Oryza sativa* L.

Dr. E. B. COPELAND, who really knows rice from long residence in the Philippines and from having grown it on a very large scale in the Sacramento Valley in California, objects to the idea of a perennial ancestor for this cereal. He states (*in lit.*) that in various regions (Japan, the Philippines and Italy; and Dr. MANGELSDORF confirms this for Mexico) there exists a weedy rice which produces an indefinite succession of culms. Some such rice is of good culinary quality and some is not. When harvested, one head at a time in Java and the Philippines, such rice can be utilized; but where harvesting is done by sickle or by machine, it is a nuisance. We admit that perennial rice may exist but it has no part in the rice industry.

I suspect that there is a little genetic problem involved here, for on one occasion I collected a very vigorous, apparently perennial, spontaneous rice near Zamboanga, Mindanao, which seemed to conform to the characters of *Oryza latifolia* Desv., its spikelet size conforming closely to that of *Oryza minuta* Presl. Incidentally *O. latifolia* Desv., the type of which came from Puerto Rico, has been reported from the southeastern United States. BACKER recognized it, for Java, as a distinct species. In view of its range, I suspect that it is nothing but a mutant of the cultivated annual *Oryza sativa* L. It would be profitable to make a cytogenetical analysis.

The statement is made, on page 28, that: "There is no necessity of starting coconuts in a seed bed and transplanting them later." SAUER would very quickly learn the reason were he to attempt, let us hope at his own expense, to establish a coconut plantation almost anywhere in the Old World tropics (*cf.* p. 266). On the same page, the statement regarding the custom of starting rice in a seed bed and later transplanting in paddies is just as unrealistic; the labor-cost for levelling, diking and irrigating, made it imperative that every square inch of space be utilized.

The statement, on page 33, regarding certain cultigens in Polynesia is grossly misleading, for the *Pandanus* was *native* there but, as a food plant, of very little value. There is no reason whatsoever for inferring that any of the few food plants mentioned, no matter where they originated, reached the Pacific Islands "at a fairly remote time", on the basis that there is great variation of some cultigens, such as the common breadfruit.

To make such a sweeping statement, one should consider that another cultigen, the sweet potato introduced into New Zealand in the twelfth or thirteenth century, proliferated into at least fifty recognizable varieties in only six centuries, and at least thirty others in Hawaii in a somewhat longer period. The peanut case (page 44), taken over from ANDERSON, but without all his conclusions, is exploded elsewhere (p. 295).

Professional nutritionists will be shocked to observe that, on page 53, maize is credited with helping to make up the protein deficiency! This was where the common bean entered the picture, for where beans were an important part of the basic diet, plus other well-known vegetables, pellagra failed to develop(16a).

A long dissertation on the time of arrival of the common domestic fowl in South America begins on page 57. This is out of my field, but SAUER certainly does not disprove NORDENSKIÖLD's argument that it was introduced into South America by CABRAL in 1500, or shortly thereafter, by someone else (I suspect it was about 1500 on the return route from Goa to Portugal via Brazil). I merely wish to point out here that no chicken bones were found in the great midden at Huaca Prieta, Peru, by Dr. BIRD (cf. p. 272). Dr. ALEXANDER WETMORE, of the Smithsonian Institution, our best informed specialist on the comparative anatomy of bird skeletons, assures me that no chicken bones have ever been found in pre-Columbian sites in America. I do not repeat his appraisal of certain genetical theories, but it was properly emphatic. Dr. SAUER's unnecessarily expanded account of the green and blue chicken egg episode was perhaps too much of an attention-arrester to be neglected, for any American audience would sit up and take notice of naturally produced colored eggs reminiscent of Easter!

It is, however, undue stretching to cite a journal entry written May 30, 1828, at Paita, Peru, probably 350 years after an introduction had occurred, to help prove a point concerning the breed of domestic fowl observed in South America and characterized by having black bones and black flesh. This breed occurs, here and there, all over the Old World tropics. In some regions, in China, for example, it is used as food and as a sovereign remedy for tuberculosis. When I first encountered this curious type in the Philippines in 1904, I ate the strange-looking flesh, thinking no more of it than did my Filipino companions who were familiar with it. Being on a field trip in a not too easily accessible part of Mindoro, and living on the country, we ate what we could get, which was never too much, and on this particular occasion we had no choice.

As to when and how the domestic fowl, which originated in Indo-Malaysia, reached South America, SAUER preferred to accept LATCHAM's diffusionist beliefs, expressed in 1922, which are opposed to NORDENSKIÖLD's who published in the same year. SAUER *wanted* to believe precisely what LATCHAM concluded. Until positive evidence to the contrary is available, I prefer to accept the current theory that the first introduction was made by the Portuguese, following the year 1500.

Perhaps it is to be regretted that the super-positive LEO WIENER who, in 1922, published his "proofs" that certain American economic

---

16a) WILLIAMS, L. O. Beans, Maize and Civilization. Ceiba 3: 77-85. 1952.

plants were established in Africa previous to 1492 (*cf.* p. 316) did not give some attention to the common domestic fowl. After all, if the African negroes or even the Arabs had discovered America a century or two before COLUMBUS, or even earlier, they might have introduced the common fowl which seems clearly to have become established first on the *east coast* of South America (*not on the west coast* — the trans-Pacific theorists might well note this!). Because of the great rapidity with which such an acquisition as the domestic fowl would spread, even among primitive people, I see no reason whatever why LATCHAM's views, even when supported by Dr. SAUER, should be taken seriously if one considers all available data.

Although it is entirely outside of my field, the blue and green egg episode arrested my attention when I read a newspaper account in late June, 1953. This account stated that the progeny of a cross between two of our standard breeds of poultry (Barred Rock and Rhode Island Red) at Montville, Connecticut produced green eggs. Dr. WALTER LANDAUER, geneticist at the Storrs Agricultural Experiment Station, informed me on July 17, 1953, that some years ago the Storrs Station imported some Araucana fowls from Chile for breeding experiments. In accordance with practice, the excess baby chicks and the cockerels were sold, as well as some of the adult stock when the experimental work was discontinued. Ever since then, he has received sporadic reports of green and blue hen eggs produced here and there in Connecticut; and in some cases, he could trace back the producers of these colored eggs to stock derived from the Storrs Station. Incidentally, he states that some of the Chilean birds carried barring.

Thus we can explain the occurrence of hens in staid New England that produce green and blue eggs, instead of conventional brown and white ones; and this occurred even anterior to Dr. SAUER's use of the blue and green egg episode in neighboring New York, as an attention-arrester. Without checking with an authority, I could very easily have concluded that here we had another case of egg-color developing independently of the original South American stock. It is a beautiful example of how it pays to check on any theory which sometimes not-too-well informed readers will accept without checking on the veracity of certain basic information. It is rather amusing to note that while the blue and green hen egg episode was being developed in New York for the edification of his audience, the lecturer never knew that for some years past these strangely colored eggs had been appearing sporadically in the adjoining state of Connecticut! This fact did not escape the notice of the New York City representatives of certain news distributing agencies, to say nothing of their Connecticut colleagues. The hens in question came from Araucanian stock introduced by the Connecticut Experiment Station for breeding purposes.

That Professor PUNNETT*(17)* had established that the color factor in the blue egg chicken is due to a dominant gene (the *cause célèbre* for the moment in poultry genetics) matters not at all. The *cause célèbre* is Dr. SAUER's own characterization. As there is no native bird in South America, according to the ornithologists, that could possibly have crossed with the domestic fowl, I believe that the indicated egg color was due to a chance mutation originating in Asia which has been perpetuated.

Dr. SAUER most willingly accepts the validity of the claims of certain authors regarding the pre-Columbian distribution on both hemispheres of the sweet potato, maize, banana and plantain, as well

17) PUNNETT, R. L. The Blue Egg. Jour. Genet. 17: 465-470. 1933.

as of the chicken, with the bare statement that each of these post-Columbian introductions can be shown to be based on errors that invalidate them (page 57). The statement, except for the sweet potato, is not true, unless he be willing to accept the discredited STONOR-ANDERSON theory which places maize in Assam in pre-Columbian times. As to the plantain, the claim that dissemination would be slow, because so few buds were produced, is invalid. Every variety with which I am personally familiar, when grown in reasonably good soil, with ample moisture, produces a good crop of "eyes" (buds). And all the Spanish accounts, that I have read, of early conditions in tropical America indicate that in Mexico, Central America, and all over the West Indies and elsewhere, the cultivation of the banana and plantain spread with remarkable rapidity, once the plants were introduced by the Spaniards and Portuguese. In less than two decades after the plants were introduced, they were very widely planted in all or most Spanish controlled parts of tropical America.

Here one cannot ignore the rapid development of the trans-Atlantic slave trade initiated in the decade following 1492. The Portuguese, in the beginning of their explorations of the west coast of Africa in 1442, had accepted slavery, and it was but natural that they took a leading part in the lucrative slave trade between their established centers on the west coast of Africa and tropical America. It was unquestionably through these slave ships that basic food plants, including certain species of the true yams (*Dioscorea*), cassava, maize, banana and plantain varieties, sorghum and other important food plants were first transmitted across the Atlantic, some from Africa to America and others in the reverse direction.

Writing about 1525, OVIEDO noted the rapid spread of what was a very valuable acquisition *to the available food supply, from across the Atlantic*. The definite date of the banana introduction into Santo Domingo was 1516, when Father TOMAS DE BERLANGA brought it from the Canary Islands. OVIEDO recorded the name *platano* as in use, for some types, less than a decade after the banana introduction. He also commented on the great abundance of the plants, stating that in his own ranch there were then (about 1525) four thousand bananas, and that there were other ranches [plantings] larger than his own. Remarks by other early observers confirm OVIEDO's statements.

I do not accept most of LEO WIENER's conclusions regarding certain other plant species (*cf.* p. 316), but even he seems to be correct in this banana-plantain case. His objective was clearly to prove, by philological data, that the conclusions of all his predecessors regarding the time of more or less universal distribution of certain cultivated plants, between the two hemispheres, were erroneous. Yet, in this case, his statement that in less than twenty years the banana and the plantain had become universal in America is correct (*Africa and the Discovery of America* 1: 130. 1920). Once the African slave trade was established within a decade after 1492, the way was open for the introduction of all available plantain and banana varieties from West Africa, and also for other economic plants.

We may reasonably admit that one, or a few, of the numerous

Polynesian plantain varieties may have been carried by the Polynesians themselves to South America, for the "eyes" (buds) can very easily be transported, over long distances, with a minimum of care and still retain their viability. It might be that a form introduced on the coast of Peru was transported over the Andes, thus reaching the upper waters of the Amazon. It has been suggested, by at least one author, that there is a "native" form on the Amazon. What is needed, of course, is a direct comparison of this with all the known Polynesian forms. Any "new" form would, of necessity, have originated as a bud sport, as there were no native parent forms in America. All this is purely hypothetical; and even if a Polynesian form had become established in pre-Columbian times, no trace of a *Musa* appeared in Dr. BIRD's very extensive excavations at Huaca Prieta, Peru (*cf.* p. 273 & 345).

A most surprising and actually fantastic surmise appears on p. 61: "The principal aboriginal marine ports of entry may have been about the Peruvian-Ecuadorean border *and their use lie as far back as the beginning of dynastic time in the Far East*" (the italics are mine). Here, Dr. SAUER accepted J. B. HUTCHINSON's *Gossypium* theory, believing in the trans-pacific carriage of cotton by man, as a proven fact; it most definitely is not. That "there are several dozen plants, cultigens, intimately associated with man on both sides of the Pacific that need critical investigation" is only in part true; as a matter of fact, if we include weeds and ornamentals, there are now involved perhaps fifteen hundred to two thousand or more species. The statement quoted above is correct, except that none of them needs or is worthy of critical investigation. The little book is really as full of holes as the proverbial sieve. The great period of trans-Pacific transmission of American and of Asiatic plants came with the early exploration of the Pacific by the Spaniards (1520-21) and for two hundred and fifty years was limited largely to the Acapulco-Guam-Manila route, the real impetus coming with COOK's first voyage in 1769, followed by his two other voyages. I may be maligned for repeating this so often, but it seems to be necessary.

SAUER's *Cucurbita* discussion is beside the point for it is *not* true that *Cucurbita ficifolia* Bouché (1837) was first described from India. BOUCHÉ did not know the place of origin of his type material, but it later developed that the plant came apparently from tropical America. The story of the fruits' having been introduced into France in 1854, as food for the Yaks which were, at that time, imported from Tibet, is intriguing as a story and correct. But it is absolutely irrelevant, for *Cucurbita ficifolia* Bouché had been previously introduced into France; it was first named in 1824, and was first described in 1837. Dr. SAUER was too intent on proving what he believed to be the case and left the *Cucurbita*-Yak story hanging by a chain of inferences. The sad point is that his inferences are purely imaginary (the *Cucurbita*-Yak story would of course intrigue the average audience). All that one needs to do is to scan what BOIS wrote. For details see the BOIS*(18)* three- or four-page discussion. To quote again from WASHINGTON IRVING, he expressed my idea perhaps better than anyone else when, in discussing the opinions of P. MARTIRE, HORNIUS, BUFFON and many other early theorists who discussed the possibilities as to how and by whom America was first occupied, he stated that they had "fastened the two continents [hemispheres] together by a strong chain of deductions."

I cannot consider the *Cucurbita* problem in detail. Several attempts have been made to settle the taxonomic problems involved. I merely mention, in passing, that COGNIAUX stated in 1881 that all the wild species of the genus were natives of America; this is true. He likewise stated that all the cultivated ones were very probably native of Asia. No one, nowadays, accepts this view, of course, as the archeological remains prove that the entire genus was American, until the Portuguese, after 1500, took certain cultigens to Goa from eastern Brazil, where they flourished. Certain types continued to vary in their new homes, first on the Malabar coast of India, then northward and then westward from what is now Iran. This Asiatic centre of variation has puzzled various theorists, who did not consider the Brazil-Goa connections that continued to persist from 1500 for some 165 years (*cf.* p. 229).

If one wishes to improve on the classification of the "species" and minor taxa of *Cucurbita,* reference is made to the extensive, well illustrated studies of Dr. L. H. BAILEY, published between 1929 and 1948. BAILEY recognized nearly thirty wild and cultivated species of the genus as well as some varieties*(19)*. Like other authors, he could not solve the problem of the botanical origin of the various cultigens; and the geneticists also failed. In his 1929 paper, BAILEY photographed the progeny of a single fruit (*C. pepo*) of one of the common ornamental gourds which is conveniently and conventionally placed as *Cucurbita pepo* L. Here the hundred and ten different fruits show a remarkable differentiation in shape, size, color, markings, etc., all from plants grown from the seeds of a single fruit. I doubt that even a national gourd society, which is very active, can ever help on this problem, except to produce new forms. This is a group of cultigens that seems to defy binomial and trinomial classification.

Then, there is a still later paper, a study of the cultivated species of *Cucurbita* of the United States, which should be mentioned. WHITAKER and BOHN*(20)* gave up on the genetics, stating that the *Cucurbita* species are not amenable to cytogenetic analysis. Thus, we find that *Cucurbita pepo* L. includes what is currently known, in the United States, as the pumpkin (with large or medium, smooth skinned, ellipsoid to depressed globose fruits), the English marrow, the Zucchini types, the yellow warted "crook neck" or summer squash, and a dozen

18) BOIS, D. Les plantes alimentaires chez tous les peuples et à travers les âges. . . . 1-593. fig. 1-255. 1927.

19) Gent. Herb. 2: 63-118. fig. 29-64. 1929; 6: 267-316. fig. 140-163. 1945; 7: 449-477. fig. 211-239. 1948.

20) WHITAKER, T. W. and BOHN, G. W. The Taxonomy, Genetics, Production, and Uses of the Cultivated Species of *Cucurbita.* Econ. Bot. 4: 52-81. illus. 1950.

other named and well known forms (in kitchen and market parlance), including various other known kinds of squash.

In some species we find rampant vines and the non-scandent types; and, in some, the fruit variation is infinite, particularly in *Cucurbita pepo* L. and *C. maxima* Duch. There is, thus, infinitely greater variation between forms placed under the same binomial, than there is between the few recognized cultivated species, so one might say that as far as botanical nomenclature is concerned, it is neither "fish, flesh, nor good red herring". It is true, as they say, that the specific name *pepo* came from the Latin, but it is manifest that the plant (or fruit) to which the name *pepo* was originally applied by the Latins was not a *Cucurbita*. It might have been the wax gourd (*Benincasa*) or the true gourd (*Lagenaria*).

Perhaps the most peculiar phrase in this treatment is the statement: "It would seem to be more appropriate to assign to the culinary words definitions in agreement with their derivations as modified by current usage, rather than to attempt to incorporate them in botanical terminology." My reaction leads me to believe that it would have been more logical had the study been strictly an economic one, and that any attempt to apply Latin binomials should have been eliminated. Perhaps one could query: "When is a squash a pumpkin, and when is a pumpkin a squash?" for in American Indian parlance what they knew as squash was botanically not *Cucurbita maxima* Duch. but was a form of the pumpkin (*C. pepo* L.). Fortunately, only five species are involved. Here is a case among the cultigens, paralleling that of many of our other cultivated plants, where it would probably be best to abandon any attempt to apply trinomial nomenclature — as in the *Musa sapientum—Musa paradisiaca* L. complex, the cultivated apples and oranges, certain *Gossypium* cultigens, maize, beans (*Phaseolus* spp.), citrus, rice and numerous other groups. The taxonomists, for the most part, wisely gave up long ago; but there are apparently always optimists in other fields.

I am not convinced that all is well with the binomial *Cucurbita ficifolia* Bouché as currently interpreted. In South America, what we know as *Cucurbita ficifolia* is a low altitude plant, as it is in India (Malabar gourd, Siamese gourd). The Guatemala form placed here grows at an altitude of from 6,000 to 8,000 feet and will not produce fruits at El Zamarano in Honduras, at about 2,300 feet, where it has been cultivated. One suspects that the form grown at high altitudes in Tibet, referred to above in the *Cucurbita*-Yak episode, is not the same as the low altitude *C. ficifolia* Bouché; in fact L. H. BAILEY suggested (*in lit.*) that the Guatemala high-altitude form represents an undescribed species. Yet Messrs. WHITAKER and BIRD[21] report that 11,000 shell fragments, 1,300 seeds, and 550 peduncle fragments from Huaca Prieta, Peru, representing *Lagenaria* (the common gourd), and two cultivated species of *Cucurbita* (*C. ficifolia* Bouché

21) WHITAKER, T. W. and BIRD, J. B. Identification and Significance of the *Cucurbita* Material from Huaca Prieta, Peru. Am. Mus. Novitat. 1426: 1-15, fig. 1-2. 1949.

and *C. moschata* Duch.) were found in Dr. BIRD's remarkable "dig." The site was continuously occupied from at least 2500 B.C. to 1600 A.D., roughly 4000 years.

This discussion of Dr. SAUER's views has been unduly drawn out. Since he is an apparently ardent and extreme diffusionist, he is convinced that his explanations are correct. I am convinced, merely from the records in botany, archeology, phytogeography, history, exploration, etc., that he is too often in error. In his bibliography, I find no record of the most important reference book of all in this field: DE CANDOLLE's *Origin of Cultivated Plants*. He has not disproved the basic truth of this work. One hesitates to charge this omission to the fact that DE CANDOLLE's conclusions are diametrically opposed to what SAUER has failed to prove.

There is only one other item that needs elaboration. In the short statement on page 56 he is exactly one hundred per cent in error. One really wonders why the statement, which follows, was included, for it is untrue, as could easily have been verified in any large botanical institution, and very misleading: "We have in North America a number of curiously distributed plants, commonly associated with man, of which we do not know the origin or whether they are identical with Old World forms. These are the sweet flag (*Acorus calamus*), the esculent *Cyperus* [*C. esculentus*], *Trapa natans* (water chestnut), the Nelumbium lotus and the *Sagittaria sagittifolia* of China and our Pacific Coast, known to the Columbia Basin Indians as *wapatoo*. Some of these plants are reproduced from underground parts, some [one!] have seeds of extreme viability; mostly their distributions are not such that animal or water transport seems likely." This is pure speculation, with a suspicion of having been deliberately slanted in favor of an early introduction idea from the Old World. Here are the facts which any real searcher for the truth could easily have determined by writing a few letters.

1) *Acorus calamus* L. — The common sweet flag was introduced from Europe by our earliest colonists, arriving, very likely, in Jamestown in 1607 and in Plymouth in 1620; it may have been a Mayflower passenger, or it may have arrived, a few years earlier, at the French settlements in eastern Canada. It was, in turn, unquestionably introduced into Europe from Asia. The only other known species of *Acorus* occurs in eastern Asia. Once introduced here, it immediately established itself. It was in great demand in Europe, for various purposes, long before America was discovered, and is one of the very easiest of plants to propagate from rhizomes.

2) *Cyperus esculentus* L. — This plant has all the appearance of being a man-distributed weed, and, within limits, primitive man may have helped in its distribution. A botanist gets the impression that most of its wide range is due to the activities of modern man, for it is basically a weed. It is now widely distributed in the temperate and tropical parts of both hemispheres, southern Europe, Africa, North and South America, India, but there is no record for it, for all of Malaysia. There is only one record of it for all the Pacific Islands (Samoa), and this (if the identification be correct) would surely indicate a modern introduction as a weed. I have seen only one immature specimen (VAUPEL 53) from Samoa and suspect that it is not the Linnaean species.

3) *Trapa natans* L. — There is no excuse for including this species in the list. We know what it is, to what it is related, where it came from and,

within a very few years, just when it was purposely introduced. What further data must the botanist supply? The actual records of introduction are lost. The somewhat variable *Trapa natans* L. is widely distributed in Europe and Asia. What we may not know is whether or not our strain is the European or the Chinese one. In China, this is a cultivated plant, as is *Trapa bicornis* L. f., and for many years the fruits of both species have been imported into the United States in bulk by the Chinese for use by them as a luxury food. It would not be strange if this second species had been established somewhere in America, but there are, as far as I know, no published records and no extant American specimens.

   Trapa natans was first collected in America by GEORGE VASEY in 1878, *in the fish ponds* that existed until sometime after 1900 on the mall at Washington, D. C., not far from the Washington monument. This is hardly a wild habitat. Finding that this alien plant quickly occupied the space intended for some kind of fish, whoever was then in charge of the fish ponds apparently raked out all of the plants and, to get rid of the mass, dumped it into the adjacent Potomac River. Here, having few pests or enemies, like the true weeds, it immediately took advantage of its opportunities and occupied all the available space to which it was adapted: muddy bottom, fresh not-too-deep water, the current none or slow. Very quickly it became a pest, interfering seriously with swimming, fishing and even canoeing. Or possibly the original *Trapa* fruits came first to the Harvard Botanical Garden and were thence generously shared with Washington, as it is noteworthy that the first Fresh Pond record for Cambridge is dated 1879, the fish pond record for Washington, D. C., being one year earlier. The first Fresh Pond records are September 12, 1879 and July 12, 1880 (C. E. FAXON, collector), so one may err in charging the first introduction of a distinctly noxious water plant to a U. S. Government agency.

   Then our local troubles in New England commenced, for soon it appeared in the Concord and the Sudbury Rivers (1884), and in the Charles River (1896). In the year 1953, a bill was introduced into the Massachusetts General Court seeking an appropriation to be used for the extermination of this very aggressive water weed — and there is about as good a chance of exterminating it as there is of eliminating all dandelions from all lawns of North America. Then, some disciple of the idea of uncontrolled dissemination of plants, be they useless or useful or even potential pests, cast some of its fruits into Sanders Lake, near Scotia, New York, which drains into the Mohawk River. The first record for Sanders Lake was 1886 as "planted"; and for the Mohawk River, 1926. A couple of decades later, it had extended its range southward in the Hudson River until it was checked by the brackish water near Poughkeepsie. This is, to date, the known range of the species in North America; there may be a few other places, unknown to me, where it is also taking over, where some one has cast its fruits into a stream or pond. FERNALD, in 1950, spoke of this plant as "locally too abund. and aggressive, Mass. and N. Y. to Md. (Introd. and natzd. from Eurasia)." So much for one of the "curiously distributed plants," from the known record of which there is nothing curious, except to the theorist who writes about plants without making himself familiar with the easily available botanical data. The actual introduction was by modern man and within our own times.

   Incidentally, although this pestiferous aquatic species increases with us, it tends to disappear in certain places in Europe. Fossil forms occur in North America, and an unusually large number of fossil species have been recorded from Japan. Last year Dr. MIKI(22) recorded sixteen fossil species from Japan alone.

   Were I to risk a guess, it would be that our form came from China and, like many other aliens of Chinese origin, found itself thoroughly at home once established in a few streams and ponds in Massachusetts, New York, and Maryland-Virginia. The best example that I know of is *Lonicera japonica* Thunb. which, within the past half century or so, has become dominant over vast areas from Maryland southward. How rapidly a very vigorous alien tetraploid weed will spread in cultivated lands is admirably shown by *Setaria faberi* Herrm. This

   22) MIKI, S. *Trapa* of Japan with Special Reference to its Remains. Jour. Inst. Polytech. Osaka Univ. Ser. 5. 3: 1-30. pl. 1. fig. 1-14. 1952.

was named and described in 1911 from a Szechuan specimen and is now widely distributed in China. The earliest record of it from the United States is dated 1932, and the first living plant was found in 1936, in (of all places) grounds controlled by the U. S. Department of Agriculture in Washington, D. C. Within two decades it had become a dominant weed in agricultural lands from New England to North Carolina, westward to Nebraska, and Minnesota and a very serious pest in the vast corn and soybean fields of the central western states. Seldom has any introduced weed in North America spread as rapidly as this vigorous one which, in favorable habitats, sometimes reaches a height of six feet (22a).

4) *"Nelumbium lotus"* Ridl. (sphalm., 1902) = *Nelumbo nucifera* Gaertn. — This species never should have been listed. It is the sacred lotus of the Old World and was not introduced into the United States, until perhaps the early part of the last century. Where it has been planted, it persists indefinitely. It did so in the Nile, until in some period of breakdown between two dynasties, the hungry underprivileged masses simply exterminated it there for use as food. It has very large edible rhizomes and large edible seeds. We may charitably presume that Dr. SAUER referred to the one other strictly American species, *Nelumbo lutea* Pers., which, thanks to the American Indian, now grows from the Canadian border southward to Cuba and Honduras (Lake Yojoa) and has also been reported from Colombia (*cf.* p. 263).

5) *Sagittaria "sagittifolia"* of China and our Pacific Coast, non L. = S. *sinensis* Sims. — The proper denomination depends on how broad an interpretation one places on the limits of a species. There may be some who would be tempted to reduce all or most *Sagittaria* species to a single one, but this would be foolish. In the latest edition of *Gray's Manual*, FERNALD critically considered those of the northeastern United States and recognized sixteen species. GLEASON, in 1952, for much the same area, recognized eleven species. Neither botanist admitted the European *Sagittaria sagittifolia* L. The Columbia River basin form is the North American endemic *Sagittaria cuneata* Sheldon. The Asiatic form is *Sagittaria sinensis* Sims(23), widely distributed in China and India, occurring in Java, Celebes, and the Philippines, as well as in the Malay Peninsula (planted there, but never seen in flower by RIDLEY), and naturalized in Hawaii. Its spread into the Philippines and Malaysia was undoubtedly due to its introduction by the Chinese, this being surely so in the Malay Peninsula and in Hawaii. The Chinese have segregated a cultigen in Kwangtung Province, a form with broad leaves and broad basal lobes. I have seen hundreds of acres of this in high-diked paddies along rivers; it is one of the most beautiful of cultivated food plants when in full flower. In considering the Chinese species in 1903, C. H. WRIGHT recognized this as *Sagittaria sagittifolia* L., and MICHELI, in 1881, considered it as a variety of the Linnaean species; but times change and the taxonomists' ideas of specific limits change with them.

I would say, off hand, that an intensive study of this and other special crop plants in China which are, here and there, produced on a very large scale, but which are not or but rarely grown outside of China would yield greater geographic dividends than the SAUER speculations.

Incidentally, one can provide just as good a meal from the tubers of *Sagittaria cuneata* Sheldon(24) (either from the eastern or the western form) as one can from Chinese tubers purchased in San Francisco, the product of *S. sinensis* Sims.

This is really not a very flattering record. If generic and specific names mean anything, it will be impossible to explain so many errors

22a) KING, L. J. Germination and Chemical Control of the Giant Foxtail Grass [*Setaria faberi* Herrm.]. Contr. Boyce Thompson Inst. 16: 469-487. 1952.

23) GLÜCK, H. Kritische Untersuchungen über das Indisch-asiatische Pfeilkraut (*Sagittaria sinensis* Sims = S. *sagittifolia* auct.). Bot. Jahrb. 72: 1-66. fig. 1-41. 1941.

24) FERNALD, M. L. and KINSEY, A. C. Edible Wild Plants of Eastern North America. i-xiv. 1-452. pl. 1-25. fig. 1-129. 1943.

and misstatements. One must hope that the conclusions drawn in the purely geographical field are more nearly correct. After all, anyone making such drastic claims as appear in this little book of 1952 might have been expected to confer with some of the botanists on the staff of his own University. Knowing most of these men personally, I cannot quite visualize *any of them* as providing such misleading data; I, therefore, am left to believe that the data came from the author's own mind or from non-botanical consultants, who may hold ideas similar to his regarding the early transmission of economic plants across the Pacific from West to East. The known facts, which cannot be repeated too often, are opposed to the possible transmission of more than a very few economic species eastward from Asia to America. The story about man's other plant commensals, the weeds, is the same.

Now, were I a historical geographer interested in plants, in relation to man and his accomplishments, where these plants originated, how and when they were distributed beyond their original ranges, I would first learn the principles of taxonomy; then I would acquire a thorough grounding in economic botany and study the basic concepts of phytogeography; consult the available annals of early exploration; read on archeology, ecology, anthropology, ethnology, comparative philology, and other fields, including paleobotany and geologic history.

By so doing, I became as dogmatic and positive as I am regarding the basic truth of DE CANDOLLE's conclusions in his classic *Origin of Cultivated Plants*. I may be accused — in fact, I have been already — of pontificating in support of DE CANDOLLE's conclusions. If my defense of DE CANDOLLE be pontification, then I am at a loss for a term to describe the opinions which I have criticized in this chapter.

It seems to me that if as much energy were devoted to matters regarding which we are rather ignorant, but which impinge on certain aspects of historical geography as they have developed in the past half century or so, we all would benefit immensely. Who knows much about certain agricultural crops and vegetable products, some of which enter international commerce on a fairly large scale?

DE CANDOLLE in 1883 limited his list to about 247 species. ANDERSON's sketchy one of 1952 included about 100, some of which, such as *Dahlia* and *Tagetes*, never should have been included. He was ten per cent in error as to claimed or inferred places of origin. Dr. AKEMINE did compile a working list between 1933 and 1940, with the rather astounding total of 1837 species. This number must be revised downward to a certain degree because he was misled in some cases by synonymy. On the other hand, certain additions must be made because the authors of reference works, from which his data were in large part compiled, did not know that various species were actually cultivated here or there in the world for food or other purposes (*see* p. 198 for further notes on this work).

Let us return to the subject of little known crop plants. Why not investigate the primitive grain plants (species of *Digitaria*) still cultivated for food in Africa? What does the economic botanist know about the history of several aquatic species very extensively cultivated for food in China and actually entering foreign commerce, such as *Trapa* (at least, two species) ; *ma tai*, sometimes called water chestnut (as are also the fruits of the *Trapa* species), *Eleocharis dulcis* Trin. ; *Sagittaria sinensis* Sims ; the *Ustilago* infected rhizomes of *Zizania caduciflora* (Turcz.) H.M.*(25)* ; *Euryale ferox* Salisb. ; *Nelumbo nucifera* Gaertn. (as a food, not as a sacred plant). All of these, with perhaps one exception, are imported in bulk into the United States from China, even nowadays (1953), reaching us via Hongkong.

There are many other species of widely cultivated plants, and many of these planted on a large scale for food in India, Malaysia and China, and even in Polynesia for which we may search in vain in standard texts of economic botany. We may cite *Canarium album* Raeusch. and *C. pimela* Koenig of southern China, the fruits of both of which enter local and foreign commerce. Then, there are many fruits which are extensively cultivated and always available, in quantity, in local markets in the Old World : the mangosteen ; duku, langsat or lansone (*Lansium*), the santol (*Sandoricum koetjape* (Burm. f.) Merr.), *Baccaurea* spp., several species of *Mangifera* and *Artocarpus* in Malaysia, as well as the tubers of *Amorphophallus* and *Cyrtosperma* and other "strange" fruits and vegetables. The same statement applies to a totally different series of species found in the markets of tropical American towns.

Odd and interesting cultivated species constantly show up. All botanists are more or less familiar with *Malva parviflora* L., a man-distributed weed of Eurasian origin, now widely distributed in the North and South Temperate Zones and at higher altitudes in the tropics of both hemispheres. How many realize that this plant is the richest in vitamins and minerals ever analyzed in the nutritional

---

25) This is actually the only extensively cultivated plant species known to me of which the normal plant, or its seeds, are not used. It is always grown from *Ustilago* infected rhizomes, which develop characteristic basal intumescences. This is *kau-sun* (known to the Europeans in China as "cane shoots"), a highly appreciated vegetable. The abnormal swollen and greatly shortened basal parts of the stem are intumescences due to the presence of *Ustilago esculenta* Hennings. HANCE ("On a Chinese Culinary Vegetable," Jour. Bot. 10: 146-149. 1872) has given an excellent account of the plant, but he had the immature form which is the one always marketed, apparently not realizing that what he so greatly admired as a vegetable was actually an infestional intumescence. D. BOIS ("Les plantes alimentaires" 1927) has provided additional information. This *Ustilago*-infected *Zizania* is grown on an extensive scale in China and Indo-China in diked paddies, similar to those in which rice is grown. A very detailed study of the normal (uninfected) *Zizania caduciflora* (Turcz.) H. M. (*Z. latifolia* Turcz.) will be found in a Russian paper with an English summary by I. V. KOZLOFF: "Manchurian Tuscarora or the Broad-leaved Zizania." Manch. Research Soc. ser. a. 12: 1-2. fig. 1-13. 1926.

The full-grown but immature intumescences of the *Ustilago* that occur on maize are widely eaten in Mexico, according to Dr. ANDERSON. The corresponding form that occurs on the form of *Sorghum* known as *kaoliang* and so extensively grown in northern China is also widely used as food. In fact, the nearly full-grown intumescences of *Ustilago sorghi* are carefully searched for and collected for food before reaching their full maturity. They are gathered immature as a sanitary measure to prevent the ripening of the spores, thus keeping the actual infestation of the next *kaoliang* crop at a minimum.

laboratories of the world?   My authority is Dr. ROBERT S. HARRIS, head of the Nutrition Laboratory of the Massachusetts Institute of Technology.   How many botanists, nutritional specialists, agronomists, geographers and others know that this "weed" is very extensively cultivated for food in southwestern China (Szechuan and Yunnan)?   It is there grown as a winter crop and covers many hundreds of acres.   Merely because we consider some peoples less "advanced" than ourselves is no reason why we should ignore what they eat and why.   Even in sedate Boston, individuals of Italian origin have been observed gathering this plant in quantity in the grounds of the Arnold Arboretum during 1953.   When questioned the answer is invariably that *Malva* is a powerful medicine.   Probably most of them never heard of vitamins.

Here is a field infinitely more worthy of investigation than the speculations, based on totally inadequate knowledge of cultivated plants, how and when species were distributed between the two hemispheres.   This subject is so complicated that closet theorists, at least, should refrain from tackling it!

I have tried to limit my criticisms of Dr. SAUER's little book of 1952 to his conclusions about plant species.   He may think that I have been harsh and acrid in my criticism.   Lest the casual reader, as well as the technically trained ones, think that I am prejudiced against this author, I refer them to Dr. MANGELSDORF's recent review of the entire SAUER *(25a)* philosophy.   The reviewer concludes: "A theory almost completely lacking in factual basis may still be stimulating and provocative and may be especially useful if it can be subjected to critical tests which would prove it wrong.   I can think of no such tests to apply to SAUER's theory.   His two principal hearths occur in regions where few archaeological remains have so far been found and where the climate almost precludes the long-time preservation of herbaceous cultigens.   Practically all of his conclusions, although unsupported by evidence, are still virtually impossible to disprove.   Indeed if one sought, as an exercise in imagination, to design a completely untestable theory of agricultural origins and dispersals, it would be difficult to improve upon this one . . ."

25a)   MANGELSDORF, P. C.   [Review of SAUER's] Agricultural Origins and Dispersals.   Am. Antiquity 19(1): 87-90.   July, 1953.

TEXT FIGURE 12. — *Zea mays* L., maize. — From
F. HERNANDEZ's *Nova Plantarum . . . Mexicanorum Historiae* (Romae, 1651). — HERNANDEZ, according to
FINAN (Annals Missouri Bot. Gard. 35: 165. 1948):
"presents a detailed picture of the uses of maize in Mexico, giving much the same information that is in the literature of exploration. For the first time in the herbals,
HERNANDEZ uses the Aztec name for maize, *tlaolli*, and
describes it as having black, white, purple, dark blue,
golden yellow or mixed-colored kernels. To illustrate his
herbal he uses woodcuts taken from the L'OBEL herbal of
1581". — The illustration at the left has, indeed, been
taken from a cut in LOBELIUS's Herbal of 1581 (according
to FINAN, this was the first illustration of prop-roots);
the right hand cut may have been made after a drawing
prepared for HERNANDEZ, in Mexico between 1571 and
1577, or after another European herbal.

E. Anderson:— As I write this, there lies before me a pamphlet bearing a quotation from a letter I wrote a few years ago: "Let us have some facts. E. D. M." This was followed by another passage: "Well, here are the first few. There are more to follow, E. A.". This friendly interchange of opinions began when I received a letter from Dr. ANDERSON outlining a hypothesis to explain how maize might have originated in Upper Burma and reached America by way of Malaysia and Polynesia. Frankly, this was a fishing expedition. I merely nibbled at the bait and, carefully avoiding the hook, I came up with a very blunt opinion against the theory, for obvious reasons.

Then came the STONOR - ANDERSON "Maize in Assam" paper which, on first sight, might seem to have settled the problem. It represented the independently developed opinions of an anthropologist, who had worked in the Assam field, and a geneticist who had received Assam maize seeds and had grown the plants in N. America. This theory has been discussed elsewhere (p. 261-262). Apparently neither author could think in terms other than of the transmission of maize from *western* America directly to India; and I can find no evidence that either considered the old much-travelled trade route, from Portugal to eastern Brazil, and thence to Goa, on the Malabar coast of India by way of the Cape of Good Hope. In 1950, I suggested a Portuguese introduction into India. The next year the Assam maize theory was killed by another geneticist-anthropologist team: MANGELSDORF - OLIVER. Yet, in 1952, Dr. ANDERSON clung tenaciously to the idea that there might be a faint ray of hope for the hypothesis that maize existed in Asia before the arrival of the Portuguese in 1500: "[It] raises for some of us the question of whether it might not have crossed the Pacific in very early pre-Columbian times". This is a beautiful example of how a hypothesis, once launched, will persist in the originator's mind. Incidentally for those who can think only in terms of transmission across the Pacific ocean from America to Asia, the form that Dr. MANGELSDORF had from Colombia matched the Assam one mentioned above. For what it is worth, this Colombian form came from the Atlantic (Caribbean) water-shed, not from the Pacific side. The kernels of both the Assam and the South American form have broad rounded apices, not sharp pointed ones, and they are iso-diametric.

The most that SAUER would admit for maize, in Asia, is that it first reached western China by way of Tibet, after it had been brought to Spain by COLUMBUS, after 1492. The Tibet idea seems very unrealistic, as almost all of that country is so high that the low-altitude form or forms of maize, originally introduced from America by the Spaniards and the Portuguese, would not grow there. My surmise is that maize travelled from the eastern Mediterranean region along the old silk route which was well known to traders before MARCO POLO's famous trip; and this was surely the route MARCO POLO followed to China. I may add that, on the seaboard of eastern China (Kiangsu Province), the common name for maize is still *yu shu shu* which means "jade millet of the west." There was no doubt in the minds of the Chinese when they received and named this cereal in the sixteenth century that it originally came to them overland from the west, and not by the sea route.

Later, they received other forms from Mexico through Manila and possibly still others from the Portuguese who reached Canton in 1516 and later established the colony of Macao south of Hongkong. Dr. BERTHOLD LAUFER, a great authority on the introduction of exotic economic plants into China, recognized the significance of the old silk route from the eastern Mediterranean across Asia to China. He secured much of his basic data from the early works in Chinese, Japanese, Korean and other oriental languages. It is lamentable that his very voluminous *"History of the cultivated plants of America and their distribution over the Old World,"* between 800 and 900 pages of manuscript, still remains unpublished, sixteen years after his death. It should be a mine of information on this subject.

I am informed by the Director of the Chicago Museum of Natural History that a careful search in the Museum archives revealed no trace of this extensive manuscript. It was not included in the material bequeathed by Dr. LAUFER to that institution. It may be extant, but where it may be found is a puzzle. It would be of so much value to know what his final conclusions were as to when and how various American cultigens reached China, especially maize, tobacco, guava, sweet potato, *Cucurbita* species and others upon which I can touch only lightly in this memoir.

There is one published paper by LAUFER that is strongly to be recommended to investigators in this field, no matter what their special interests may be*(26)*.

The following remarks concerning ANDERSON's views are based, as was the above, on his interesting and instructive series of essays published in 1952. One will easily agree with the majority of his interpretations, but one wonders about some of his conclusions*(27)*. Many of his ideas are stimulating, but others are merely exasperating.

My mind on these problems is not closed, but I am personally concerned because Dr. ANDERSON, on page 35, says that, when I was identifying certain very large recently received collections of botanical material from various parts of Asia, Malaysia, and Polynesia, and when I came to a well-known weed I "would mutter 'a pantropic weed' and throw the specimen in the waste basket." Such a statement is out of place, unfair and true only in part. For the past fifty years I have concerned myself with the significance of weeds, when, how, and by what special adaptation they came to be so universally distributed. Dr. ANDERSON neglected to say, or perhaps did not know, that every one of these discarded specimens was named, the name was entered in the identification lists and reported back to the senders.

I confess that, at times, when I have reported on large collections from densely settled areas in Asia and Malaysia, I have discarded as high as 75 per cent of all the specimens, and I still see no reason for changing this custom. But very often, instead of resorting to the waste basket method of elimination, I have taken the trouble to complete the labels and have supplied many thousands of these unwanted and too-often unappreciated weeds to newly established herbaria in the United States and other countries, where, as I know from experience, they will be appreciated and used. Anyone, who is familiar with modern descriptive floras, will realize that in many of them the descriptive data for the weeds are so greatly abbreviated as to be practically valueless in identification work. The KING and GAMBLE descriptions, in their Malay Peninsula flora (1889-1936), are remarkable exceptions to this general rule. BACKER should also receive credit for his careful and ample descriptions of the weeds of Java.

26) LAUFER, B. The American Plant Migration. Sci. Monthly 28: 239-251. 1929.

27) ANDERSON, E. Plants, Man and Life. 1-245. fig. 1-16. 1952.

But, after all, when one has a reasonable number of collections of a common, well-known weed from a specific region, the immediate needs of the situation are taken care of. Now some of these despised tropical weeds fall in the Fernaldian category of the "oh my" flowers, such as *Asclepias curassavica* L., *Argemone mexicana* L., *Euphorbia heterophylla* L., and some species of *Hibiscus* or *Abelmoschus*, which all new collectors secure in abundance, merely because they are showy and attractive, even if weeds. There is a much larger number of wholly unattractive weed species, often preempting all the available space, in waste places in most or all tropical countries. The simian strain mentioned in the discussion is really not overdeveloped in my nature, for I prefer to pass on to others what is not really needed, wherever I happen to be working.

Incidentally, I am also the American botanist (not named in the text), who wrote the long passage, quoted on p. 71, and who is characterized as not illustrating "a distinctly scientific approach to a complicated problem." This covers what I had to say in my summary of the J. B. HUTCHINSON cotton miscegenation theory between an Asiatic and an American species (*see* p. 335 & 370). It was naturally irritating to a true believer in early transmission of plants *by man* from one hemisphere to the other; it was also irritating to HEYERDAHL who made a minor caustic comment about it in his large volume of 1952. He apparently did not like what I said, but all he could do was to quote another Biblical passage to offset the one I used.

Prior to preparing the manuscript for this memoir, I spent much time compiling data on independent inventions and developments which are known and which can be proved to be correct. The list is an extraordinary one, and the fields covered are very wide indeed. If a thorough diffusionist has any doubts in his firm belief that all advances developed in one region and spread from an original centre to all parts of the world, as the romanticists among them claim, my advice is to avoid the field of independent invention as he would the plague. I do not pursue this phase of the subject in detail, because there is a limit to what I can accomplish as I approach my seventy-eighth year.

If the extreme diffusionists would approach the subject with an open mind, they would be shaken in their firm belief that there cannot be such a phenomenon as independent invention. In the world as a whole, independent discoveries or inventions happened over and over again, both among primitive peoples and among our presumably more advanced groups. To accept blindly the idea that every advance depended on diffusion is short-sighted in the extreme, for while there was undoubtedly some limited diffusion, independent invention has ruled the day since before the dawn of history.

Having strayed from the field I started to develop I will now return, although the subject that intrigued me was not a plant, but merely a plant product: cotton. The extremists usually try to prove that the highly specialized spinning and weaving industry in Peru, as developed in the pre-Inca and Inca periods, *must* have been introduced from India directly by civilized man. Dr. BIRD's discoveries clearly demonstrate that, apparently, nothing of the kind took place. *Gossypium* occurred here and there in Polynesia as a wild plant; but, up to 1769, the Polynesian people had no knowledge of weaving cloth, or, apparently, even of spinning cotton. They depended on bark cloth as did the early Malayan peoples, until the arts of spinning and weaving were brought in from Asia. At Huaca Prieta, Dr. BIRD recovered

CEMPOAL XOCHITL, *seu*
Giuhnaxochitl. Tzneycepohual.
Caryophyllus Mexicanus I.

TEXT FIGURE 13. — *Tagetes*, a strictly American genus. — Various Mexican forms were among the earliest Mexican plants introduced in Europe, following 1520. HERNANDEZ gives a number of illustrations of simple and double flowered forms of this interesting, sacred Aztec flower, now often wrongly known as "African Marigold". The woodcut reproduced above represents a hybrid (*T. erecta* L.), as are all double flowered forms of *Tagetes*, and is of interest to show the high degree of development the art of hybridization had reached in Mexico in the 16*th* century. — From F. HERNANDEZ's *Nova Plantarum . . . Mexicanorum Historiae* (Roma, 1651), probably drawn in Mexico, between 1571 and 1577.

about 3,000 fragments of cotton fabrics. These early people were evidently very skillful with their hands. They learned to spin cotton and then developed primitive looms, lacking the heddle. A simple field analysis of the techniques used in weaving cloth showed that about 78 per cent of these cloth fragments are of twined construction; fish nets and pouches came next; then followed looping and coiling; true weaving came last.

Were I an extreme diffusionist, I should be very much impressed and upset by what Dr. BIRD has incontrovertibly demonstrated. There is little reason to believe that the knowledge of weaving cotton reached Peru from across the Pacific, but there is, on the other hand, every reason to believe that this art was independently developed among the American Indians. Surely if these primitive agriculturists were capable of first developing their simple agriculture, and then the more complex types, as well as the arts of spinning and weaving cotton, why question the ability of their successors to continue the development to a point where, at the time of the conquest, the art of spinning and weaving had reached a very high degree of perfection? The answer to this is cast into the laps of the diffusionists; they probably will not deem it worthy of being considered. What they often accept as absolute proof of a contention would generally be discarded by an experienced biologist, for biology offers acid tests which the diffusionists and the neogeographers usually avoid; or if they venture a guess, the guess is wrong.

In Dr. ANDERSON's book of 1952 on page 72 in the second paragraph, following the long quotation which I am pleased to acknowledge, from tobacco to cotton and *Rosa*, there is not a case, except cotton, where different species of the eastern and western hemispheres are involved. We accept the cytological evidence in tobacco, all the citrus fruits, the apples, pears, roses, chrysanthemums, dahlias, bananas, and all the others, but we do not agree with the final line of the chapter that: "One of the chief services of the new evidence from cytology and genetics has been to show up the experts". It simply shows how a real expert in his own field may be led astray when he enters a different one that he does not understand. I scarcely know the rudiments of either of these two modern sciences, but it is clearly evident that both Drs. ANDERSON and SAUER take a very dim view of DE CANDOLLE's classic *Origin of Cultivated Plants*, even to the extent of not mentioning it in their suggested reading lists and bibliographies. The contrast is very great, for DE CANDOLLE approached the subject with an unbiased mind and, after a critical search of the vast literature as available to him some seventy-five years ago, he presented his conclusions which still stand, in spite of those who argue against them. He was beautifully equipped by his classical education and his wide knowledge of taxonomy, fields unfamiliar to most of his ultra-modern critics.

Dr. ANDERSON states (page 153): "If I knew less about the subject, I could authoritatively quote the great Swiss botanist, DE CANDOLLE, who last set this suite of rooms in order some sixty years ago and let it go at that. Unfortunately, for this simple solution, I have spent a good deal of time recently in poking around these dusty chambers, trying to make some sense out of the collections there, and I realize what a mess the place is in." In his roster of our most important crop plants and their probable origins, ANDERSON did raise plenty of dust, but not much else. And now as the dust settles, as rapidly as he raised it, practically everything remaining *in statu quo ante*. As against DE CANDOLLE's 247 species, ANDERSON briefly discussed about one hundred, but one wonders at the word "important" when one notes such entries as castor bean, pepper (black), turmeric, dahlia, marigold, grain amaranths, Job's tears, pearl millet, quinoa, sunflower, cowpea, the true gourd (except among the more primitive peoples), jack beans, pigeon pea, guava, jujube, mombin, quince and pomegranate. It is true, here and there, some of these are locally important, but scarcely one of them deserves a place in a list of major economic plants, and some should have been left out entirely. I estimate that there may be perhaps four hundred species of plants which are not even mentioned in any list of cultivated plants, except the one of AKEMINE of 1933-1940, but which are cultivated throughout the world, for food, some of them on a very large scale and over vast areas. Many of these are infinitely more important, both to primitive and to advanced peoples, than most of those in ANDERSON's sketchy list (*cf.* p. 285).

I can mention only a few specific cases. By oversight perhaps, the hemisphere where the castor bean (page 154) originated is not mentioned: it came from the Old World. One could spend a lifetime studying its forms, but it would be a lifetime wasted. Turmeric (page 156), while important in early times as food, faded into insignificance as soon as better food plants became available. It is cultivated here and there, but in all my travels in tropical countries, in both hemispheres, I never saw it grown as a crop plant. The dahlia (page 157) is not worthy of mention except as an ornamental. Had I written the entry, I should have added that this manifest hybrid had become extensively naturalized in all its glory and variability in the Himalayan region in modern times. If WILLIAM ROXBURGH, the father of Indian botany, be an authority, we may accept from him that the dahlia was not introduced into cultivation in India before 1814.

Tagetes (page 157) is strictly an American genus, except where it has been introduced and naturalized in those parts of the Old World, to which it is adapted. It was sacred to the Aztecs but to follow this with "and the ancient sacred flower of the Hindus" creates an utterly false impression. The Hindus merely took it over from the Portuguese, quite as the Buddhists took over the American *Plumeria* after it was introduced (probably from Manila), on such a scale that it early became known as the temple tree and received a partly Sanscrit name. The name *genda* (Hindi and Bengali) and *gendu* (Uriya) for *Tagetes* means "ball". It is of Sanscrit origin, but has nothing to do with the Sanscrit name *ganda* which refers to fragrance, as in the epithet *gandasuli* (*Hedychium coronarium* Koenig). Incidentally, in parts of

Brazil, this *Hedychium* has become so widely naturalized that the uninformed visitor observing it in immense quantities would unhesitatingly call it an indigenous species, never considering it an introduced one. The now well known family name GANDHI came from the same Sanscrit root and merely indicates that some ancestor of the recent Indian leader dealt in perfumes. These data have been supplied by my friend, Mr. BURKILL *(28)*.

It cannot truthfully be said that any form of Job's tears (*Coix*, page 160) is anywhere an important tropical cereal. Years ago, Mr. P. J. WESTER attempted to popularize it in the Philippines under its Tagalog name *adlai*, but the attempt was a dismal failure. *Coix lachryma-jobi* L. was once a primitive cereal and still is planted on a small scale for special purposes in backward parts of the world. The best variety is *ma-yuen* Stapf. Up to the time of the European expansion *Coix* was still unknown from tropical America, although the FORSTERs had collected it in the Pacific basin on Captain COOK's second voyage.

Cotton (page 164) has been discussed elsewhere (*see* p. 335, also p. 291 *supra*). I can see no reason whatever why pre-Columbian man should be brought into the picture as the distributor of the Asiatic form.

Regarding the peanut (page 167), there is certainly nothing exciting. ANDERSON says: "The most primitive type of peanut, the same narrow little shoestrings which are found in the Peruvian tombs, are commonly grown today, not in Peru, but in South China. How did they get there?" Here he apparently could think only in terms of direct communication in ancient times across the Pacific from South America. The explanation is simple. The centre of *Arachis* differentiation is Brazil; it is strictly an American genus. The second Portuguese trip to India in 1500 was effected by way of Brazil and the Cape of Good Hope to Goa. In 1516, the Portuguese reached Canton and later established their own colony of Macao, a short distance south of Hongkong. The same type of peanut, now grown in southeastern China, may be expected to be found in East Africa, Madagascar, southern and western India, Ceylon, Malacca, and even in the Moluccas and Formosa, for the Portuguese once dominated those areas.

ANDERSON, disregarding the much travelled Brazil-Goa trade route, took his data from AMES (*Economic Annuals* p. 44-49. fig. 1-13. 1939). But AMES merely observed that it had little to recommend it in view of the much better varieties now available. He did hint that it might be argued that a prehistoric Peruvian peanut has persisted in the Old World cultivation, but he did not set up such a hypothesis. He too did not realize how the old Portuguese route (eastern Brazil to Goa and

---

28) Mr. BURKILL also calls my attention to the fact that for *genda* (= a ball) there is a synonym, *gol-mariyam* (literally "Mary's ball"), which, he suspects, arose among the Portuguese Christian converts in southern India, just as *mariyam* means "Virgin Mary" while *gol* is a natural substitute for *genda*. On the Malabar Coast, another name for *Tagetes* is *genda rojia*, the *rojia* derived apparently from the Portuguese *rosa de ouro* which means merely "golden rose."

thence to Canton and a few decades later, Macao) fitted into the picture, but he approached the problem wisely*(29)* (FIG. 14).

The Jack bean (*Canavalia,* page 172), as a cultigen, did not occur in Polynesia. There were certain native species present, but these have nothing to do with the cultivated forms. It is agreed that critical work is needed to ascertain the place of origin of the very few cultigens in this genus. The pods and beans of these are of distinctly secondary importance as a food.

There is no supposition as to the provenience of the pigeon pea (page 174), for it originated in the Old World. One who is really familiar with it will immediately understand why it fell from grace as a food plant, when better species became available. In the oriental tropics with which I am familiar, it is widely and thoroughly naturalized, and only once, in my long career, did I ever see it cultivated for food and then on a very small scale for household use. It is planted sometimes as a green manure to enrich the soil. To say that: "Its origin is as much of a puzzle as is that of *Zea mays*" gives an erroneous impression. It maintains itself unaided, year after year, in various parts of its Old World range; maize is absolutely dependent on man, for it never occurs as a wild plant and cannot maintain itself.

The statement on page 177, under *Cucurbita,* that: "Primitive varieties of winter squash are known from the same parts of China which have ancient popcorns and primitive peanuts" is very misleading, for the casual reader might well infer that all three were in Asia long before the Europeans crossed the Pacific. This is definitely not the case (*see* under *Arachis,* above, and maize, p. 261). In this instance of *Cucurbita* (as in *Arachis, Zea,* and the grain amaranths, to say nothing of the numerous tropical weeds of American origin), this author apparently knew nothing of the large scale and long continued Portuguese operations between Brazil and Indo-Malaysia, China and Japan. The aggressive Portuguese actually reached Japan only two years after appearing at Canton.

The statement on page 180 under guava that one species of *Psidium* reached the Old World at such an early date that it is referred to as the "Chinese guava" certainly infers that it might have been there in pre-Magellan times. This is not true. I have been through a number of the beautifully maintained guava orchards in Kwangtung Province, and the Chinese guava is nothing but a selected form of the common

---

29) ANDERSON must have depended on his memory (as I, to my sorrow, have sometimes done) and forgotten to check on what AMES said about the form he illustrated. "Shoe-string shaped" would be the poorest descriptive phrase that anyone could apply to the peanut which AMES illustrated, for it was 3-4.5 cm long and 1-1.5 cm in diameter, in general cylindric. I should have used the term "hump-backed." There is nothing shoe-string-like about it; nor is it a primitive form. If one wishes to see a "shoe-string peanut," *vide* HOEHNE's *Arachis diogoi* Hoehne var. *subglabrata* Hoehne (Fl. Brasil. XXV. II, 122, plate 3. 1940). Its very slender fruits are up to 9 cm long and 3 mm in diameter. This author, incidentally, recognized ten species as occurring in Brazil, with a number of minor taxa, illustrated by sixteen plates, one of them being of the fruits and seeds in color. One of the fruits shown strongly suggests the form that AMES illustrated from China and from Inca graves in Peru.

Psidium guajava L. with fruits larger than the common wild form. It is merely another of the Mexican introductions into the Philippines by way of the Acapulco-Manila Galleon route in the last half of the sixteenth century. It naturally reached China very soon after it was established in the Philippines (FIG. 15).

I dislike being obliged to tear down a very weak attempt to dis-

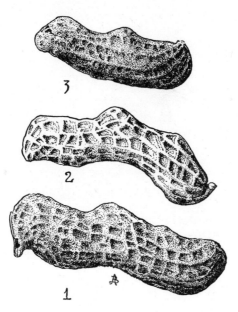

TEXT FIGURE 14. — *Arachis hypogaea* L. — 1 and 3, prehistoric peanuts, from Peru. 1, from the necropolis at Ancón. 3, from the necropolis at Paracas. 2, a modern specimen from China (purchased in a Chinese store in Boston, and imported, two or three decades ago, from Canton). — *Arachis* is strictly an American genus. Its centre of differentiation is in Brazil, whence the Portuguese transferred it to Africa, Madagascar, India, Ceylon, Malacca, Moluccas, Kwangtung, Formosa and Japan, and other areas which they dominated from 1500 until about the middle of the next century. — Drawings by BLANCHE AMES, somewhat enlarged, from O. AMES's *Economic Annuals and Human Cultures*. 1939.

prove the widely accepted and, to me, very thoroughly proven de Candollean conclusions of 1883: that there was essentially no evidence of any trans-Atlantic or trans-Pacific associations between the peoples of the Old and the New Worlds, previous to 1492, which, in any basic manner, affected the food plants available to the peoples of either hemisphere.

A casual examination of ANDERSON's list of "Important Crop Plants" shows that his conclusions, as to origins and times of distri-

XALXOCOTL
Pomum Arenoſum.

TEXT FIGURE 15. — *Psidium guajava* L., the Guava.
— A typical Mexican introduction, via the Acapulco-
Manila galleon route, after 1565, into the Old World
Tropics (*cf.* p. 231). Possibly introduced into China from
Brazil by the Portuguese after they occupied Goa, in the
early 1500's. There seems no reason whatsoever to infer
that the oriental form might have been a different species
introduced earlier into China. — According to GEO. D.
RUEHLE (The Common Guava. Econ. Bot. 2: 306-325.
1948) the guava offers possibilities for future development of excellent fruit through plant breeding and selection. The fruit is rated as a fair source of vitamin A
and as an excellent source of vitamin C. The better vars.
commonly eaten as fresh fruit in Florida contain from 2
to 5 times the vitamin C content of fresh orange juice.
Research on the guava has been stimulated by the discovery of the high vitamin content of the fruit. — From
F. HERNANDEZ's *Nova Plantarum . . . Mexicanorum Historiae* (Romae, 1651).

bution, are false in about 10 per cent of the species considered. I could have added other species (such as two in *Nicotiana*, as well as in other genera) where loose statements are made, but I refrain from further discussion of the "proofs" that my friend has compiled to support a strange theory he wants to believe.

What one may reasonably object to in popular or semi-popular books, destined for non-critical reading by the general public is the inclusion of unsupported statements, with no hint that there is often another side to the story from the one being given. It is not exactly an approved scientific method to infer a claim, but very carefully never to make a direct statement that a given species of American origin existed in the Old World in pre-Magellan times. Inferences may become just as devastating as positive claims which often are very easily disproved in the field of plant distribution.

The last chapter of the ANDERSON book is entitled "Adventures in Chaos", the opening line (page 207) reading in part: "It should be evident that this is largely a book about what we don't know". This is obviously a true statement. I have elsewhere reviewed the volume and recommended it for general reading with purely perfunctory reservations, for it is a volume that is really worth while from many points of view. Its author, a personal friend of mine of long standing, is a geneticist who really appreciates the value of taxonomy in connection with many or most genetical problems. He is also a staunch supporter of the taxonomic method and it has perhaps not been fair to include a discussion of his views and writings in the same chapter where the wild theories of Messrs. CARTER, HEYERDAHL, SAUER, *et al.*, are analyzed.

Now that I have pointed out certain cases where he has read altogether too much in the record, or where in other cases, he has merely by inference arrived at what I believe to be unwarranted conclusions, my detailed consideration of certain of the opinions which he accepts must not be interpreted along the lines of the quotation from the Book of Job: "Oh! . . . that mine adversary had written a book", more frequently cited as: "Oh, that mine enemy had written a book". There is altogether too much that *must* be known about the innumerable phases of a very complex subject to warrant an author, no matter who he may be and no matter in what field he specializes, making too many dogmatic or, as one of my opponents expresses it, "pontifical" statements on controversial matters.

While reading the proofs of this memoir I feel that, as a result of the well meant efforts of my editors, I appear often much too lenient in judging certain individuals. Here is a case where most of our modern American theorizers obviously never considered the Portuguese colonizing ventures in the orient. These operated from Portugal by way of Brazil to the Cape of Good Hope, Goa and eastward to Japan and the Moluccas for 165 years following 1500. As outlined elsewhere, in greater detail, there were not one or sometimes two ships in a single year, like the Acapulco-Manila galleon route, but there were whole fleets of commercial vessels, and sometimes supplementary war ships, year after year. The areas explored were East and West Africa, South Africa, Madagascar, Red Sea, Gulf of Persia, parts of India, Ceylon, Siam, Malacca, the Moluccas, Canton and Macao, Formosa and Japan; so extensive was this

ACHIOTL

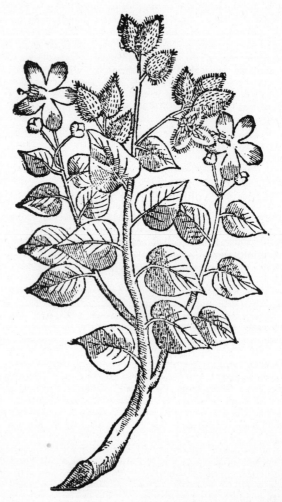

TEXT FIGURE 16. — *Bixa orellana* L., the Anatto Tree. — The genus which belongs to a strictly American family reached its present wide distribution during the second part of the 19*th* century (*cf.* p. 370), except for its earlier introduction by the Portuguese into India, after 1500, and by the Spaniards into Guam and the Philippines, after 1565. The red seed coats were widely used by the American Indians from Mexico to Brazil for staining their bodies; it is probably from this habit that the use of the term "Red Indian" was derived. — From F. HERNANDEZ's *Nova Plantarum . . . Mexicanorum Historiae* (Romae, 1651).

exploration that one is appalled that these vast regions were overlooked, to such an extent, by our modern theorists. Yet, the bulge of Brazil, with a direct connection to the Orient by way of the Cape of Good Hope and a very extensive long continued commerce cannot be ignored. This is whence came the oriental representatives of Indian corn (for the type of popcorn in India is matched by forms in South America and from the Atlantic watershed).

Just for the record, I list a few of the Brazilian cultigens of strictly American origin that reached the Orient by this old *direct* route to India following 1500. This situation is one where our present theorizers insist on setting up unnecessarily complicated theories to explain when the distribution of economic species over the world happened: in other words, when the interchanges of economic plants (through the agency of man) between the eastern and the western hemispheres commenced. The favored idea is several thousand years ago. What useful purpose is served by laboriously charting the places where a given cultigen is now grown (such as popcorn for example) without first determining *when a specific form was first introduced*? It becomes more and more evident that the transmission of American plants to Eurasia and *vice versa*, with two or three exceptions, did not even commence until 1500 when the Portugese reached India from Brazil.

First amongst the Brazilian cultigens that reached India by way of the Brazil-Goa trade route, perhaps, were the squashes and pumpkins, for up to 1500 *Cucurbita* was strictly American in distribution. The grain amaranths are clearly from South America. The peanut, as well as *Averrhoa carambola* L. and *A. bilimbi* L., were both early Portuguese introductions into India from Brazil. *Eugenia uniflora* also falls into this class, as does the Brazilian popcorn which should have reached India many centuries ago, according to the STONOR-ANDERSON explanation. The total would number scores, probably comparing with the approximately 200 introduced into the Philippines and Guam in the 250 years over the old Acapulco-Manila route briefly discussed on p. 237.

I have claimed elsewhere in this memoir that there is no evidence that any of the ubiquitous pantropic weeds were apparently common to the two hemispheres at the time COLUMBUS made his first voyage; one set of species came from tropical America, another came from tropical Asia, immediately the routes were established in the period between 1492 and 1565. It cannot be too strongly stressed that the Portuguese venture in the Orient was developed, on a large scale, sixty-five years before the Spaniards established their Philippine colony.

When I am informed, as I was in a recent letter, that *Tagetes* was established in India 2000 years ago, I am not impressed. The genus is Mexican; it reached India sometime after 1550 from Portugal. When I read in CARTER's work of 1953 (p. 70) that *Bixa orellana* L. "needs study as ANDERSON suggests", I am reminded of O. F. COOK's pontifications, for *Bixa* is a strictly American genus, first introduced into Guam and the Philippines from Mexico following 1565. Some time ago, I provided Dr. ANDERSON with the pertinent data for the Polynesian introductions of this very characteristic species. Of about twenty-five individual collections of *Bixa* reported from Polynesia, all but two or three were recorded within the present century. The oldest one (from Hawaii) was recorded as naturalized in 1865. There is not the slightest indication of an early introduction here! (FIG. 16).

There is no reason why a theorizing geneticist, much less why botanically uninformed geographers, should continue to push their pet foibles when these run up against stone walls of fact. Dr. O. F. COOK was about 100 per cent in error in his fantasic claims on the time of distribution of cultivated food plants and it is, indeed, strange what a strong hold his ideas of *direct* connections from India to America across the Pacific has taken on the minds of certain workers.

I have deliberately left out J. D. SAUER's *(30)* excellent study of the grain amaranths, for the ANDERSON inference is that two species possibly were present

30) SAUER, J. D. The Grain Amaranths: A Survey of Their History and Classification. Ann. Missouri Bot. Gard. 37: 561-637. pl. 12-14. fig. 1-6. 1950.

in both hemispheres from very early times. In the Arnold Arboretum herbarium, dedicated mostly to shrubs and trees, there are but four sheets of *Amaranthus*. I can no longer accomplish herbarium work, nor am I able to visit the Gray Herbarium to inspect the *Amaranthus* specimens there. *Amaranthus*, incidentally, is one of the last genera I would be tempted to study from a monographic point of view. I have no reason whatever to question the correctness of JONATHAN SAUER's identifications. As to the old world distribution of the grain amaranths, for practical purposes, about all he did was to verify the correctness of MOQUIN's conclusions of 1849 that they were present in India and in tropical America at that time. A mere hint about the old Portuguese trade route via Brazil to the Malabar coast of India, which existed from 1500 on, would have been of material assistance to this student.

What I do question are certain conclusions that some infer as to when the cultivated forms may have reached Asia. It seems to be evident that some of the species were of very ancient cultivation in Mexico and parts of South America, but, without going into detail, I may state that I have the impression that the Asiatic forms were certainly brought from Brazil to Goa by the Portuguese over that apparently forgotten trade route from 1500 to 1665; but I know nothing about *Amaranthus* in Brazil. Even the younger SAUER, in speaking of the ancient history of the grain amaranths in Asia, states that the American and the Asiatic forms are very closely related, which is indeed evident, and that the group must have been originally domesticated in America, which is acceptable. It is striking that the crop is still grown for grain in the mountains back of the old Portuguese-controlled areas on the Malabar coast, and the Abyssinian localities are not too far inland from ports on the west African coast often visited by the early Portuguese sailing to the Orient by way of Brazil. From southern India, the grain amaranths would very naturally be carried northward. In further studies on *Amaranthus* the possible rôle played by Portuguese colonizers (post 1500) should receive more attention.

I am not impressed by the young SAUER's reference to *Amaranthus* in China in 950 A.D. as "a clear reference to a grain amaranth." My view is based on the reason that the early Chinese record appears in a work on *materia medica*, and at that time there were several species of *Amaranthus*, other than the grain-producing ones, widely cultivated in China, some of which may have been used for medicinal purposes. As far as I know, the tender parts of all species of *Amaranthus* are edible as pot herbs, and their seeds are also edible; but they are not noted for their medicinal qualities. I suspect that the suggestion that the figure to which SAUER refers was clearly a grain amaranth does not appear in BRETSCHNEIDER's work.

The younger SAUER did, I believe, clearly demonstrate that two identical species of *Amaranthus* do now occur in both America and Asia, but he was wisely non-committal as to when the dissemination occurred. The other weedy species of the genus such as *A. spinosus* L., *A. viridis* L., and all the other types cultivated for their colored leaves, no matter where they may have originated, have attained pantropical distribution through the medium of modern man, *i.e.*, since 1500. Very likely this author's statement that there never will be much more evidence available from Asiatic sources is true and, therefore, we may never know just how and when the grain amaranths reached one hemisphere from the other. As I see the picture, the chance of securing real evidence to support an early trans-Pacific distribution is very, very remote. I extend my sympathy to any young botanist who has the courage to attack such a knotty problem. Young SAUER is, apparently, very much more critical and conservative, as to the possible early trans-Pacific distribution of economic plants, than is his father or Dr. ANDERSON, the professor who supervised his thesis. For this, he is to be congratulated.

R. C. Bakhuizen van den Brink, Sr.:— This Netherlands-Indies botanist became interested *(31)* in the problem of American plants in Malaysia, but, like all of us who have considered the matter, he lacked detailed knowledge, except for the limited area of Malaysia. Because of this, like myself and others, he inevitably made a number of errors. With his intimate knowledge of such languages as Sundanese, Javanese, and naturally of Malay (the *lingua franca* of the Archipelago), it is rather surprising that he made certain linguistic claims, such as those under *Plumeria*, which cannot be supported. All one needs to do is to turn to RUMPHIUS who was writing in Amboina, perhaps about 1680 (*Flos convolutus* Rumph. Herb. Amb. 4: 65. pl. 38. 1743) to find the key.

From the standpoint of phytogeography, the problem, as to any possible part pre-Columbian man may have played in the deliberate or accidental transmission of certain plant species from one hemisphere to the other, is very complicated and under no circumstances should anyone, botanically trained or not, approach the subject with his mind made up in advance.

To recapitulate, the overall picture remains the same. We have seen that up to 1492, there was no general inter-communication between the peoples of America with those of the Old World or *vice versa*, at least as far as the distribution of cultivated species of economic plants shows. There were rare and accidental communications across a part of the Pacific and probably across the much narrower Atlantic; but such as they were, these early and largely accidental voyages had little or no effect on the dissemination of plant species.

BAKHUIZEN's general summary of the activities of the early European explorers in the Malaysian region is excellent, although he did overlook certain important early source books. He presents a list of eighty-three binomials indicating species which he assumed to be of American origin established in Malaysia by the middle of the seventeenth century. In some cases a question mark is added, as for *Adenostemma lavenia* (L.) O. Kuntze, *Cassia tora* L., *Ipomoea pes-caprae* (L.) R. Br., *Poa annua* L., *Sesuvium portulacastrum* L., *Solanum nigrum* L., *Vigna marina* (Burm.) Merr., and *Ximenia americana* L. Included, without expressed doubt as to their American origin, are *Remirea maritima* Aubl. and *Boerhavia repens* L. It is, indeed, curious to note how naturally distributed pantropical strand plants are included, such as the two above listed and the *Ipomoea*, *Sesuvium* and *Ximenia* just mentioned, for they all attained their present distribution by natural means in previous geologic periods, man having had no

---

31) BAKHUIZEN VAN DEN BRINK, R. C. De Indische flora en hare eerste Amerikaansche indringsters. Natuurk. Tijdschr. Nederl. - Ind. 93: 20-55. pl. 1-4. fig. 1-2. 1933.

rôle in their spread. He is, however, to be congratulated for *not* including *Hibiscus tiliaceus* L. and for expressing doubt that O. F. COOK could possibly have erred when he "proved" that this halophytic species was of American origin and man-distributed across the Pacific from America.

The doubtful *Ximenia* record was, apparently, taken from my 1904 paper. The oriental form of this has been described as *X. elliptica* Forst. f., the type coming from Polynesia; man certainly had nothing to do with its distribution. One could question the correctness of including certain other species as of American origin. From the Philippine records of the pre-Linnaean period, a considerable number of species might be added. One may safely admit at least one hundred American species as being established in Malaysia, by 1750 or earlier; for the Moluccas lay on the Portuguese circuit shortly after 1500, soon followed by the much longer continued Acapulco-Manila connections.

The six species which BAKHUIZEN discussed in detail (pages 32 to 55) fall in a different category, and each rates a few words. The first is the well known silk-cotton tree, *Ceiba pentandra* (L.) Gaertn. The Malaysian form definitely belongs to this species, for the original Linnaean binomial was based wholly on the Indo-Malaysian form, identical with the one which RUMPHIUS illustrated and described. The genus is typically American. CHEVALIER*(32)* considered only the four or five species of economic importance, but binomials were assigned to but four: (1) *Ceiba pentandra* Gaertn. of Indo-Malaysia of which he says: "Il est sans doute venu d'Amérique à une époque très ancienne (bien avant le voyage de COLOMB)"; (2) *C. thonningii* A. Chev. n. sp. (African, but not spontaneous there); (3) *C. guinensis* (Thonn.) A. Chev. (with two varieties); and (4) *C. caribaea* (DC.) A. Chev. (the giant *Ceiba* of the West Indies and tropical America; this is properly *C. occidentalis* (Spr.) Burkill). Another synonym is *Ceiba pentandra* Gaertn. var. *caribaea* (DC.) Bakh. (1924). The fifth is an unnamed taxon from the Amazon region. He states that: "Sous le nom de *Ceiba pentandra* on a confondu jusqu'à ce jour plusieurs espèces jordaniennes toutes originaires sans doute de l'Amérique chaude mais réparties aujourd'hui en diverses régions de l'Ancien et du Nouveau Monde". There is no evidence whatsoever that there was any early trans-Pacific distribution via Polynesia to Malaysia of any Ceiba, as all the Pacific Islands records have been made since 1900. It is highly probable that the Indo-Malaysian form was introduced from tropical Africa by the early Malay voyagers. BAKHUIZEN assumed that *Ceiba* reached Indo-Malaysia from Africa, as does Dr. H. J. TOXOPEUS*(32a)*. I have no records of possible Portuguese introductions into Africa from Brazil after 1500 A.D., but doubtlessly such introductions were made.

32) CHEVALIER, A. Arbres à kapok et fromagers. Rev. Bot. Appl. Agr. Trop. 17: 245-268. pl. 4-6. 1937.

32a) Natuurwet. Tijdschr. Ned. Ind. 101: 23-25. 1941. Chuo Noozi Sikenzyoo Contr. 14: 1-20. 1953; later reprinted in Meded. Alg. Proefstation Landbouw 56: 1-19. 1948.

BAKHUIZEN*(33)* also attempted to prepare a general revision of the entire family. Unfortunately, he lacked American and African material, so that his final copy represented a very sketchy treatment of other than the Malaysian representatives of the group. Thus, in *Ceiba*, he recognized ten species as valid, one in the tropics of both hemispheres, the other nine strictly American (lacking material for study, he left nine strictly American species as of doubtful status or as insufficiently known). For *Ceiba pentandra* (L.) Gaertn., he made the Asiatic form, with which we are concerned, var. *indica* (DC.) Bakh., and united the American and African forms as var. *caribaea* (DC.) Bakh. The latter, a tropical giant American tree, is now generally recognized as a distinct species, *Ceiba occidentalis* (Spr.) Burkill (*C. caribaea* (DC.) A. Cheval., 1937), and there seems to be no valid reason for including these two very different forms within the limits of a single species. The time of introduction of the kapok tree into India and Malaysia cannot be proved, but, apparently, it was introduced from Africa by the Malays who had reached and colonized Madagascar and had reached the east coast of Africa long before the Europeans arrived in the Orient. I find no dependable evidence that kapok is native to any part of Indo-Malaysia.

Heliconia.—This is basically an American genus. In the last monograph of the family by K. SCHUMANN, in 1900, he recognized twenty-nine species. Since that time, about fifty new binomials have been optimistically proposed by various authors which complicates the situation. SCHUMANN treated *Heliconia bihai* L. (1771) (*Musa bihai* L., 1763) as a collective species, citing about fifteen synonyms, the indicated range being Mexico, Central America, West Indies, and South America from Colombia and Guiana to Brazil and Peru, Samoa, Solomon Islands, New Guinea and the Moluccas; he should have added New Caledonia as he interpreted the species. This was his disposition of *Folium mensarium album* Rumph. Herb. Amb. 5: 142. pl. 62. fig. 2, 1747, accepted by Dr. VALETON in 1917. In 1933, Dr. BAKHUIZEN correctly, I believe, accepted Dr. BACKER's disposition*(34)* of it as *Heliconia indica* Lam. (1785) as the proper name for the Moluccan and Papuasian form. The next older name for the Amboina form is *Heliconia buccinata* Roxb. (1814, 1832). Another synonym is *Heliconopsis amboinensis* Miq. (1859). Then there are *Heliconia edwardus rex* Hort. Sand. (1903) from New Guinea, *H. illustris* Hort. Bull. (1893) (*cf.* Ill. Hort. 42: 288. 1895), from the "South Sea Islands" (*see also* ANDRÉ, Rev. Hort. 68: 36. 1 pl. 1896, var. *rubricaulis*), and *H. micholitzii* Ridl. (1908) from the Bismarck Archipelago. There is also *Heliconia austro-caledonica* Vieill. from New Caledonia. Until a new and critical monograph of this entire genus appears, little can be done except to guess what may have happened. But I do not choose

---

33) BAKHUIZEN VAN DEN BRINK, R. C. Revisio Bombacacearum. Bull. Jard. Bot. Buitenz. III. 6: 161-240. pl. 26-38. 1924.

34) BACKER, C. A. *Heliconia indica* Lamarck. An Insufficiently Known Species of the East-Indian Archipelago; *in his*: Contributiones ad cognitem Florae Indiae Batavae. Bull. Jard. Bot. Buitenz. III. 2: 315-319. 1920.

to follow the rather wild guessing of Dr. O. F. COOK *(35)*. Having no firsthand knowledge about the botany of the Pacific region, with superb indifference he did not hesitate to postulate that *Heliconia bihai* L. reached the Old World through the agency of man and died out in the Pacific Islands because, for some purpose for which its leaves were used, the native *Pandanus* was superior. *Heliconia*, once introduced and established in the tropics, is one of those groups of plants that simply do not "die out", unless there be a very radical change in climatic conditions.

Having no specimens for study, and never having seen *Heliconia* in nature, except for a few species in Central America, I remain conservative in this case. It may be that some of the few Polynesian records are based on specimens actually introduced within the past century. From BACKER's study (and Dr. BACKER is a taxonomist upon whom we can depend), it seems to be evident that the Papuasian-Moluccan-Celebes form is very distinct from the American *Heliconia bihai* L. It has not been shown that the former is the same as any described American species. If it be shown to be identical with any of the latter, there is a very remote possibility that QUIROS may have introduced it into the Santa Cruz Islands in his abortive attempt to establish a colony there in 1606; and there is perhaps an even more remote possibility of a Portuguese introduction into Amboina. What I suspect, but cannot prove, is that, as in the families *Centrolepidaceae* and *Proteaceae*, and such genera as *Nothofagus, Araucaria, Uncinia, Nicotiana* and various others, this discontinuous distribution of the genus *Heliconia* in the southern hemisphere represents the end products of what may have happened in earlier geologic times, when Antarctica supported a luxuriant vegetation. Here probably also belongs the Araceous genus *Spathiphyllum,* mentioned incidentally by Dr. BAKHUIZEN (twenty-five species in tropical America, one in New Guinea, Moluccas, Celebes, Philippines and two described from Palau in 1940).

Of course any one can object that the Sumatra localities cited by Dr. BACKER are very distant from New Guinea, Amboina and other known localities, but before rushing into print it would be well to remember that the Achinese war continued for about forty years, and that many of the soldiers who took part in it were from Amboina. The species was well known to RUMPHIUS about 1680.

The critical BACKER paper, referred to above, is also most important for his corrections of false translations or interpretations of certain descriptive data given by RUMPHIUS. In this case, all we have to depend upon as to the characters of *Heliconia indica* Lam. are the data provided by RUMPHIUS, and published in 1747.

Ipomoea batatas (L.) Lam.:— I hesitate to discuss the sweet potato again *(see* also p. 321 & 371). It was carried across the Pacific by the Polynesians, as far to the southwest as New Zealand; its range was extended to parts of Papuasia and as far north as the

---

35) COOK, O. F. Food Plants of Ancient America. Ann. Rept. Smithsonian Inst. 1903: 481-497. 1904.

Marianas Islands, before the Europeans reached the Orient. PIGAFET-
TA recorded *"battatas"* from Guam, when MAGELLAN discovered that
island in 1521 and also from Cebu in the Philippines and from the
Moluccas. The early Chinese record from the second or third century
of our era is erroneous, as Dr. LAUFER has demonstrated in one of his
later papers. This was due to a misinterpretation of an early reference
to a yam (*Dioscorea*) in Chinese literature, just as early crude illustrations of the kaoliang *Sorghum* have been misinterpreted as representing the American maize.

Merely because its tubers form the chief food of the Stone Age Pese-
gem and Timorini peoples, inhabiting the remote Belem valley in central New Guinea, is no proof of its early introduction into that island,
for a series of airplane photographs of the valley, made by Mr. BRASS
on the third Archbold expedition, give the impression that the valley
had not been occupied by man for more than a very few hundred
years. The appearance, two or three times, of the current Polynesian name for this plant, *kumara*, in the Peabody Museum Library's
extensive index of names of this plant for British New Guinea is
undoubtedly explained by the fact that, when the southern part of
eastern New Guinea was taken over by the British in 1884, many
educated Polynesians were brought in as teachers and as civil servants.
The occasional use of the name *kumara* in New Guinea probably dates
from that time. The species may well prove to be of African origin.

Nicotiana tabacum L.:— The proponents of the idea that this
plant was of pre-Magellan introduction into New Guinea will have a
task to convince the taxonomists. If pre-Magellan man introduced it
from America, he by-passed the Polynesian islands. It has even been
suggested, by at least one author, that its seeds might have been transmitted in the chinks of floating logs from western America! This is
far too visionary to consider further, when one evaluates all the factors involved.

What we would like to have explained is how the Caribbean
(Taino) name *tabaco* for the *cigar* (*not the name of the plant or the
pipe*) was transmitted to the Orient, other than by the Europeans, and
there applied to the plant. Even the Spaniards accepted the original
Taino usage and have perpetuated it for the cigar. In a few Spanish-
speaking countries, one hears the name *tabaco* used exclusively in
place of the word *cigarro*, which is apparently of Mayan origin. In
the Caribbean region, *tabaco* was not the name of the plant. Thus,
in the Philippines, where the term for the cigar is universally *tabaco*,
we find it also in current and practically exclusive use for the plant.
In Malaysia the name of the plant is *tabaka, tambako, tebak, tembako,
bako, bhako,* etc.

I asked Dr. L. O. WILLIAMS to check on the currently used names
for the cigar in Latin America among students at the Escuela Agricola
Panamericana at Tegucigalpa. Among the fifty questioned, all Cubans
said *tabacos* was the only term universally used there. The most
widely used name (eight countries) is *puro*: *tabacos* also used in

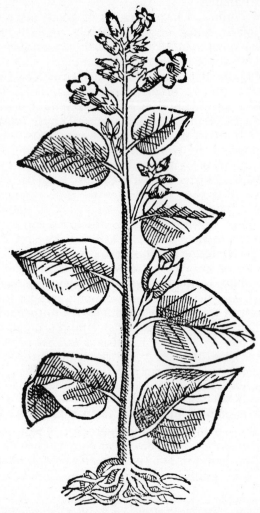

TEXT FIGURE 17. — *Nicotiana rustica* L., a hybrid of South American origin, was the first tobacco to be cultivated by the North American aborigines and by the early colonists of Virginia, and is still grown occasionally by Indians today (*cf.* p. 311). This is probably the first illustration of the species. Early in our colonial history it was replaced by the better *Nicotiana tabacum* L., also a hybrid originating in South America. — From F. HERNANDEZ's *Nova Plantarum . . . Mexicanorum Historiae* (Romae, 1651), probably drawn in Mexico, between 1571 and 1577.

Colombia (as is *cigarro* and *puro*), and *cigarro* in Dominica as well as *habanos* in Panama.

From New Guinea, I have records of about sixty different names used for the plant, many of them merely cognate forms of *tabaco*: such as *babaku, kemaki, tabake, tabaok, tafaki, sakapa, sakape, sakupe, sepuke, sitrube, sokuba, suguba,* and *sukaba*.

HADDON*(36)*, in 1946, added many more for New Guinea, including *tabaka, tabaku, tabak, tavo, tembaku, tampaku, tavora, tamok, temuka, tamuku, tamuk,* and at least a couple of dozen others which are all cognate forms of the Caribbean (Taino) *tabaco*. One might think that this impressive list of cognate forms of the Taino name of the cigar, applied to the plant all over Malaysia and Papuasia, would impress such anthropologists as VAN NOUHUYS who insists that this American cultigen existed in New Guinea long before the arrival of Europeans.

Under the circumstances, it is very easy to understand how the West Indian name for the artifact, which we call the cigar, was applied to the plant in the Orient. I still believe that European sailors disseminated the smoking habit and that some acute European pioneer fostered the idea of growing tobacco in the Orient for trade purposes!

As of this date, to the best of my knowledge, *Nicotiana tabacum* L., a *hybrid* of American origin, is the only species known from New Guinea where it is very widely planted. An anthropologist's recollections of the flower color as "greenish" might suggest that the other cultivated species, *N. rustica* L., also a *hybrid* of American origin, occurs there too. Unfortunately, as usual, the anthropologists in question failed to collect a specimen for determination.

It has long been known that there was at least one species of *Nicotiana* on Norfolk Island, one in Australia, and one in New Caledonia. But now it develops that instead of one species in Australia, there are fifteen, according to one classification*(37)*. There is still no native species of *Nicotiana* known from all of New Guinea or Malaysia. Further data will be found in Dr. GOODSPEED's comprehensive monograph of the genus to be published shortly by the Chronica Botanica Co.

In 1946, I perhaps erred in assuming that the common Papuan method of smoking tobacco was merely a modification of the Chinese method of smoking opium. Undoubtedly Dr. LAUFER was correct in his statement that the opium pipe was not developed until the beginning of the seventeenth century; but, after all, the Chinese were then actively engaged in trade with the Moluccas, allowing two hundred fifty years; and this period for the most part covers the time when the cultivation and use of tobacco spread very rapidly all over the world, from the middle of the sixteenth to the beginning of the seventeenth centuries.

Few cultivated plant species of the several hundred involved can match the speed with which the knowledge and use of tobacco spread in the world at large. In 1939, AMES provided a carefully compiled list of early records of tobacco. First observed in 1492. First leaves introduced into Spain in 1519. Introduced into France in 1556. Cultivated in Lisbon in 1558. Known in Italy in 1561, in

36) HADDON, A. C. Smoking and Tobacco Pipes in New Guinea. Philos. Trans. Biol. Sci. 232: 1-278. pl. 1-7. fig. 1-197. 1946.

37) WHEELER, HELEN-MAR. Studies in *Nicotiana* II. A Taxonomic Study of the Australian Species. Univ. Calif. Publ. Bot. 18: 45-68. 1935.

Germany in 1565, in West Africa in 1570, in England in 1573 and in Holland before 1590 (smoking), in Asia in 1595, in Turkey in 1599, in Russia in 1600 (smoking), in Persia in 1600, in the Philippines in 1600, at Java in 1601, in Egypt in 1603 (smoking), cultivated in India and Japan in 1605, cultivated in China in 1608 and in Ceylon in 1610. The last four entries were certainly due to Portuguese influence.

Some years ago, Dr. CHEVALIER(38) gave considerable attention to the origin and distribution of tobacco. He concluded correctly that no representative of *Nicotiana* was native of Africa, but thought that it might have been present in southern Asia in pre-Columbian times (which has never been proved) and argued for its pre-Magellan arrival in New Guinea through the flotsam and jetsam method, *i.e.*, by its seeds floating from the western coast of South America by way of the Polynesian islands to New Guinea or perhaps by being carried by birds. My idea is that it reached Africa, Madagascar, and southern India probably by the now too often forgotten Portuguese trade route (*cf. infra* & p. 229).

I find no reason whatever for considering that either of the commonly cultivated *hybrid* species of tobacco occurred anywhere in the Old World, until after the pioneer voyages of the Spaniards and Portuguese were made in 1492 and 1498-1500. It is worthy of note that Portugal began the development of its far-flung oriental conquests six and a half decades before Spain undertook its colonization of the Philippines. CHEVALIER did record a number of local American Indian names for the tobacco plant, but unfortunately he did not provide the names of the places where they were used. They are: *yoli, cozabba, gisia, yelt, picielt, quantyetl, upwoc, uppuwoc, petum,* and *petun,* but never *tabaco.* The name *petun* found more or less common usage in Europe and is still used in France and the French West Indies for tobacco or certain tobacco products. In botany, it is the basis of the generic name *Petunia* Juss., applied to an allied genus. Further data of interest will, undoubtedly, be available in the rich, but widely scattered, ethnobiological literature on the American Indians.

The present natural generic range of *Nicotiana* (North and South America, a very few Pacific Islands, and Australia) was attained, in the Tertiary Period, by way of Antarctica, when that continent supported a luxuriant vegetation. This, of course, long antedates the periods with which the anthropologist is concerned, but it should not antedate the time in which phytogeographers, systematists, taxonomists and even historical geographers ought to be interested. The natural *Nicotiana* distribution, like that of *Gossypium*, is hardly exciting.

In 1930 I took certain exceptions to a paper on tobacco in New Guinea written by Dr. A. B. LEWIS under the supervision of Dr. BERTHOLD LAUFER. The latter was such a well-informed student of oriental botanical problems that it is hard to understand why he agreed with some of the claims by Dr. LEWIS. Dr. MILLSPAUGH, to whom some dried leaves of tobacco from New Guinea were referred for identi-

38) CHEVALIER, A. Les Origines du Tabac et les Débuts de sa Culture dans le Monde. Rev. Internat. Tabacs 2: 305-312. 1926; 4: 13-16, 86-91, 171-174. 1927.

fication, was concerned in this study in a peculiar way. Admitting that species identifications in *Nicotiana* could not be made from leaves alone, he, nevertheless, suggested that the leaves he had might represent *Nicotiana suaveolens* Lehm. He confused New Guinea with the Guinea coast of Africa, and his statement that *Nicotiana suaveolens* Lehm. was cultivated in South Africa is an extraordinary mistake, based upon his geographical error.

We know today that there are no native species of *Nicotiana* from New Guinea; that the only known cultivated species is the American hybrid, *N. tabacum* L.; that a great many of the local names of the plant in New Guinea are derived from the Spanish, Portuguese and Dutch names of this plant, and that the name *tabaco, tobacco* (with its cognates) spread all over the world with the plant itself and with the smoking habit — this during the past three hundred fifty years or so; and, finally, these "tabaco" names in all languages are derived from the word originally applied to the cigar (not the pipe and not the plant) in the West Indies. We see, then, even from Dr. LAUFER's attempt in 1931 to support his associate, Dr. LEWIS, that altogether too much guessing has appeared in print.

The *Nicotiana* situation has been greatly complicated by the free and easy early description of various new species and varieties which now prove to be nothing but forms of the very variable hybrid *Nicotiana tabacum* L., as well as by the scarcity of early herbarium specimens (*cf. infra*).

When I became interested in the other tobacco, *N. rustica* L., at one time widely planted by our North American Indians, I found this species poorly represented in half a dozen of our larger herbaria. Most of the few specimens were collected about a century ago. Within the present century, however, it has been collected at the town dump at Stoughton, Mass., in waste places at Lynn, Mass., and it is still grown on the Seneca Reservation, Cattaraugus County, New York. The species is planted and comes up as a volunteer, but Dr. WITTHOFF, State Anthropologist of Pennsylvania, reports that it is not a truly wild escape. Many families cultivate it in rows in vegetable gardens. The border-bed, from which the planting stock is taken, gets a minimum of cultivation; the plants are self-sown for as long as the house is occupied, persisting for ten to fifteen years after a house has been abandoned.

Years ago, Dr. E. M. EAST carried out much genetical work at the Bussey Institution adjoining the Arnold Arboretum. *Nicotiana* was one of his specialties. In his experimental plots, which are still in use, no tobacco has been planted during the past eighteen years, and no volunteer plant has been permitted to mature its seed in that period. Nevertheless, young *Nicotiana tabacum* plants still appear, year after year, from seeds buried deeply in the soil.

Only once have I seen self-sown *Nicotiana tabacum* L. in Latin America, a small patch near a small house not far from the Escuela Agricola Panamericana, in Honduras, where some tobacco plants had been planted for home use at least ten years ago. I have never seen anything like this in the oriental tropics.

In my two score years of service in the Philippines, I myself collected *Nicotiana tabacum* L. only twice, for there it is almost never found outside of cultivation. Once I found a very few mature plants in the great tobacco region of the Cagayan Valley, Luzon; these few plants were self sown, occurring near the door of a tobacco warehouse.

The second occasion was when I found a solitary plant growing in among the rocks of a loose stone wall, while assembling data for my *Flora of Manila*. In the Philippines, ants eat all germinating tobacco seeds they can find, so that, in practice, planters must protect their seed flats against the ants (let no theorist cite this as an example of early propagation of such plants as rice and the coconut).

The paucity of herbarium specimens of cultigens reminds us of Dr. ANDERSON's lament that collectors and taxonomists pay no attention to and collect no cultivated plants. A good example of the dearth in our standard herbaria of cultigens is that mentioned by Dr. H. J. LAM(39) in reference to the great herbarium at Buitenzorg (Bogor), Java. As of about 1921, there were only two specimens of *Nicotiana* from New Guinea in the Buitenzorg herbarium, both *N. tabacum* L. No specimens of *N. rustica* L. are known from any part of Malaysia.

The two *Nicotiana* cultigens which we considered, *both hybrids,* became almost wholly dependent on man for their very existence. This, incidentally, has been the case with all of the improved forms of our cereals, fruits, tubers, corms and leafy vegetables. It is high time that our younger anthropologists gave more attention to this general subject. Obviously, whatever man has been able to accomplish in improving his condition throughout his existence as a race has been governed and limited by his food supply.

HADDON's very sane attitude in 1946 is by far the most logical, best balanced and best documented one that I have noted. On the other hand, I have no faith whatever in VAN NOUHUYS' claims and assertions, in spite of the fact that he had the opportunity of prosecuting anthropological field work in the interior of New Guinea. All I can do is to refer him to the simple problem of the numerous Malaysian and Papuasian names for the tobacco plant which are derived from Portuguese, Spanish and Dutch names for the plant.

To summarize, we may say that no forms of the American *Nicotiana rustica* L. or *N. tabacum* L., both hybrids, reached any part of the Old World until after the Portuguese had established themselves in India, Ceylon, Malacca, the Moluccas, China, Formosa, and Japan following 1500, and the Spaniards had also established themselves in Guam and in the Philippines in 1565. *Nicotiana,* as I see it, is a very unconvincing example if one must "prove" trans-Pacific transmission by man previous to 1521. The hybrid origins of the two cultivated species of *Nicotiana* have been proved. If one insists that tobacco was known in New Guinea before the coming of the Europeans, then one has two alternatives: it was either carried across the Pacific or else across the Atlantic and the Indian Oceans by pre-Columbian man and left no traces behind.

I close this long discussion by citing a few references(40) to what is still a controversial question, where, indeed, careful genetical analysis of various proposed "species" should throw a ray of light on a situation which is not clear taxonomically.

39) LAM, H. J. Fragmenta Papuana (Observations of a Naturalist in New Guinea). Sargentia 5: 1-196. 1945. (Translated from the original Dutch of 1927-29 by Dr. L. M. PERRY), p. 148, footnote 15.

Plumeria acuminata Poir.:— This is another case scarcely worth
a discussion. For details one is referred to a paper which I published
in 1937*(41)*. We may, in review, point out that Mr. BAKHUIZEN was
misled by a belief that a bas-relief on the ninth century Borobudur
temple, in Java, represented this strictly American species; whatever
this might have been intended to represent, it is definitely not a *Plumeria*. RHEEDE did not know the plant in India; it at least does not
appear in his classical *Hortus Malabaricus* (1678-1703). Yet, less than
a century later, it was found in temple grounds, all over India, had
become sacred and was known as the "temple flower." Forms of the
Sanscrit names used in Java are in part modified ones, meaning a
kind of *champaca*, and another, *kambodia*, is a place name rather clearly indicating the country whence the plant was transmitted to Java,
which in turn had received it from Manila.

It is not generally known that the Spanish associations with Cambodia were close enough that, on occasion, a galleon for the Manila-Acapulco route was built in Cambodia. The attempt to derive the
names, cited by RUMPHIUS in 1743 (he wrote between 1681 and 1692),
from Malay words failed, for *culong tsjutsju*, etc., are merely slightly
modified forms of the Philippine *kalachuche*, which in turn is a slightly
softened form of its original Mexican (Nahuatl) name. There are
fifteen variants of this name in the Philippines alone. Then, too,
BAKHUIZEN did not know of the early Philippine published records:
first, MERCADO*(42)*, writing in the last third of the seventeenth century, definitely stated that the species was brought from Mexico (via
the Acapulco-Manila galleon route) and that, at the time, there was
scarcely a town in the Philippines where it did not occur. KAMEL
(CAMEL, CAMELIUS) *(43)*, whose work was published in 1704, written
probably in the last decade of the previous century, described it from
the Philippines as *Cacaloxochitl mexicana*.

Furthermore, a minor historical episode was overlooked, for Spain
occupied the islands of Ternate and Tidore in the Moluccas in 1609,

40) LAUFER, B. Tobacco in New Guinea: An Epilogue. Am. Anthropol. 33:
138-140. 1931.

LEWIS, A. B. Tobacco in New Guinea. *Op. cit.* 134-138.

MERRILL, E. D. Tobacco in New Guinea. *Op. cit.* 32: 101-105. 1930; Further
Notes on Tobacco in New Guinea. *Op. cit.* 48: 22-30. 1946. Reprinted Chron.
Bot. 10: 386-393. 1946. (*Merrilleana*).

MIKLOUHO-MACLAY, A. DE. List of Plants in Use by the Natives of the Maclay-
Coast, New Guinea (with Botanical Remarks by Baron FERD. VON MUELLER).
Proc. Linn. Soc. N.S. Wales. 10: 346-354. 1886.

NOUHUYS, J. W. VAN. Over de herkomst en het gebruik van tabak op Nieuw
Guinea. Mensch en Maatschappij 8: 75-99. 1932.

A discussion of WIENER's theory of the origin of the smoking of tobacco will
be found on p. 316.

41) MERRILL, E. D. On the Significance of Certain Oriental Plant Names in
Relation to Introduced Species. Proc. Am. Philos, Soc. 78: 112-146. 1937. Reprinted Chron. Bot. 10: 295-315. 1946. (*Merrilleana*).

42) MERCADO, I. Libro de Medicinas de Esta Tierra, *in* BLANCO, M. Fl. Filip.,
ed. 3, 4[2]:i-vi. 1-63. 1880. (Manuscript written in the last third of the seventeenth century).

43) KAMEL, J. G. Herbarium aliarumque stirpium in Luzone Philippinarum
primaria nascentium, *in* RAY, Hist. Pl. 3: Suppl. 1-96. 1704.

and retained control of one or both of them for over fifty years as part of its Philippine colony; and it was just at the time when this particular ornamental tree was being distributed through the Orient. When the islands were given up, their Christian converts were transported to Luzon and settled in Cavite Province in a place that still bears the name Ternate. In view of this not entirely obscure bit of history, it is strange that no attention should have been given to RUMPHIUS's warning: "Andere zeggen, dat ze in de Manilhas te vinden is, en van daar nevens de volgende bloem [*Flos manhilanos* = *Tabernaemontana divaricata* (L.) R. Br. = *Ervatamia divaricata* (L.) Burkill] in Ternaten gebragt zij".

This is a very simple case. All the evidence — botanical, philological and historical — in all respects indicates Mexican origin, transportation to the Philippines by way of the Acapulco-Manila galleon route, and its dissemination from Manila southward to Celebes and the Moluccas, and westward to Cambodia, thence to western Malaysia, India, and other parts of the oriental tropics. Its slightly modified Mexican name went along with it in the seventeenth century. The record of the post-Magellan transmission of a plant species from one hemisphere to the other, across the Pacific, is rarely clearer than in this case(*44*).

That Dr. WOODSON reduced POIRET's species, with nineteen other binomials, to synonymy under *Plumeria rubra* L., signifies only differences of opinion as to the limits of species, for all species of the genus are of American origin.

In 1904, I perhaps foolishly published my first paper on introduced species in the Philippines. This was completed in August, 1903, when I had been in the islands only a few months more than one year(*45*). It was, to be frank, but a compilation, for the entire herbarium then available to me contained only a few thousand sheets, library facilities were very limited, and my knowledge of Philippine botanical problems was equally limited. I considered briefly about one hundred species which I then believed had been introduced from tropical America. As I know the situation now, I may say that the list could have been about doubled.

---

44) Another case is *Theobroma cacao* L. BLANCO (Fl. Filip. 601. 1837) stated that Father GASPAR DE SAN AGUSTÍN recorded that in "Año de 1670 un Piloto llamado PEDRO BRAVO DE LAGUNAS, trajo en una maceta un pie de Cacao de Acapulco." This one plant, through a series of mischances, was planted in Lipa, Batangas Province, Luzon, and within a few years its seeds had been widely distributed — it was the beginning of cacao cultivation in the Philippines.

45) MERRILL, E. D. The American Element in the Philippine Flora. Govt. Lab. Publ. 6: 19-36. 1904.

It seems to me that when ill-informed workers use such phrases as "virtually unassailable proof" referring to data which a specialist, equally as ill-informed botanically, has cited in support of a thesis, or that when another, after quoting a long passage, challenges the author of the quotation "to put up or shut up" merely because of a difference of opinion, it is then time to review the evidence supporting the other side of the argument in an attempt to avoid prejudice and bitterness.

At the same time, I would be the last to claim that traditions are always correct. In dealing with certain "authorities", some of whom are deservedly rated as being at, or very near the top, of their respective professions, I have shown that some of them tend to argue from not too faultless premises arrived at often by mysterious processes. It is ironic that some leading historical geographers fail to consider (or are ignorant of) certain historical aspects of the situation, such as the problem as to when, how and whence maize first reached Asia, or the equally simple problem as to how and when certain cultivated forms of another strictly American genus, *Cucurbita,* reached western India and Persia, to say nothing of the common peanut.

The few taxonomists, whose work I discuss in this chapter, are here only incidentally involved, because they worked in institutions whose herbaria were distinctly limited. One must have material from all parts of the world, in order to avoid errors in studies of plant distribution. Other offenders are certain geneticists who theorize too much in ignorance of what has happened in the past entirely outside of their own branch of science. Those concentrating on chromosome studies must realize that many factors must be considered when phytogeographical problems are involved.

I deliberately express no opinion about those anthropologists, ethnologists and philologists who, from time to time, have condescendingly attempted to make contributions to our knowledge of plants and plant uses. Up to the present century, plants and agriculture, although basic to civilizations and cultures, apparently meant little to most of the workers in these fields. In my twenty-one years in the Philippines, where I was, for most of that period, associated with professional ethnologists and working in the same building with them, I do not remember a single one of them ever bringing in a botanical specimen or asking a botanical question. On the other hand, I used continually to ply them with ethnobotanical questions, most of which they could not answer, if the query applied to other than some of the most common species.

Above all, those who are ignorant of the published annals of the history of exploration, from the beginnings of the fifteenth century onward, but who like to theorize as to when economic plants and weeds were transmitted from one hemisphere to the other, should, before proceeding further along their way, familiarize themselves with the principles of phytogeography and simple taxonomy, and then master the annals of exploration. Most of the data they need are available in English in the publications of the *Hakluyt Society* and similar serials. They should, however, not confine their reading to the early authors, including and succeeding MARCO POLO and PIGA-FETTA, but should continue to give full consideration to all travel accounts up to, at least, the middle of the last century. Then, there is a vast amount of information available in the published annals of botany which non-botanists tend to overlook entirely because it is such dull reading (the published annals of general explorations are, in general, anything but dull).

Leo Wiener:—To conclude, I must refer to an astonishing work by LEO WIENER *(46)*, onetime Professor of Slavic Languages at Harvard University. This work, in my judgment, is Rafinesquian in the extreme and should not have been published until after the manuscript had been thoroughly revised by a widely experienced taxonomist and an equally widely experienced anthropologist. In 1946, HADDON took the trouble to consult it and spoke of it as subversive, which is a very mild characterization.

WIENER asserted that the smoking of tobacco originated in Africa with *Nicotiana tabacum* L. and *N. rustica* L., and that from Africa the smoking habit found its way into America, half a century, possibly a century, before COLUMBUS made his first voyage to the West Indies in 1492. It was not known then that both of these "species" are of hybrid origin and that all the parent species involved are still confined to America. The parentage of *Nicotiana rustica* L. is *N. paniculata* L. and *N. undulata* L., both native to Peru and that of *N. tabacum* L. is *N. silvestris* Speg. & Comes, of Argentina and *N. tomentosa* Ruiz & Pavon from Peru. Both of the Linnaean hybrid species have been reconstituted by the long continued, critical breeding work prosecuted by Drs. GOODSPEED and CLAUSEN, and their associates, at the University of California, within the past three decades. The two hybrid cultigens must have been introduced into Africa from America. But why the ignorant American Indians had produced or at least detected and widely distributed these species in both North and South America, without knowing how to smoke, is not convincingly explained. There is no native *Nicotiana* in Africa. This is a wonderful example of how far a theorist will go to "prove" correct his preconceived theory; and yet WIENER is no more to be censured than are certain other specialists in totally different fields whose theories are discussed in this memoir.

Among the other strange "facts" that WIENER proved—at least to his own satisfaction—are that the sweet potato (*Ipomoea batatas* (L.) Lam.) was a native of Africa and that *camote* (its name everywhere in the Philippines) originated in that archipelago and was thence

---

46) WIENER, L. Africa and the Discovery of America, 3 vols. 1920-22.

transferred to Mexico, where it was adopted by the Nahuatl peoples. But here he forgot to check his dates. I am not a philologist, but I challenge WIENER's statement that: *"Camote* is . . . . . a native Philippine word which means 'root' "*. This is one of his very numerous positive statements that do not stand the strain of critical investigation. Highly educated and widely experienced Filipinos whose native tongues are Tagalog, Bisayan, Bicol, Ilocano and others (Dr. E. QUISUMBING being an example) insist that such Philippine words as *gamot, gamut, gamoy, lamot,* and *yamot* meaning "root" (all cited by WIENER) have nothing to do with *camote,* the resemblances in form being merely accidental. There are still other equivalents of "root" in the Philippine languages, such as *ugat* (Tagalog), *uyat* (Pampango), and *ramot* (Ilocano), but these are never associated with *camote.* Dr. QUISUM-BING says that *c* (or *k*) and *g* are not interchangeable in Philippine languages but that *r* and *l* are.

Taking up WIENER's positive statement that *camotli* (often spelled *camotl* in the sixteenth century) is not a Mexican (Nahuatl) name, but is a Philippine one introduced with the plant itself, one immediately queries: How, when, and by whom was this introduction made? There were no direct eastward connections between the Philippines and Mexico until 1565, except for the return of the Spanish expeditions of LOYASA in 1526, SAAVEDRA in 1529, and GAETANO in 1546. Yet in 1521, PIGAFETTA recorded batatas from Guam, from Cebu (unfortunately without their local names), and from the Moluccas (with the local name *gumbili*). The first recorded local name for the sweet potato that I have succeeded in locating for the Philippines is the Bisayan *kurintagos* for Negros which appears in the POVEDANO manuscript of 1578, to which I have referred on p. 365. There is positive evidence that this species did occur in parts of America, all over Polynesia and even in parts of Malaysia and Papuasia in pre-Magellan times. I can find no evidence that it occurred in western Malaysia or in India at an early date. It is very easy to understand this Polynesian distribution if one considers how various peoples expanded over the Pacific basin, particularly the true Polynesians. One must remember the long continued rôle of the strong northeast monsoon, year after year, and the frequency by which castaways from the Marianas and the Caroline Islands reached the eastern coast of the Philippines and presumably the Moluccas, New Guinea and other points.

WIENER confused the issue when he said categorically that "HER-NANDEZ . . . does not give *camotli*". But HERNANDEZ *(47)* did record this in his "De camotli, seu Batata" and described four varieties *acamotli, yhoicamotl, xochicamotli,* and *camopalcamotli* or *poxcauhcamotli.* WIENER apparently did not know of this HERNANDEZ publication but depended on other works published by that early writer. Here there are reasonably good descriptions also of *camopatli* (*seu Batata venenata*), p. 353, *quauhcamotli* (*seu Yuca*), p. 354 (this is *Manihot utilis-*

---

47) HERNANDEZ, F. Opera, cum edita, tum inedita (De Historia Plantarum Novae Hispaniae) 1: 351. 1790. One must keep in mind that the manuscript was written before 1575, within the decade following the arrival of the first galleon from the Philippines.

sima Pohl = *M. esculenta* Crantz, the tapioca or cassava plant), *chichiccamotic* (*seu amara Batata*), *tepecamotli* (*seu Batata montana*) both on p. 355, *cacamotic tlanoquiloni* (*seu Batata purgativa*), *cacamotic hoaxtepecensi*, both on p. 356, *cacamotic tricuspide* and *cacamotic yacapichtlae*, both on p. 357, and finally *cacamotic altera*, p. 358. Furthermore, in the library of the Arnold Arboretum there is an undated *Indice de los nombres Mexicanos de las plantas descriptas en la obra del Dr. Hernandez* p. 1-256 (author unknown) in which there are seven additional references to the words *camotl* and *camotli*, these chiefly in entries appertaining to other species which were compared one way or another to the sweet potato. The descriptions all apply to vines with thickened or tuberous roots in several unrelated families of plants.

It is my contention that the terms *camotl, camotli* and *camotic* were used by HERNANDEZ rather in a generic sense, based on obvious resemblances in habit alone, to signify vines with thickened or tuberous roots. I cannot condone WIENER's overlooking the twenty definite entries cited above; yet in his work (1: 267, 1920) following his definite statement that: "HERNANDEZ, who does not give *camotli* or *quahcamotli*," he did record *cacamotic tlanoquilonis* but was not impressed, apparently because of his preoccupation in proving only what he wanted to believe.

Then there is the record of SAHAGUN*(48)* of 1569, only four years after the return of the first galleon from the Philippines, who describes both *camotli* and *quauhcamotli*.

I can but conclude that the Spaniards in Mexico accepted the Nahuatl name *camotl* or *camotli*, modified it slightly to *camote* and carried the word to Peru, Guam and the Philippines. As they quickly and easily extended their control over the newly occupied regions in the orient after 1565, whatever native names for this plant which might have been in use were quickly abandoned in favor of the term *camote* introduced and sponsored by the Spanish. That the plant was known in parts of the Orient when the first Europeans reached the Philippines is certain.

To complicate even more the picture, WIENER says: "*Camotli* is as little Nahuatl as *camote* is Peruvian". Nobody ever claimed that it was Peruvian. It is evident that the Spaniards in Mexico accepted the Nahuatl name, changed it slightly and took it to Peru and to the Philippines. I venture to state that the original Nahuatl form in Mexico was *camotl*, in spite of WIENER's elaborate, involved and unconvincing argument to the contrary.

I mention this strange work mainly because a certain geographer assumes that the Pacific barrier was passed by pre-Columbian man with at least some of his cultivated food plants and expressed to me (*in lit.*, 1953) his belief that the Atlantic barrier would not stand. WIENER, incidentally, "proved" that the Atlantic was no barrier in pre-Columbian times. Lately, a romantic diffusionist

---

48) SAHAGUN, B. DE. Historia general de las cosas de Nueva España. 1829-30. The manuscript in twelve books was written in 1569, but not published until two hundred sixty years later.

in South Africa is out to prove it again*(48a)*! I admit that there is increasing evidence that a very few African species reached tropical America, a few hundred years before COLUMBUS made his successful trip in 1492. The sweet potato is perhaps an example. On the other hand, a few American cultigens, such as maize, possibly the peanut, and even the squash or pumpkin and cassava may have reached Africa before COLUMBUS. But WIENER's views according to which *cassava had been introduced into South America from Africa and the Africans had taught the American Indians the art of its cultivation and use,* cannot be correct. The genus *Manihot* (to which cassava belongs) is strictly American. PAX and HOFFMAN who monographed it in 1910 then recognized 129 species, mostly from Brazil. New species have been described since that date, but the phytogeographical picture remains unchanged.

Lest I be accused of not having studied a valuable source book merely because its author had reached conclusions in some respects diametrically opposed to those of A. DE CANDOLLE and others, I examined the WIENER volumes very carefully. After reading most of the text rather critically, my conclusion remains unchanged. The author, a philologist, cites with authority and positiveness words from between four and five hundred different Eurasian, African and Amerindian languages. It is a study which shows that the author possessed a vast store of philological knowledge but which, apparently disorganized, he utilized, too often, unwisely. He proved to his own satisfaction his preconceived idea that the African Negroes had discovered America at least one or two centuries before COLUMBUS. But even if we could grant this hypothesis to be true, it does not affect the general picture of the interchange of certain economic plants between the two hemispheres; it would merely give certain theorists one or two hundred years more with which to play. This same statement applies to any possible Arab discovery of America. I cannot reverse my opinion that *Africa and the Discovery of America* is a work that never should have been published, until after careful editing with the assistance of specialists, such as HOOPS apparently secured before completing his *Waldbäume und Kulturpflanzen im germanischen Altertum* in 1905.

As soon as the first volume of his work appeared in 1920, it was subjected to one of the most scathing reviews I have ever read. The critic was Dr. R. B. DIXON, who certainly knew whereof he spoke (*see* Am. Anthropol. 22: 178-185. 1920). I cite only a part of his first paragraph: "This unquestionably interesting but in many ways unfortunate volume presents the reviewer with something of a puzzle, for a careful reading leaves one in doubt as to

---

48a) JEFFREYS, M. D. W. Maize and its old world introduction. Sou. Af. Jour. Sci., May 1953. Pre-Columbian maize in Africa. Nature 172: 965-966. 1953. The history of maize in Africa. Hist. Sect., Eighth Int. Bot. Congress, Paris, July 1954 (Abstracts). — *If the Arabs had introduced maize into Africa, as early as JEFFREYS indicates, they would have transmitted this important food plant to all parts of Indo-Malaysia (this was the time they expanded over the entire region)!*

whether the author really intended his work to be taken as a serious contribution or has attempted to perpetrate a rather elaborate jest. For while he has brought together material of much interest and arrives at startling conclusions there is . . . so much in the way of unsubstantiated assumption, hasty correlation, false reasoning, misunderstanding and misrepresentation of sources . . . that it is difficult to take the volume seriously." Then comes the real dissection. The closing sentence is: "It is clear that there is a problem here which demands a scientific and scholarly study, but this the volume under discussion cannot be said to supply." The vast amount of reading that WIENER obviously did in searching for proofs of his claims represents time and effort wasted, for he did not secure the assistance and advice of reliable specialists to help him interpret and correlate his material. There seems to be no DIXON reviews of volumes two and three of WIENER's work.

I could not resist the temptation to read this three-volume work, for the reason that some, as weak in their botanical knowledge as WIENER proved himself to be, may have utilized the WIENER work which gives inexperienced theorists the "proof" they seek. Yet, most American theorizers on the subject seem to be as ignorant of this three-volume work as they are of the very large scale Portuguese operations by way of Brazil to the Orient which persisted for 165 years following the year 1500. I could not forego discussing it in order to forfend any use of it by later and unsuspecting writers as a serious work.

Further Remarks on the Sweet Potato Controversy: — There is one recent, short paper that seems to be worthy of note here in connection with this sweet potato controversy. Its author *(49)* says: "DIXON says that the word camote is of Mexican origin, introduced by the Spaniards into the Philippines, but I think the reverse is more likely." WIENER had foolishly accepted this twenty years earlier. All data that I have assembled indicate to me that DIXON was right and that WIENER and PIERCE's pleas, even from a philological standpoint, were but wild guesses. Now it is admitted that there is a chance that *Ipomoea batatas* (L.) Lam. may have originated outside of America, but as yet I have seen no data that would prove that this was the case. Nevertheless, Dr. JUNIUS BIRD informs me that none of the plant remains unearthed by him in his remarkable excavations at Huaca Prieta, Peru, have as yet been associated with the sweet potato, and the site so critically explored by him has been inhabited since pre-maize and pre-pottery days, from about 2500 B.C. to 1600 A.D. I can only admit that, though I follow the almost universally accepted idea that the sweet potato originated in America, here is a case where this may ultimately be shown to be erroneous. Even if it be shown eventually that this economic cultigen originated in the Old World, we still have the definite dates when it was introduced into China, Japan and elsewhere in post-Spanish and post-Portuguese times. Unsupported claims that it was in the Malay Peninsula in the eleventh century leave one rather unconvinced, and I can find no evidence that it was in India until after the arrival of the Portuguese in 1498 and 1500.

PIERCE's second point was an entomological one and is well worthy of serious consideration. What is the significance of certain species of weevils of the subfamily *Cyladinae* (about twenty species) in such genera as *Cylas, Protocylas,* etc.? He says that, the world over, the sweet potato is the host of these weevils; sometimes other species of *Ipomoea* are involved. As yet too little is known from which to draw any final conclusions as to the host plants; in 1940, Dr. PIERCE knew the host plants of only one fifth of the twenty weevil species in this group for the entire world. It may well be, as PIERCE says, that the sweet potato weevils belong to a group that is typically Asiatic and African in origin, but we cannot forget that the host species has been distributed by man for the most part by means of its tubers, and the weevils would naturally travel with the tubers. It is an interesting point which really ought to be pursued in detail as a possible source of clews to where this important food plant originated. He states in conclusion: "I think that this lends strong

49) PIERCE, W. D. A few Remarks on the Possible Origin of the Sweet Potato. Bull. South. Calif. Acad. Sci. 39: 229-230. 1940.

TEXT FIGURE 18. — *Ipomoea batatas* (L.) Lam., the sweet potato, the only cultivated plant of *possible American* origin which was widely distributed throughout the world in pre-Columbian times. — As discussed in a postscript on p. 371, the almost universally accepted idea that the sweet potato originated in America, may have to be revised; it may even prove to be of African origin. It is obviously a hybrid. — Reproduced from the *Historiae Naturalis Brasiliae* (1648) by PISO & MARCGRAVE who call this plant: *Ietica brasiliensibus . . . Lusitanis Batata*. This early cut shows well the diverse forms of its leaves and tubers.

arguments to the contention that the plant is of African or south Asiatic origin". The latter may be ruled out, but Africa is a possibility. But even though it be conclusively shown that the sweet potato originated in Africa, the dates of its pantropic distribution are relatively recent, not ancient, and for the extreme diffusionists would carry the dates back only a very few hundred years before the great expansion of the Spanish and the Portuguese between the years 1492 and 1565.

On Vernacular Names of Economic Plants: — To those who theorize in part or wholly on the significance of the local names of economic species, I call attention to a very important source of Papuan plant names for a few economic species. In 1945, Miss HENRIETTE A. NEUHAUS kindly compiled for me the local names of four important economic plants in New Guinea from the set of the Annual Reports of the Territory of New Guinea available to her in the office of the Archbold Expeditions, American Museum of Natural History, New York. The area covered was limited to what was, at the time, British New Guinea. The dates covered extend from 1886 to 1927. The tabulated data cover the local names used, the dialect, the station or division involved, the village or settlement, the date, page, and the names of the compilers. Here are the results for the four species considered.

Tobacco (*Nicotiana tabacum* L., a hybrid of American origin), 103 different names (a very high percentage clearly derived from the Spanish and Portuguese *tabaco* and the Dutch form *tabak*).

Sweet potato (*Ipomoea batatas* Lam.), 111 different names.

The greater yam (*Dioscorea alata* L.), 140 different names.

Taitu = *Dioscorea* sp., probably *D. esculenta* (Lam.) Burkill *fide* Mr. L. J. BRASS, 52 different local names.

I am incompetent to analyze these numerous, elsewhere mostly unlisted, names from a philological standpoint. The document prepared by Miss NEUHAUS I have deposited in the library of the Peabody Museum at Harvard University.

A good example of how one may easily be misled by similarities in local names in such a region as Malaysia is that presented by the local terms for the introduced and cultivated arrow-root plant (*Maranta arundinacea* L.) of tropical American origin. When I was working on this part of the manuscript, Prof. BARTLETT published his paper on *English Names of Some East-Indian Plants and Plant-Products* (Asa Gray Bull. II, 2: 159-176. 1953). He has recorded sixteen variant spellings of what is widely known in the Philippines as *arurú*. In all of Malaysia, the variations extend from *ararú* to *waherút*. HEYNE, in the third edition of his *Nuttige Planten van Indonesië* in 1950, recorded nearly thirty different local names for this cultivated food plant, including about eight more variants of the *arurú* form. Prof. BARTLETT thought that this Malay name might have been the source of the English name arrow-root. In 1904, I held the same theory briefly when I first learned the local

name for this plant commonly used in the Philippines — in fact
I then actually started in to write a note on the similarity of the
Tagalog *arurú* and the English arrow-root. I then discovered that
this particular species of *Maranta* had not been introduced into the
Philippines until sometime after 1850, and probably not until after
the Suez canal was opened in 1869. MIQUEL did not know the species
as a Malaysian one in 1855, and HEYNE's earliest record for Malaysia
is an item appearing in the Bataviasche Courant of April 11, 1829.
Dr. HANS SLOANE had recorded the name arrow-root as used in
Jamaica about 1700. Thus it is clear that the *arurú* variants in
Malaysia all resulted from attempts of the illiterate native peoples
of the various parts of Malaysia to render some sort of an equivalent
of the English word arrow-root. This is a remarkable illustration
of what may happen on occasion in the proliferation of plant names
particularly to those applied to introduced species. Thirty different
names originated in less than 125 years and applied to a single
species is rather a record!

BARTLETT was undecided about which way the word travelled, and
commented on the use of the form "araroetoe" and "arraroet" in
Curaçao as follows: "This may have been an introduction of an Indonesian word from one Dutch colony to another, by colonial planters,
or just a perversion of English by the Dutch, which makes us wonder
if the same thing could have happened in Indonesia and have led to
the long list of words which I suppose to be good Indonesian."

It seems fitting to cite here a very pertinent quotation from
page 12 of STEVENS's*(50)* work, published in 1930, on the discovery
of Australia in which he criticized wholly unwarranted claims, made
a few years earlier, that QUIROS made the discovery at the time he
attempted to colonize the New Hebrides in 1606. QUIROS had never
made such a claim and actually never got closer than about 1400
miles to Australia. STEVENS states: "The writer pointed out to the
editor of the journal in question the inaccuracy of its statements (as
did at least one other correspondent), but, as far as he is aware, no
correction or retraction was ever vouchsafed. It can only be pre-
sumed, therefore, that the editor and his contributor are still of the
opinion that QUIROS discovered Australia, and are peacefully enjoy-
ing that blissful state which GRAY seems to suggest 'twould be folly
to disturb'. *For that reason this most amazing journalistic 'bloomer'*
of modern times, which has so amused the geographical world, is
placed on record here as an excellent example of the modern pernici-
ous, but very prevalent, practice of writing on historic subjects with-
out first verifying the prime sources of information. By the neglect
of this precaution, the erroneous deductions of the writers of one
generation become the accepted truths of the next. Fictions and the
facts from which they emanate become so inextricably mingled that

---

50) STEVENS, H. N. New Light on the Discovery of Australia as revealed
by the Journal of Captain Don DIEGO DE PRADO Y TOVAR. Hakluyt Society II,
64: i-xvi. 1-261. 1929.

often the original modicum of truth is distorted, obscured and finally lost. Only by an independent analysis of basic facts and the sweeping away of the superincumbent fictions of successive writers, quoting and enlarging one from another, can we hope to arrive at a solution of some of the many mysteries which becloud early geographical history(51). The present investigation, as will be seen, has brought to light several curious and flagrant examples of the way in which historic facts have gradually become distorted over a long period of years, owing to mistranslations or misinterpretations of the meaning of the original writer."

To many of those I have criticized in this chapter, the above quotation applies in all respects. They in turn can apply it to me if they be so inclined, but I reserve the right to require reasonable proofs for their adverse claims.

Apologia:— It may be appropriate to conclude these notes with some general comments on the work of one of the botanists of the diffusionist school. The following remarks were recently received from a distinguished colleague who went through most of the proofs of this book and are being quoted with his permission, not to add criticism of a personal nature to a work in which I have been forced already to criticize so many workers, but as they make an excellent summary of some of the principal errors which I have endeavoured to analyze in the preceding pages: ". . . as guilty as the others in searching for evidence to support his preconceived ideas and ignoring evidence which is in conflict with them. . . I would criticize him severely for condoning the outrageous botanical errors of his [non-botanical] colleagues. . . As a botanist he must know that hundreds, if not thousands of genera occur in both the Old World and the New and that the existence of cultivated forms of the same genus in both the Old World and the New may be nothing more than the reflection of the facts of plant geography and does not necessarily provide the slightest evidence of diffusion. He is just as guilty as the others of employing 'attention arresters', sensational hypotheses and sweeping conclusions. . . While the anthropologists tend to dismiss the geographer-diffusionists, having encountered their errors in other fields, they regard him as a true botanist and indeed a reputable one. Your only way to neutralize the effect of his errors was to show where he is wrong."

---

51) The italics are mine.

Chapter VIII

ON THE BINOMIALS APPEARING IN
PARKINSON'S JOURNAL (1773)

From a casual examination of the title page of PARKINSON's work*(1)* one might, perhaps, overlook the fact that it was an unofficial account of COOK's first voyage around the world (1768-1771). In it (pages 37-50) appears a section entitled: "Plants of use for food, medicine, &c. in Otaheite." SYDNEY PARKINSON was one of the artists, employed at the expense of JOSEPH BANKS who accompanied the latter on the *Endeavour* (PLATES 90 and 91). There were also employed, at BANKS's expense, four or five servants and helpers.

All the artists, Messrs. BUCHAN, PARKINSON and REYNOLDS, died on the trip. Two of BANKS's personal servants froze to death on Tierra del Fuego in January 1769, as a result of their indiscretion in absorbing all the liquor that was brought ashore for the use of the entire party (the trip was planned for a single day but due to adverse circumstances all who accompanied BANKS and SOLANDER were forced to spend the night on shore without shelter). Mr. PARKINSON died at sea on January 26, 1771, about a month after the *Endeavour* left the then notoriously unhealthy port of Batavia, Java. Thus, when the *Endeavour* reached England, BANKS's personal staff was greatly reduced.

Upon the return of the *Endeavour* to England, SYDNEY PARKINSON's personal effects were turned over to his brother, STANFIELD PARKINSON. Various misunderstandings between the principals fol-

---

1) PARKINSON, S. A Journal of a Voyage to the South Seas, in His Majesty's Ship, the Endeavour... i-xxiii. 1-212 [1-2]. pl. 1-27. 1773. In 1774, a German translation of those pages dealing with plants appeared under the title "Die Pflanzen der Insel Outahitée, aus der Parkinsonischen Reisebeschreibung und mit Anmerkungen erlautert." Naturf. 4: 220-258. pl. 2, 3. 1774. The translator masked his identity by signing it "Z.". This I have ignored, as it impresses me as being most noteworthy for its high percentage of misspelled scientific names, such as *Anistum* for *Aniotum*, *Chaitea taua* [*tana*], *Terminalis debrata* [*glabrata*], *Mimusops kanku* [*kauki*], *Epipapetis* for *Epipactis*, etc., all due to errors in transcription. A French translation was published in Paris, in 1797, under the title: "Voyage autour du Monde, sur le Vaisseau de Sa Majesté Britannique 'Endeavour'."

The PARKINSON data on plants occupy pages 71-91 of the first volume. A second volume consists of a summary of the data excerpted from the official reports of COOK's second and third voyages. This I have not seen, but it may, in part, have been based on the London edition of 1784, i-xxiii. 1-212 [1-2]. pl. 1-27; 2: i-lxi. 1-253, for following the preface to the "Additional Part" of this 1784 edition (there is no proper title page), which is in Dr. VERDOORN's library, are the data excerpted from the accounts of the trips of Messrs. BYRON, WALLIS, CARTERET, BOUGAINVILLE, COOK and CLERKE.

lowed.   After all, SYDNEY PARKINSON was employed by JOSEPH BANKS, and certainly the latter was within his rights in retaining the illustrations prepared by that artist.   As one reads the STANFIELD PARKINSON introductory statement (pages v-xxiii), one gets the impression that he was a very difficult individual.   He did not hesitate to express what he apparently believed about BANKS, as well as about Messrs. LEE, FOTHERGILL and HAWKESWORTH, who became involved in the matter.

The STANFIELD PARKINSON imbroglio is clarified by Dr. JOHN FOTHERGILL (who died at the end of 1780) in the greatly amplified edition of PARKINSON's Journal, printed in London in 1784.   The amplification consists of the inclusion of abbreviated data from HAWKESWORTH and, perhaps, other sources.   There is evidence that the introductory part (pages 1-18), including the postscript (pages 19-22), which was prepared from data written by a friend of Dr. FOTHERGILL, was prepared for the printer shortly after 1777.   For some unexplained reason, printing was deferred until four years after FOTHERGILL's death.   STANFIELD PARKINSON, who even at the time of his controversy with BANKS and others, displayed strong evidence of mental unbalance, had to be placed under restraint at the time Dr. FOTHERGILL wrote the explanation.   He soon became insane and was committed to an asylum.   There is evidence that this unfortunate affair was a contributing cause of Dr. HAWKESWORTH's death.

It is, on the whole, fortunate that PARKINSON's Journal was published, because it contains various data which were not included in the other published accounts of COOK's first voyage.   I do not here consider the three-volume HAWKESWORTH Voyages, likewise published in 1773 in two editions, based on the papers of Messrs. BYRON, WALLIS, CARTERET, COOK, BANKS, and SOLANDER, for the simple reason that many of their entries were eliminated, others "edited", while some statements were interpolated by the editor.   As Captain WHARTON stated, when he edited COOK's Journal in 1893, "Dr. HAWKESWORTH, into whose hands the Journals were put, not only interspersed reflections of his own, but managed to impose his own ponderous style upon many of the extracts from the united Journals; and, moreover, as they were all jumbled together, the whole [COOK, BANKS, SOLANDER documents] being put into COOK's mouth, it is impossible to know whether we are reading COOK, BANKS, SOLANDER, or HAWKESWORTH himself." (PLATE 92).

HAWKESWORTH was immensely indebted to the data included in BANKS' Journal.   I have not seen the account in J. H. MOORE's Collection of Voyages and Travels (1780?), nor that in R. KERR's General History and Collection of Voyages and Travels, vol. 12 (1824), but I assume that both were taken from HAWKESWORTH.   Apparently, STANFIELD PARKINSON tried to, and actually did, anticipate the HAWKESWORTH publication.   COOK's own account was not published in full until 1893, and BANKS' Journal had to wait until 1896.

HAWKESWORTH's three-volume account was published in London in 1773, shortly after the PARKINSON Journal had been issued.   There is a copy of the original edition in the Arnold Arboretum Library.   It was reprinted in the same year; this is the so-called "second edition", which I have not seen. Mr. A. C. TOWNSEND, librarian of the British Museum (Natural History), kindly examined this edition for me and reports that Volume I contains a "Preface to the Second Edition", dated August 2, 1773, in which Dr. HAWKESWORTH replies to a pamphlet by Mr. DALRYMPLE entitled: "A Letter from Mr. DALRYMPLE to Dr. HAWKESWORTH, occasioned by some groundless and illiberal imputations, in his account of the late voyages to the South Seas." In this second edition, the continuous pagination of Vols. II & III was changed to an individual pagination for each of the volumes concerned.

In the PARKINSON "botanical" paper, seventy-four binomials appear (including the several cases where alternative names occur). There is no botanical or other arrangement. First, the native name is given; this is followed by the binomial; then comes a shorter or longer statement chiefly regarding the uses of the plant. At the outset, I wish to make it clear that, in no case (except where typographical errors may occur), is PARKINSON the true author of any binomial, for they were taken, either from the illustrations of the various species he had prepared for BANKS, from SOLANDER's descriptions (which were written mostly on the *Endeavour*), or from the actual specimens SOLANDER named. One may prefer to credit the new names to BANKS and SOLANDER, but clearly the latter wrote the descriptions. The numerous, unpublished manuscripts prepared by him, appertaining to the floras of Madeira, Brazil, Tierra del Fuego, Tahiti, New Zealand, Australia, Java, Cape of Good Hope, St. Helena, etc., are also all catalogued under his name. Had these carefully prepared documents been published, doubtless they would have appeared under the joint authorship of BANKS and SOLANDER, for the former was an experienced botanist, and, as the financial backer of the entire program of natural history, he had certain rights. In the PARKINSON paper, as far as the new generic names of SOLANDER included are concerned, all new specific names, associated with them, form binomials of the generico-specific type.

In only one case, as far as I know, has an author taken up any of these "PARKINSON" binomials as validly published prior to 1941 — WARBURG in 1900 accepted *Pandanus tectorius* Solander (1773) in preference to the later *P. odoratissimus* L. f. (1781). MARTELLI(*2*) devoted ten pages to a discussion of this problem, rejecting *Pandanus tectorius* Soland. (1773) and accepting *P. odoratissimus* L. f. (1781).

WARBURG, at least, had no misconception as to the real author of the binomial when he accepted it. FOSBERG(*3*), nevertheless, in 1941, accepted *Sitodium* "Parkinson" and *Aniotum* "Parkinson" as validly published generic names, as of 1773. There is, of course, no indication whatever in PARKINSON's *Journal* that SOLANDER was the originator of these names; one must search back of the PARKINSON record to determine what happened. In accepting *Sitodium altile* "Parkinson"

2) MARTELLI, U. *"Pandanus odoratissimus"* o *"Pandanus tectorius"*? Nuovo Giorn. Bot. Ital. II. 36: 328-337. 1929.

3) FOSBERG, F. R. Names in *Amaranthus*, *Artocarpus*, and *Inocarpus*. Jour. Wash. Acad. Sci. 31: 93-96. 1941.

and *Aniotum fagiferum* "Parkinson" as validly published in 1773, it
was inevitable that the two specific names involved be accepted in
Artocarpus and *Inocarpus* to replace the currently used but later *Artocarpus communis* J. R. & G. Forst. (1776) and *Artocarpus incisa*
(Thunb.) L. f. (1781) (*Radermachia incisa* Thunb., 1776), and *Inocarpus edulis* J. R. & G. Forst. (1776). FOSBERG's claim that PARK-
INSON's use of these names has priority is clear; the problem is
whether or not valid publication was effected in 1773.

PARKINSON's paper is, in all respects, a curiosity. The writer of
it had no authority to use the SOLANDER names, nor did his brother
STANFIELD, who edited the *Journal*, realize that he was publishing
under SYDNEY PARKINSON's name a series of new technical names
originated by SOLANDER. In this published work of 1773, seven new,
or almost new, generic names appear, as well as forty-six new binomials. We know just what genus or species, in terms of currently
accepted scientific names, is represented in all, or nearly all, of the
cases because of the extant specimens, the excellent PARKINSON illustrations, which were never published, and the ample technical So-
LANDER descriptions which, likewise, were never published, except
in a very few cases.

These specimens and documents are available and were studied by
me in the Department of Botany of the British Museum (Nat. Hist.)
in 1951. The voluminous SOLANDER manuscripts are all listed in the
library catalogue of that institution. Among these, the most important one, from the standpoint of this study, is the beautifully prepared
descriptive flora of Tahiti*(4)*. It is a clear copy, prepared for the
printer, the data being transcribed from the original slips prepared
by SOLANDER while at Tahiti or on the *Endeavour*. There is a photo-
stat copy of this document in the Arnold Arboretum Library, thanks
to the courtesy of Dr. GEORGE TAYLOR of the British Museum (Natural
History) (*cf.* p. 164) (FIGS. 1, 3 and 21).

As noted above, there is not a hint in PARKINSON's volume that
the technical names used by him were originated by SOLANDER. With
the situation as it is, and since there is no botanical arrangement,
no technical descriptions of the new taxa, and no sufficiently definite
data, in any one of the PARKINSON discussions, by which one might
place a new genus in the proper order or class, in the simple Linnaean
system, I feel that most or all of the new names, so casually "published" by PARKINSON, should be ignored. If cited at all, the authority
should be indicated as "[Solander ex] Parkinson".

Very few of the "PARKINSON" new names have found their way
into *Index Kewensis*. Most of those, which have been included, there
appear as SOLANDER species, chiefly from the selected complete So-
LANDER descriptions actually published by SEEMANN in his *Flora Vitiensis* (1865-1873). The 1773 "PARKINSON" use of various SOLANDER
generic and specific names antedates certain J. R. & G. FORSTER names
of 1776 and other FORSTER f. names of 1786.

4) SOLANDER, D. Primitiae Flora Insularum Oceani Pacifici, sive catalogus
Plantarum in Otaheiti, Eimeo, Otaha, Huaheine & Ulaietea A.C. MDCCLXIX,
diebus 13 Aprilis-9 Augusti collectarum, pp. 199-379 [1-5 (index)].

I note that FOSBERG, in his publication of 1941, stated that in a longer paper then prepared (but as yet still unpublished), he had considered the validity of the new names used by PARKINSON in 1773. In a very few cases, there may be reasons for accepting selected PARKINSON entries as more or less validly published; but the vast majority of the new names certainly cannot be accepted, because of the utter lack of botanical data. *Pandanus tectorius, Spondias dulcis, Sitodium altile*, with perhaps a nod in favor of *Aniotum fagiferum*, are about as far as I would be willing to go.

Yet, as Messrs. EXELL and DANDY note, *in lit.*, regarding *Sitodium altile* "Parkinson": while this binomial of 1773 would have some claim to validity as to the specific name, it has to stand or fall on the basis of a generico-specific description. In this category, as to the generic part of the binomial, the data are insufficient, as no generic characters are given and there is no attempt at generic differentiation. It is admittedly a borderline case. PARKINSON, clearly, had no intention of publishing new scientific names.

Among the twenty-four new generic names, originated and characterized in the SOLANDER manuscript, seven were considered by PARKINSON in 1773: *Aniotum* = *Inocarpus* J. R. & G. Forst. (1776); *Chaitea* [*Chaitaea*] = *Tacca* J. R. & G. Forst. (1776); *Galaxa* (changed by SOLANDER to *Alyxia*) = *Alyxia* Banks ex R. Br. (1810) (*Gynopogon* J.R. & G. Forst., 1776); *Sitodium* = *Artocarpus* L. f. (1781); *Telopea* [*Telopaea*] = *Aleurites* J.R. & G. Forst. (1776); *Thespesia* = *Thespesia* Soland. ex Correa (1807); and *Zizyphoides* = *Alphitonia* Reisseck (1840).

The single binomials, under all of these generic names, in the PARKINSON publication are strictly generico-specific ones. In no case, was an attempt made to differentiate the named, but previously never published or characterized, genus involved. Some might be inclined to add the earlier Rumphian names *Casuarina* and even *Pandanus*, because they appear in the PARKINSON work, without proper descriptions, while SOLANDER provided very detailed descriptions for both. *Betonica*, in the PARKINSON document, is an error for *Butonica* Solander. Certainly such "descriptions" as: "the leaves of this plant, baked, are eaten as greens"; "the leaf of this plant is one of the ingredients in their manoe"; "the stalks of this plant they give to their young children to suck"; and "the expressed juice of this plant they drink to intoxicate themselves" are not botanical descriptions, and hence do not validate the binomials accepted by later authors.

Yet, in all cases, we know definitely just what plant species was intended. Between these brief non-descriptive statements to the long discussion of *Sitodium altile*, which occupies nearly one and one-fourth small folio pages (incidentally PARKINSON's illustration of the breadfruit appears without a scientific name in HAWKESWORTH's Voyages 2: pl. 11. 1773), there are various intergrades, from one full line of print to as many as eleven lines; and, in the cases of *Sitodium* and *Cocos*, forty and fifty-five lines. Most of the entries contain three lines or less. Technical botanical characters are always lacking.

Because I have, in the past four or five decades, detected so many overlooked, misinterpreted, little known and, in too many cases perhaps, unlisted technical botanical names, my attitude regarding these fugitive "PARKINSON" names may shock some of that group, of which I am one, who believe that the accepted priority and homonym rules in botanical nomenclature mean what they say. I have reinstated so many of these forgotten names that I suppose my name is anathema among those who object to changes in names of plants with which they are familiar. There are, strangely, taxonomists in this group who do not hesitate to change names in accordance with the code, but who find all kinds of reasons why changes, made by others, should not be accepted. Thus it is, that there are among my critics some who write extensive essays to prove the errors of certain conclusions. I agree with the critics in some cases; but in other cases, I still insist that my original interpretations, which conform to the provisions of the code, were correct. We assume that these colleagues will not be too shocked at my refusal to recognize, as validly published, these "PARKINSON" names of 1773.

With the situation what it is, as to the validity or non-validity of the publication of these "PARKINSON" (or actually SOLANDER) names of 1773, I do not believe that acceptance or non-acceptance of any of them should be left to individual choice. In a very few cases, one may safely interpret a "PARKINSON" (SOLANDER) name by the data which PARKINSON gives, without reference to the extant specimens, the PARKINSON plates, and the extant (but unpublished), complete SOLANDER descriptions.

In the enumeration, which will be found in the next chapter, I have in very many cases quoted all that PARKINSON published about each taxon, but as to his long discussions I have been content to summarize the "botanical" characters, always, more or less casually, included in the original text. It is clear that PARKINSON, who was an artist but not a botanist, did not realize what he was doing when he recorded the SOLANDER generic and specific names, and his brother STANFIELD who had the copy edited was even less informed.

So I suggest that PARKINSON's Journal (1773) be included in the short list of titles which have been officially outlawed, as an addition to our botanical "Index Expurgatorius." Those, who believe in absolute priority, will accept certain "PARKINSON" names; those, who may be ranked among the conservatives, will reject most or all of them.

I have divided the binomials considered by PARKINSON in 1773 into two series. This I have done deliberately. The first, immediately following this section, consists of the Linnaean binomials used by PARKINSON (*after* SOLANDER), including those correctly and those incorrectly interpreted by SOLANDER. The second list (p. 346 - 363) includes the new names, mostly unlisted in botanical literature, proposed by SOLANDER and incidentally but very inadequately "published" by PARKINSON in 1773. The actual identity of each is indicated.

Chapter IX

THE LINNAEAN BINOMIALS
USED BY PARKINSON

The new SOLANDER generic and specific names, which PARKINSON so casually considered in 1773, are individually discussed below (p. 346). If cited at all, they should, in my judgment, be indicated as "[Solander ex] Parkinson". In a few cases, PARKINSON used binomials that SOLANDER did not include in the final copy of his manuscript, most of which appear on the slips prepared by SOLANDER on the *Endeavour* which were available to PARKINSON. For one reason or another SOLANDER changed certain names when the final draft was prepared in London, an example of which is *Galaxa* on the original slip which PARKINSON used, changed to *Alyxia* in the final copy. There are also certain errors in transcription, such as *Betonica* for *Butonica*, and *Erythoina* for *Erythrina*. In many cases SOLANDER correctly interpreted and applied Linnaean binomials, but in others he misinterpreted and misapplied them, as do many taxonomists up to the present day. It is not so strange, perhaps, that the younger FORSTER accepted practically all of the SOLANDER misinterpretations (*see* p. 206).

In the following list, the Linnaean binomials from the SOLANDER manuscript appearing in the PARKINSON paper are considered. Where no comment is made, it is apparent that SOLANDER's interpretations were correct as the various species are understood by modern taxonomists. The species were all from Tahiti.

Abrus precatorius L. p. 63. — Man-introduced from the west.

Arundo bambos sensu [Soland. ex] Parkins. p. 39, non L. = *Bambos arundo* Soland. ex Seem. Fl. Vit. 323. 1873, *nom. in syn.,* sphalm. = *Schizostachyum glaucifolium* (Rupr.) Munro. — In the unpublished SOLANDER manuscript the description appears as "*Arundo Bambos*" on page 217. SEEMANN inadvertently reversed the order of the generic and specific names. In the margin of the manuscript is pencilled "specimen not found"; *i. e.,* SEEMANN did not find a BANKS & SOLANDER specimen in the British Museum herbarium.

Arum esculentum L. p. 63 = *Colocasia esculenta* (L.) Schott. — Man-introduced from the west.

Calophyllum inophyllum L. p. 39. — An Indo-Malaysian strand tree, extending to Polynesia.

Casuarina equisetifolia [as *equisefolia*] L. Amoen. Acad. 4: 143. 1754; [Soland. ex] Parkins. Jour. 44. 1773, *nom., nota*; J. R. & G. Forst. Char. Gen. 103. pl. 52. 1776. — LINNAEUS did not characterize the genus (or species) in 1754. In the appendix under "Sin-

gulares" he merely listed "*Casuarina equisefolia* 3-57". The specific
name was corrected to *equisetifolia* in Amoen. Acad. ed. 2, 4: 143.
1788. The "3-57" is a reference to *Casuarina litorea* Rumph. Herb.
Amb. 3: 86. pl. 57. 1743, where there is an ample description and an
excellent illustration. This is, therefore, an intermediate between
a legitimately published generic name *(Casuarina)* and a generico-
specific binomial. If this be not acceptable to taxonomic perfectionists, then the remedy is to accept *Casuarina* Adans. Fam. 2: 481. 1763
as to the generic name and its authority, and *C. equisetifolia* J. R. &
G. Forst. (1776) for the binomial. As PARKINSON indicated no botanical characters, in 1773, when he used the name of SOLANDER's
proposed genus and species, I do not accept this as valid publication.
He merely mentioned certain wood characters and uses. It is an interesting commentary that LINNAEUS, SOLANDER, and the FORSTERS
should all have selected the Rumphian group name, and that all of
them should have changed his trivial name *litorea* to *equisetifolia*.
Here the FORSTERS undoubtedly were familiar with the SOLANDER
manuscript. In PARKINSON's *Journal* the generic name *Casuarina*
is, by error, curiously associated with the Tahitian local name *E toa*,
rather than with the specific name *equisetifolia*. An Indo-Malaysian
strand species extending to Polynesia, in some places occurring also
inland in light sandy soil. There is a bare possibility of its having
been man-introduced on some of the more eastern islands of Polynesia.

Cocos nucifera L. p. 47. — Man-introduced from the west.

Convolvulus brasiliensis L. p. 38 = *Ipomoea pes-caprae* (L.) R.
Br. — One of the very few species of naturally pantropic strand
plants; by some placed as a variety of *I. pes-caprae* (L.) R. Br., but
even then credited to both hemispheres.

Cordia sebestena sensu [Soland. ex] Parkins. p. 37, non L. =
Cordia subcordata Lam. — Curiously SOLANDER's misinterpretation of the Linnaean American species likewise misled FORSTER f.
(Prodr. 18. 1786), who also accepted *C. sebestena* L. for the Tahitian
species. An Indo-Malaysian-Polynesian strand tree.

Dioscorea alata L. p. 50. — Man-introduced from the west.
Curiously, many erroneously insist that this, the greater yam, was established in tropical America in pre-Columbian times. There is not
a shred of evidence to support such a belief. It was introduced about
the middle of the 16*th* century, although the African *D. cayanensis*
Lam. had been established about half a century earlier; the latter was
deliberately introduced to provide food for slaves. The large tubers
of the greater yam, weighing sometimes 50 to 60 pounds, were very
resistant to decay. Thus they became very important as food on long
voyages such as those early trips of the Malays to Madagascar and East
Africa. Naturally, the Polynesians carried the species to the Pacific
islands. As Mr. BURKILL has shown, this Asiatic food plant declined in
popularity after the sweet potato was introduced into the Old World
tropics. If one of the theorizers should visit the Atlantic coast of Pan-

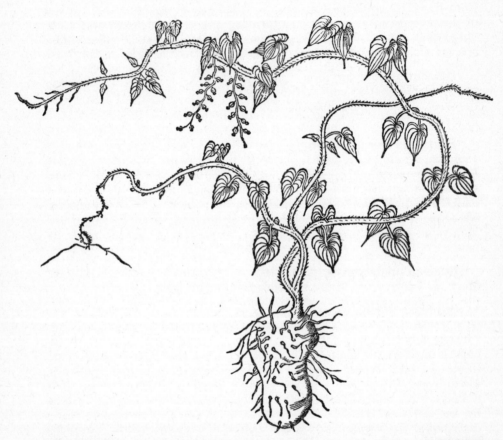

TEXT FIGURE 19. — *Dioscorea* sp., a yam established in Brazil in colonial times.
— Reproduced from the *Historiae Naturalis Brasiliae* (1648) by PISO & MARCGRAVE
who give the following native names: *cara brasiliensibus, inhame, camaranbaya,
quingombo,* and *inhame de S. Thome,* indicating that the yam which originated in
S. Asia may have reached Brazil via Africa. Dr. BERNICE SCHUBERT suggests that
this species is possibly *D. cayanensis* Lam. This is an African species and the first
Dioscorea introduced into tropical America, by Negro slaves.

ama, where, according to Dr. PAUL ALLEN, the greater yam is now thoroughly naturalized, he might easily jump to the conclusion that this species is a native of America!

Dodonaea viscosa Jacq. p. 67. — A pantropic strand plant, in various regions also occurring inland.

Dracaena terminalis L. p. 38 = *Cordyline fruticosa* (L.) A. Cheval. (*C. terminalis* Kunth). — SOLANDER recognized six forms of this species in Tahiti. It was formerly much more extensively cultivated than now, being an important food plant in early times. This species was probably an early introduction from islands to the west.

Dracontium polyphyllum sensu [Soland. ex] Parkins. p. 47, non L. = *Amorphophallus campanulatus* Blume — Man-introduced from the west. Here again FORSTER f. accepted SOLANDER's misinterpretation of the Linnaean species.

Erythrina corallodendron sensu [Soland. ex] Parkins. Jour. 43 (sphalm. *Erythoina*), non L. = *E. indica* Lam. = *E. variegata* L. var. *orientalis* (L.) Merr. — Here PARKINSON not only misspelled the generic name but also by error associated it with the native one *E atae*, not with the specific one. FORSTER f. in 1786 accepted SOLANDER's misinterpretation of the Linnaean species. An Indo-Malaysian-Polynesian strand tree, in various places also occurring inland.

Eugenia malaccensis L. p. 40 = *Syzygium malaccense* (L.) Merr. & Perr. — Man-introduced from the west.

Gardenia florida sensu [Soland. ex] Parkins. p. 37, non L. = *G. taitensis* DC. — Here FORSTER f. was misled by SOLANDER's erroneous identification (Prodr. 20. 1786). SOLANDER said that it occurred on slopes and that it was also planted near houses. It occurs in other Pacific Islands such as the Marquesas, Samoa, Fiji, Tuamotu, Mangareva, Ellice, and Austral groups, Tonga and Rarotonga. It is a Polynesian endemic and was clearly distributed within the region by the early Polynesians themselves, even as they introduced and distributed the ornamental shrub *Hibiscus rosa-sinensis* L. from the west; local names, *tiare, tiare tahiti, tialo, tiale tofe,* and *tiale feutu.*

Gossypium religiosum sensu Parkins. p. 42 (an Linnaeus ?) = *G. taitense* Parl. Sp. Cot. 39. pl. 6. fig. A. 1866; Watt, Cot. Pl. 248. pl. 43. 1907. — PARKINSON merely said for *E wawei*: "This is a species of cotton of which they have not yet found out the use". This is a very significant statement. It might be interpreted to mean that the cotton found by the first explorers of Tahiti may have been man-introduced, possibly at about the same time the sweet potato was brought in; but if so, the early navigator failed to bring back the techniques of spinning thread and weaving cloth. I do not think we need consider more than what may have happened in previous geologic times, when the Antarctic regions, in places at least, supported a luxuriant vegetation, perhaps in the Tertiary or even earlier when the genus

De YCHCAXIHVITL, seu Gossipio. Cap. LXXII.

HERBA est *Ychcaxihuitl*, Gossipium à nostris nuncupata, quæ et huic nouæ Hispaniæ frequentissima, & cuius per singulos annos messis fit vberrima. Nascitur in calidis, humidisque, cultis præcipuè, locis. Germina rusa, atque epota ex aqua, atque epota ex aqua, mirè resistere puncturis Scorpionum, Viperarum, cæterorumque animalium venenatorum. caulis videtur frigidus, succusque, & adstringens. & vlceribus medetur leuigatus, & admotus. folia verò glutinosæ naturæ.

Gossipium Europæ notissimum, cuius descriptio vberior extat apud Matthiolum, Herbarium Lugdunense, & alios Botanicos.

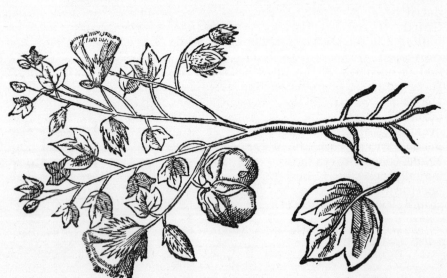

Gossypium was attaining its world wide distribution, to explain the situation. STEBBINS has suggested that the circum-Pacific generic range might have been attained in pre-glacial times via the Arctic regions but considering the distinctly larger number of *Gossypium* species that now occur in the southern Pacific region, as compared with those of the northern Pacific, I would consider the southern connection more plausible; and then we should consider the evidence that tends to support the general idea that there are in the Pacific Islands certain floristic elements that reached these islands from ancient Antarctica. SOLANDER (MS. p. 274) gave the local name as *ewavai*, recorded the species from Tahiti, Huaheine, Ulaitea, and Otaha, and provided a detailed description in which he characterized the calyx as: "albidus, monophyllus, urceolatus, exteriori duplo brevior, *quinquifidus. Lacinae subulatae acuminatae, longitudine tubi*" (the italics are mine). I have emphasized a part of the quoted descriptive phrase to point out a problem raised by WATT*(1)*, whose taxonomic treatment of *Gossypium*, which even the geneticists, who disagree with his system and who reduce a great many of his species to synonymy, admit "will always remain the starting point for taxonomic studies in *Gossypium*." In the treatment of *G. taitense* Parl. which J. B. HUTCHINSON *et al.(2)* reduced without question to *G. hirsutum* L. var. *punctatum* (Schum.) J. B. Hutchinson *et al.*, WATT probably correctly cited a J. R. & G. FORSTER collection under *G. taitense* Parl., but he cited a BANKS and SOLANDER collection from the same island under *G. purpurascens* Poir.; and POIRET's species is also reduced by J. B. HUTCHINSON *et al.* to *G. hirsutum* var. *punctatum*. Strictly *G. taitense* Parl. has *very slender elongated calyx lobes* as indicated in the above quoted passage, while *G. purpurascens* Poir. has *cupshaped, truncate or undulate calyces;* and most curiously I can find no mention of the calyx characters in the ample description of *G. hirsutum* L. or of its variety *punctatum* (Schum.) J. B. Hutchinson *et al. (op. cit.* 40-43). Somehow I feel that calyx characters are perhaps as important as are those of other floral and fruit parts in evaluating and delimiting species or minor taxa in this particular genus. In any case, the WATT identification of the BANKS and SOLANDER collection (as figured by him; it is *not* the form that SOLANDER actually described), may well indicate that there existed more than one form of *Gossypium* at Tahiti in the early 1770's. *G. religiosum* seems clearly to be one of the numerous hybrids between New World

---

1) WATT, G. The Wild and Cultivated Cotton Plants of the World. i-xiv. 1-406. pl. 1-53. 1907.

2) HUTCHINSON, J. B., SILOW, R. A., and STEPHENS, S. G. The Evolution of *Gossypium* and the Differentiation of the Cultivated Cottons. i-xi, 1-160, pl. 1-9. fig. 1-10. 1947.

TEXT FIGURE 20 (*opposite*). — An American cotton species, *Gossypium hirsutum* L. — As discussed in detail on p. 335-342, *Gossypium* has a natural pantropic distribution. Native species were domesticated independently in both hemispheres at early dates. HERNANDEZ recognized this figure as a species of *Gossypium* under the Nahuatl name ycheaxvitl. — From F. HERNANDEZ's *Nova Plantarum . . . Mexicanorum Historiae* (Romae, 1651).

and Old World cotton species. This hybrid may well have reached Tahiti, through the agency of man, before the long voyages of the Polynesians had ceased.

Miss D. HILLCOAT of the herbarium staff, British Museum (N. H.), kindly reexamined the Tahiti *Gossypium* specimens for me, and reported that the FORSTER specimen conforms to *G. taitense* Parl. as originally described and illustrated and as verified by Sir GEORGE WATT; but that the BANKS and SOLANDER specimen has calyces with three short obtuse to subacute lobes and two elongated caudate-acuminate ones, thus not agreeing with the calyx characters of *G. taitense* Parl. nor with WATT's description and illustration of *G. purpurascens* Poir. This specimen is in fact, as to its calyx characters, intermediate between *G. taitense* Parl. as illustrated by both PARLATORE and by WATT, and *G. purpurascens* Poir. as illustrated by WATT. It actually has the appearance of being of hybrid origin.

I casually mention the fact that in the first two decades of the last century the missionaries introduced various other types in their attempt to establish a cotton industry in Tahiti, as detailed by WILLIAM ELLIS in his *Polynesian Researches* (1829). I am neither a geneticist nor a cotton specialist, but the four systems of classification for the species of this one genus within the present century, to say nothing of that of WETTSTEIN, are so radically different from each other, that a mere *Gossypium* tyro is lost in the maze, and, without access to historical collections, is not in a position to judge the work of others. These four systems are those of WATT (1907), J. B. HUTCHINSON *et al.* mentioned above (1947), that of HARLAND *(3)* (1939), and that of ROBERTY *(4)* (1938; 1942-46; 1952). Each of these "systems" could be subjected to severe criticism of one type or another; yet it should be conceded that each author or group of authors attempted to do the best that could be done with what was available. J. B. HUTCHINSON *et al.* shrug off ROBERTY's work because "he failed to give sufficient weight to genetic evidence and his arrangement cuts across well established natural groupings in several important respects"; I could violently disagree with ROBERTY because of the inordinate number of varieties he has proposed. Frankly I suppose that it is about as useless to attempt to apply the trinomial system here as it is in the case of the cultivated forms of *Musa, Cucurbita, Malus, Citrus, Pyrus, Brassica,* and any other large genus (or small ones like *Zea* for example) where man has deliberately interfered with nature by selecting and perpetuating various of the better strains for his own benefit. Yet this HUTCHINSON, SILOW and STEPHENS treatment is clearly subject to much more severe criticism than the three other attempts. The closing paragraph is, in places, utterly fantastic, apparently an attempt being made to justify a pre-conceived theory. *Theoretically,* what they seriously propose is possible, but *practically,* it is utterly impossible; for most certainly, no matter how pleasing their conclusions may be to the extreme diffusionists and the neo-geographers, no advanced Indian peoples made the long trip across the north Pacific, missing all the Pacific and Malaysian islands, *direct* (or for that matter indirectly) from India to South America two or three thousand years ago; this simply could not be done! In claiming or inferring that early civilized man did introduce an Asiatic cotton species into America, the simple fact *that not a single Asiatic cultivated food plant made the journey* is overlooked; and food was infinitely more important 2000 to 3000 years ago than mere cotton! The Manila-Acapulco route developed from 1565, was in my opinion too late for consideration and at that time (1565, and later) this certainly was no possible explanation of the Polynesian distribution of the *Gossypium* types found in Tahiti a couple of hundred years later; by the time of the indicated date the long voyages of the Polynesians had largely ceased. When HUTCHINSON *et al.* stated that all the available evidence supported the idea that the domestication and distribution

3) HARLAND, S. C. The Genetics of Cotton. 1-193. 1939.
4) ROBERTY, G. Hypothèses sur l'origine et les migrations des cotonniers cultivés et notes sur les cotonniers sauvages. Candollea 7: 297-360. 1938; Gossypiorum revisionis tentamen. *op. cit.* 9: 19-103. pl. 1. 1942; 10: 345-398. 1946; 13: 9-165. 1952.

of crop plants was "intimately bound up with the origin and spread of civilization," this may safely be accepted with limitations, but that "civilized man, his domestic animals and his crop plants has grown from a single root and spread to the New World by trans-Pacific migration," is not true; this is rather a revival of G. ELLIOT SMITHism. This idea is repeated, *op. cit.* 76: "Only one alternative remains, that they [cotton seeds] were carried across the Pacific by man among the seeds of his crop plants and with the tools of his civilization." Nobody has yet proved that any single basic cultivated food plant or any domestic animal (other than the common dog) was common to the two hemispheres (including temperate and tropical zones) previous to the voyages of COLUMBUS and of MAGELLAN; the common gourd, yes, but it was never an important food plant. The pre-Columbian agriculture in America was based on strictly native American plants and animals, not one of which, other than the common gourd, was known in either Europe or Asia, until after the expansion of the European colonizing nations beginning in the closing decade of the fifteenth century. I do not count the Old World coconut which had somehow reached the west coast of Panama and northern South America (it is everywhere now in tropical regions of abundant rainfall, but this was not the case in most of tropical America and apparently also in much of tropical Africa at the time of the Spanish and Portuguese expansion). The common gourd *(Lagenaria)* which was also pantropic in distribution is not basically a food plant (except for certain forms which are about as exciting a food and probably as nourishing as a boiled cucumber). I maintain that three cultivated plant species, *only one of which was more or less universal in cultivation in the warmer parts of Asia, Africa, and America* (and this was not basically a food plant), is absolutely insufficient evidence on which to base such sweeping statements as those above referred to.

Yet in justice to Dr. HUTCHINSON, with whom I have had some interesting correspondence, and to whom I sent a copy of my comments on this *Gossypium* statement, I wish to make one point clear. Referring to my statement regarding the extreme diffusionist school he says: "May I add that I have been somewhat disturbed at the way in which diffusionists tend to run my own diffusion theory [regarding cotton] a good deal further than I think it should possibly go." He objects to STEBBINS' idea that the transmission of *Gossypium* could have been via the Arctic regions as this would involve a humid climate and "if you want to prove that a wild *Gossypium* spread by natural means, you *must* first show that the area over which it spread was desert at the time." This I do not accept, for all over the world we even now do have in all continental and large insular areas the long alternating wet and dry seasons and the associated constantly wet regions (such as East Java *versus* West Java). A long dry season of six months or so is all that is needed but naturally cotton would be out of place in constantly wet regions such as in West Java; and these contrasting regions occur in Africa, Australia, Asia, North and South America, and here and there in all of Malaysia and among the Pacific Islands. And there is every reason to believe that in previous geologic times here and there corresponding conditions prevailed.

Gossypium is a genus of natural pantropic distribution, and certain native species were domesticated *independently in both hemispheres* at an early date in the development of civilizations. To pose a simple question: do those who stress the chromosome counts insist that in nature the doubling of the chromosomes in any single genus occurred but once? The answer is found in the published record, unless perchance this or that published record was based on a miscount; and a possible miscount cannot be proved, for in most cases no voucher specimens were preserved by the counters. Claims have been made that in the latest published chromosome atlas, a compilation, not more than ten percent of the chromosome counts associated with binomials could be proved to be correct as to the cited binomials, simply because no voucher specimens were preserved. The herbarium technique really has some very obvious advantages.

My conclusion is that in *Gossypium* we must go back to Tertiary times for the true explanation as to when its species attained more or less universal distribution in the warmer parts of the world. In what are now the Arctic and the Antarctic regions, both areas were characterized at times since the Eocene by having typical tropical and subtropical conditions, with, in places, highly developed vegetation as is proved by the presence of coal deposits and from the paleobotanical records. These conditions would permit the migrations of plants that now have no living representatives in vast areas to the north and to the south. Consider, for a moment, the very impressive list of genera now known only from limited areas in eastern Asia and similarly limited areas in eastern North America; curiously, these are now both cotton growing areas. LEO WIENER, knowing no botany, solved the *Gossypium* problem very easily: there were no American species, which probably no taxonomist or geneticist will accept. The Arabs or WIENER's favorite Mandingos introduced *Gossypium* from Africa perhaps 200 years before COLUMBUS discovered the West Indies — it is as simple as that if one wishes to accept WIENER as a reliable authority, which I do not.

The latest summary is that by Dr. LI*(5)*. His maps bring out the condition very graphically indeed. The evidence is so strong that it simply cannot be ignored, because fifty-six different genera in many families of plants are involved, wherein numerous very characteristic small genera are known only from restricted areas in eastern North America and eastern Asia, such as *Liriodendron, Halesia, Carya, Epigaea, Zizania, Saururus, Buckleya, Pyrularia, Podophyllum, Menispermum, Illicium, Astilbe, Itea, Hamamelis, Gymnocladus, Cladrastis, Wisteria, Apios, Pieris, Shortia, Campsis, Catalpa, Croomia* and others; and in their most remarkable generic distribution it is really needless to state that man was not in any manner involved. In addition to this very striking north temperate zone distribution, there was perhaps an even more impressive south temperate zone, one involving the floras of South America, New Zealand, Tasmania, Australia and South Africa. Most of the groups involved have no representatives north of the equator and there is very much evidence to the effect that Antarctica was the source of many elements of the flora of what is now Polynesia. Then, there is a third distribution going back to early times (millions of years, before man was a factor), for a number of genera have representatives in tropical America and in the tropical parts of the Old World, but no living representatives in present north or south temperate zones, or in the Pacific Islands. Yet, in some cases, fossil forms of these genera have been found far north of the tropics. Thus it is my belief that more than chromosome numbers must be taken into consideration. No one should ignore the importance of considering *all* factors, when an attempt is made to explain the present distribution of the recognized representatives of this or that natural group (genus), no matter whether or not species of economic importance (or those actually cultivated by man) are involved. ASA GRAY, in 1857 and 1859, first elaborated the suggestion that there were striking similarities between the floras of eastern North America and eastern Asia.

In the same letter referred to above is a dissertation on the problem of early versus late distribution of cultivated economic plants. DR. HUTCHINSON does not accept any conclusions and yet neither he (nor anybody else) can disprove them. To think in terms of *genera* rather than of *species* proves little. He lists *Cucurbita, Phaseolus, Gossypium, Solanum, Amaranthus, Canavalia,* and *Ipomoea* as all being genera common to both hemispheres in pre-Columbian times, which is true *(6)*; these happen to contain a few species of originally limited distribution that man has domesticated here or there. But there may be a couple of thousand additional genera which have native species in both hemispheres with the geographic distribution of the individual species of which man has had nothing whatever to do. One is too apt to forget about the significance of the old Portuguese trade route that continued from 1500 to 1665 via eastern Brazil to Goa on the Malabar coast of India thence to Malacca, Amboina, Canton, Macao, Formosa and Japan. With a great many ships following this route year after year for over a century and a half, a great deal happened, in this period, in plant

5) LI, H. L. Floristic Relations between Eastern Asia and Eastern North America. Trans. Am. Philos. Sec. II. 42 (2): 371-429. fig. 1-56. 1952.

6) *Cucurbita* must be eliminated, as the cultigens in this genus were introduced into India from eastern Brazil by the Portuguese following 1500. This explanation is long overdue, for the genus is strictly an American one except as various cultigens have been distributed in the Old World by modern man.

distribution, including economic species and weeds which traveled in both directions. This is when and how the American species of *Cucurbita* reached the Malabar coast — Brazil to Goa — *direct*. It is nothing to get excited about, even if this apparently anomalous distribution did mystify COGNIAUX in 1881, and has continued to confuse various theorists who simply do not know the history of exploration. When a non-botanical neo-geographer claims that certain American weeds (chiefly those of Brazilian origin) were first described from specimens collected in India, this is true, but when he states that this proved that these plants (all weeds and ruderals) were universally distributed long before the Europeans reached the Orient, this is an absurd claim.

This was the rock on which the short-lived STONOR-ANDERSON theory of maize in India in pre-Columbian times was thoroughly wrecked within two years after their paper was published (*see* p. 261 and *infra*). To list *Phaseolus* is meaningless, as the American and Asiatic cultivated species are totally different from each other. The footless *Gossypium* controversy may continue for many years to come. To list *Solanum* is meaningless, this being a very large genus in the tropics of both hemispheres, but the few native American cultivated species, such as *S. tuberosum* L. are so totally different from the few Asiatic cultivated ones, such as the brinjal or egg plant (*S. melongena* L.), that the non-taxonomist may well ask why they should be placed in the same genus. *Amaranthus* is of world wide distribution with many indigenous (and endemic) species in North and South America, Africa, Australia and Eurasia; it includes many weeds of modern distribution. The case of the two cultigens claimed and "proved" as common to America and Asia since very early times, so enthusiastically accepted by ANDERSON in 1952 is, as I see it, to be explained as due to the long overlooked ancient Portuguese trade route (as is the Chinese peanut to which ANDERSON refers). The *Amaranthus* case is one of which we have not as yet heard the last. One does not deny the specific identities of the two American and Asiatic taxa among the grain amaranths, but the point at issue is when the seeds were transmitted from America or Asia. There is no reason to believe that this distribution took place before 1500. *Canavalia* is like the other genera here discussed, a group of natural pantropic distribution. Indeed one species occurs back of sandy beaches all over the tropics (*C. rosea* DC.). There are two generally recognized cultivated species, neither of great importance. *C. ensiformis* (L.) DC., possibly native of India, and the very large fruited *C. gladiata* (Jacq.) DC. which may have originated in America, but neither was pantropic in distribution in pre-Magellan times. The whole group is very badly in need of revision. To invoke generic distribution here is just as meaningless as it is in the last case. *Ipomoea* is a large genus with indigenous and endemic representatives in both hemispheres, and also a considerable number of universally distributed weeds that owe their present ranges to post-Columbian man. There is only one important cultigen, *I. batatas* (L.) Lam. This is possibly of American origin and through the agency of man reached Polynesia in pre-Magellan times extending as far to the west, through the agency of the Polynesians themselves to New Zealand by the twelfth or thirteenth century, and even reaching parts of Papuasia. But it apparently did not reach Malaysia proper, China, or India until after its independent introduction by the Spanish from Mexico to the Philippines in the last half of the sixteenth century. BURKILL has most effectively demonstrated that all of its local names in Malaysia are borrowed or descriptive ones, and of course *camote*, its universally used name in the Philippines, came from Mexico with the plant itself via the early Acapulco-Manila galleons. It was deliberately introduced from the Philippines into Fukien Province, China as a famine food as Dr. LAUFER has proved. Yet PIGAFETTA in 1521 definitely recorded it from Guam, Cebu in the Philippines and from the Moluccas. . . . LEO WIENER in 1920 proved to his satisfaction that this species was a native of Africa, but while he had a remarkable knowledge of philology, his botanical information was very faulty and is not to be trusted (*see* p. 371). Yet, there are good reasons to believe that he may have been correct in his expressed belief that this species originated in Africa; but we have no proofs as yet.

LAUFER(7) has beautifully covered the situation for China, drawing his data from the Chinese, Korean, Japanese and other oriental records. He emphasized the fact that from these oriental records the economic plants of American origin first appeared in eastern Asia in the latter half of the sixteenth and the beginnings of the seventeenth centuries. He adds that we find the same story in Siam, India, Persia, and Europe, and emphasized the fact that these American plants were entirely unknown in Eurasia previous to 1492. He concluded that none of the Eurasian cultigens was found in America previous to that date. It is recommended that this paper be read and pondered by all who strenuously support the opposite views. Here spoke an authority who was not only an eminent Sinologist, with a remarkable command of the early published literature of eastern Asia, but also one whose knowledge of the botany of the crop plants we may all respect.

It is of interest to note that some geneticists are by no means in accord with the HUTCHINSON, SILOW and STEPHENS theory regarding this theoretical *Gossypium* miscegenation, whereby an Asiatic species somehow got across the Pacific and promptly hybridized with an American one. It is scarcely necessary to discuss this here, but in very thoroughly dissecting the STONOR-ANDERSON idea that maize occurred in Assam long before the European trans-Pacific and trans-Atlantic explorers reached India, MANGELSDORF and OLIVER not only effectively pricked the STONOR-ANDERSON maize balloon, but also with equal effectiveness dealt with the HUTCHINSON, SILOW and STEPHENS *Gossypium* hypothesis. In the MANGELSDORF(8) treatment of *The Origin of New World Cultivated Cotton and Its Bearing on Asiatic Maize* (p. 286-287) the HUTCHINSON, SILOW and STEPHENS *Gossypium* theory is as thoroughly discredited as is the STONOR and ANDERSON Asiatic maize idea.

Guettarda speciosa L. p. 39. — An Indo-Malaysian-Polynesian strand species.

Hernandia ovigera L. p. 44. — I believe *H. peltata* Meisn. to be a synonym of the Linnaean species. In SOLANDER's detailed but unpublished description the leaves are described (in part) as "ovata, acuta, obtuse cordata juniore et majora peltata," indicating peltate and non-peltate leaves on the same plant. An Indo-Malaysian-Polynesian strand species, in some places occurring inland.

Hibiscus rosa-sinensis L. p. 42. — A pre-Magellan man-introduced ornamental species from the islands to the West.

Loranthus stelis sensu [Soland. ex] Parkins. p. 38, non L. = *L. forsterianus* Schult. = *Amylotheca forsteriana* Danser, Bull. Jard. Bot. Buitenz. III. 10: 301. 1929; Verh. Akad. Wetensch. Amsterd. Afd. Nat. (Tweede Sect.) 29 (6): 37. 1933, cum syn. — Here FORSTER f. accepted SOLANDER's misapplication of the specific name for this strictly Polynesian species.

Melastoma malabathricum sensu [Soland. ex] Parkins. p. 39, non L. = *M. denticulatum* Labill. — The SOLANDER misinterpretation of the Linnaean species was also accepted by FORSTER f.

Morinda citrifolia L. p. 38. — An Indo-Malaysian-Polynesian strand plant, perhaps in Polynesia in part man-distributed.

Morus papyrifera L. p. 44 = *Broussonetia papyrifera* (L.)

7) LAUFER, B. The American Plant Migration. Sci. Monthly 28: 239-251. 1929.

8) MANGELSDORF, P. C. and OLIVER, D. L. Whence Came Maize to Asia? Bot. Mus. Leafl. Harv. Univ. 14: 263-291. 1951.

Vent. — Man-introduced from the West. This plant has a very interesting history. It was a native of eastern Asia, extending from Korea and Japan to Formosa and Hainan, in most of the Provinces of China from Hopei in the north to Kwangtung in the south, westward to Szechuan; also in Indo-China, Siam and Burma. It was unquestionably introduced into Malaysia by man and from Malaysia into the most distant Pacific Islands and to New Zealand by the Polynesians. RUMPHIUS knew it from Celebes before 1680 (*Frutex lintearius* Rumph. Herb. Amb. 4: 114. pl. 53. 1743). It is no longer included in descriptive floras of New Zealand, being apparently extinct there, and has largely disappeared from Malaysia; some recent collections in Polynesian islands bear the note "nearly extinct." Yet judging from the accounts of early explorers, it was apparently in early times the most carefully cultivated species among the few cultivated ones in Tahiti, New Zealand, and in other parts of Polynesia. It was highly prized, because from its bast the best tapa cloth was made. One may safely assume that it was once important in Malaysia before tapa cloth was replaced by woven fabrics. RUMPHIUS noted that in Celebes some 270 years ago it was used for making a paper-like cloth (*i.e.*, tapa). The species is as rapidly disappearing in Malaysia as it is in Polynesia. There is no record of its ever having been found in the Philippines.

Musa bihai sensu (Soland. ex) Parkins. p. 47, non L. = *M. troglodytarum* L. (*M. uranoscopos* Colla, 1820, non Lour., 1790; *M. fehi* Bertero, 1862). *See* MACDANIELS, Bishop Mus. Bull. 190: 1-56. pl. 1-10. fig. 1-15. 1947 (syn. p. 20). — The Linnaean species was based wholly on *Musa uranoscopos* Rumph. Herb. Amb. 5: 137. pl. 61. fig. 2. 1747, one of its striking characters being its strictly erect, not pendulous, fruiting racemes. PARKINSON said that there were four varieties of this in Tahiti. When LOUREIRO adopted the binomial *Musa uranoscopos* Lour. in 1790, while he took his specific name from RUMPHIUS, his description was wholly based on what proves to be the very different *M. coccinea* Andr. (1799), and thus LOUREIRO's binomial replaces that of ANDREWS. Just where *Musa troglodytarum* L. originated is not certain, but the Polynesians distributed it all over their culture area (except the low islands and New Zealand), and they, like the Malay peoples of the Moluccas, may well have secured it from the Papuasian region which extended eastward and southeastward to Fiji and New Caledonia. The form RUMPHIUS so clearly described in 1747 is still to be found in gardens in Amboina. It occurs also in the Kei Islands, in New Guinea, in the Solomon Islands, New Hebrides, New Caledonia and on the high islands of Polynesia eastward to Hawaii, the Marquesas and Mangareva. It probably originated in the southwestern Pacific region, and is undoubtedly a man-introduced species in the Pacific Islands.

Musa paradisiaca L. p. 47. — Man-introduced from the West. As interpreted by SOLANDER mss. this included 23 forms recognized by native names in Tahiti, including both the banana and the plantain. These are considered by most authors as belonging to two species,

Fig. B. Nux magnitudine parum aucta longitudina-
liter dissecta ut loculamentum lunatum ap-
pareat.

POLYGAMIA

MONOECIA.

paradisiaca. MUSA. Linn. Sp. pl. 1477.1.
     α.) Maya.
     β. Faï.   } Insularibus Oceani Pacifici.
Hab. in Otaheite, Huaheine, Ulaietea. Otaha. et
     Ohiteroa.

Inter Principes Regni vegetabilis locum certissime
merentur Musæ; si vel formam externam con-
temples vel utilitatem consideres illas invenies
fere omnibus plantis palmam præripientes. Et
expertissimus nostram in Insulis Oceani pacifici
cultam, Musarum nobilissimam pronunciare
Fructus Musæ nullibi sapidiores (a nobis gusta-
ti) vel pro quavis occasione melius adaptati
sunt.
Utut Incolis utilissima hæc est planta, ita etiam
illorum cura magis commissa fuit quam ulla
alia, unde Varietates numerosissima pullula-
verunt; ex his alia dulcissimos gerunt fructus
quos crudos uti bellaria comedere placet, alia
probent fructus quos asare vel coquere opor-
tet et tunc ipso pane nequaquam inferiores
sunt. Diversis anni temporibus diversa varietates suos maturescunt, ut fere semper in
promtu suat; omnes vero cultura esse probles
vadet defectus seminum, illas itaque in species dispescere vanum erit, in duas autem famili-
as omnes facile subdividi possunt, et hoc, con-
sensu omnium Incolarum. Primaria familia
ab Incolis vocatur Maya, altera Faï; prior —
suppeditat fructus dulciores, posterior austeri-
ores et hi vix nisi cocti ad cibum vocantur.
Varietates maxime notabiles sequentes sunt:

α.) Maya.	β.) Faï
1. Orhea.	15. Mata matahi.
2. Ehuerao.	16. Ohai.
3. E Tulita.	17. Taapeape.
4. E Tivahi.	18. Mamala.
5. Aletoa.	19. Etapua.
6. Aaa.	20. Ovori.
7. Aivau.	21. Erenrai.
8. Ehumalai.	22. E Tawhili whili.
9. Ehuapoto.	23. Palahatu
10. Etorho.	β.) Faï.
11. Tayo urha.	1. E pautea.
12. E pute pute.	2. Ove.
13. Epauta.	3. Erhu rheva.
14. Pou rhoini.	4. Oa iti.
	5. E whata

Obs. Septendecim anteriores Maya, et duas prores
Faï;

M. sapientum L., and *M. paradisiaca* L.; but the geneticists have now demonstrated that all the myriads of forms of the two supposedly distinct Linnaean species are actually hybrids of *M. acuminata* Colla and *M. balbisiana* Colla. This is interesting, but we still have to consider the Linnaean binomials. Some emphatic claims have been made that the plantain occurred in South America before the arrival of the Spaniards, but if so it must have been very local. If present I suspect that it may have been introduced shortly before the Spaniards reached Peru. SAUER in 1952 says dogmatically that the case for the plantain being in tropical America in pre-Columbian times is as good as that for the pre-Magellan trans-Pacific carriage of cotton, the gourd, sweet potato, and the coconut. Unfortunately, he did not prove this bald assertion. If the Polynesians did reach the west coast of South America in pre-Columbian times, which seems manifestly to have been the case, the plantain would certainly have been taken along, it being one of the most easily transported plants. The very recent report of a fossil banana (unnamed) from the Cretaceous of Colombia (Revist. Colomb. 9: 115-116. 1953) of the *Musa sapientum* L. group is curiously unconvincing and *Musa mexicana* Matuda (Madroño 10: 167. fig. 1. 1950) is certainly a garden escape, one of the ornamental species of the subgenus *Rhodochlamys* introduced in modern times from the Old World (*cf.* p. 273).

Nauclea orientalis sensu [Soland. ex] Parkins. Jour. 37; Forst. f. Prodr. 15. 1786, non L. = *Nauclea forsteri* Seem. = *Neonauclea forsteri* (Seem.) Merr. (*Nauclea *forsteriana* Drake, Fl. Polyn. Franç. 84. 1893). — FORSTER f. accepted the SOLANDER misapplication of the Linnaean binomial. The unlisted synonym, *N. forsteriana* Drake, was due to an error in transcription on the part of DRAKE DEL CASTILLO.

Urena lobata L.; Parkins. Jour. 42. — A man-introduced weed from the islands to the West, now pantropic in distribution, but apparently of Indo-Malaysian origin.

TEXT FIGURE 21 (*opposite*). — Another page from SOLANDER's unpublished manuscript flora of Tahiti. — The large number of banana varieties listed is interesting to note. Twenty-three varieties of *Musa paradisiaca* L. and five varieties of the Fehi banana (*Musa troglodytarum* L.) are distinguished (*cf.* p. 343). Banana thickets which occur as high as 5000 ft. are a remarkable feature of the vegetation of Tahiti. They consist of the seeded Fehi type, the seeds being widely scattered by birds. The fruiting racemes are erect, hence its name in the Moluccas: toncud langit ("to watch the sky").

Chapter X

THE NEW AND MOSTLY UNLISTED TECHNICAL
NAMES IN PARKINSON'S JOURNAL (1773)

I have deliberately not used the term "published" in the above heading, because clearly, most or perhaps all of the new SOLANDER generic and specific names used by PARKINSON in 1773 were not validly published by him, as he provided no technical descriptions. In most cases, no botanical data, other than economic notes, appear in his work. The few new generic names involved are all in the generico-specific category, and in no case was a generic description provided. As a matter of fact nowhere are sufficient botanical data supplied whereby, from the PARKINSON discussions alone, a single one of the few new generic names used could be placed in the simple Linnaean system of classification. The names used by PARKINSON were all taken from SOLANDER's descriptions prepared on the *Endeavour* before the former's death, or were copied from the plates that PARKINSON prepared.

In this chapter, the new generic and specific names which will not be found in the *Index Kewensis* and its Supplements have been indicated with an asterisk (*). Those which are listed, but with references to later places, have been marked with a dagger (†). With one exception all of those in the following list either need to be added to the *Index Kewensis* or the existing entries corrected; and, as will be seen, most of the binomials are not even listed. There are a few in this category proposed by other authors; these appear in the discussions. Yet, in my judgment, it makes little or no difference whether or not the additions and corrections are made, for these "[Solander ex] Parkinson" names should not affect nomenclature, because the basic technical data were not provided when the PARKINSON paper was published in 1773. They are usually not strictly *nomina nuda* but some will rate as *nomina subnuda*. I have compromised by adding after each reference the expression *nom., nota.*

I have already noted that PARKINSON — an excellent artist but not a botanist — did not originate the technical names he used. Perhaps in a few cases, where manifest errors in transcription were made, the authorship should be credited to him. It is admitted that one need not officially qualify as a trained or partly trained botanist in order to name and describe new species of plants. Anyone who chooses to do so can master the simple technique required. There is, however, a limit beyond which taxonomists should not be required to go in their attempts to account for all published technical names of plants. Certain media of publication, such as daily or weekly newspapers, are already outlawed, but the field of published books, and technical or semi-technical serials needs some attention; only certain publications of a few botanical mavericks have been officially outlawed. I could cite the case of a new technical name of a succulent plant, appearing in what is now an established and recognized serial, which was selected at a meeting of the sponsoring group where those present voted that a plant exhibited by a certain member was a new species and that its specific name should perpetuate the name of the exhibitor! After all, it is not supposed that it matters much one way or the other whether or not this particular new cactus binomial finds its place in our standard indices. Maybe its authority should be that often used abbreviation "Anon." Such is extreme democracy, at times, even if, in this case, it is well laced with ignorance of proper procedure.

Aeschynomene †**speciosa** [Soland. ex] Parkins. Jour. 43. 1773, *nom., nota;* Soland. ex Seem. Fl. Vit. 55. 1865, *nom. in syn.* Tahiti = *Sesbania speciosa* F. H. B. Brown, Bishop Mus. Bull. 130: 110. 1935, non Taub. (1895) = *S. coccinea* (L.f.) Pers. (*Aeschynomene indica* L. f.; *Coronilla coccinea* Willd.). — Dr. BROWN published a description of this species as *Sesbania speciosa* (Soland.) F. B. H. Brown in 1935, but carelessly cited no name-bringing synonym and overlooked the fact that the specific name was invalid in *Sesbania*. For *E owhaee*, the modern *oufai*, all that PARKINSON said was: "This shrub grows wild, in great abundance, on the island of Toopbai [Tubai]; and is planted on the other islands, to shade their houses; and the flower of it, which is very beautiful, they often stick in their ears." This is not a botanical description. The species is little more than a color variety of *Sesbania grandiflora* (L.) Pers. with red flowers, the latter having white flowers. The locality "Nova Zeelandia" as given by the younger LINNAEUS is erroneous; New Caledonia was intended. His specimen came from Mr. BÄCK, the donor, not the collector, who was a great personal friend of the older LINNAEUS and who from time to time acquired and presented botanical specimens to him. The BÄCK specimen was collected by the FORSTERS, for the younger FORSTER in 1786 recorded the species as from "Societatis insulae, Botanicesque insulis"; WILLDENOW in 1802 and PERSOON in 1807 repeated this. This species does not grow in New Zealand. The Botany Islands of COOK are between New Caledonia and the Isle of Pines.

*Aniotum *fagiferum [Soland. ex] Parkins. Jour. 39. 1773, *nom., nota;* Fosb. Jour. Wash. Acad. Sci. 31: 95. 1941, *nom. in syn.* Tahiti = *Inocarpus edulis* J. R. & G. Forst. (1776) (*I. fagiferus* Fosb. *l.c.*). — PARKINSON's entire description consists merely of: "*E hee* or *E ratta. Aniotum-fagiferum.* This is a tall and stately tree which bears a round flat fruit, covered with a thick tough coat, and when roasted and stripped of its rind, eats as well as a chestnut." There is no generic description, the binomial being merely a generico-specific one. In my opinion this does not constitute valid publication, even though we definitely know what SOLANDER had in mind when he prepared his ample but never published description. Neither can I see any valid reason for conserving *Inocarpus* J. R. & G. Forst. (1776) against *Aniotum* [Soland. ex] Parkins. (1773), as FOSBERG recommended, for the simple reason that PARKINSON did not publish a generic description. FORSTER f. provided a greatly detailed description of the species in *De plantis esculentis* p. 50-52. 1786.

Arum *costatum [Soland. ex] Parkins. Jour. 43. 1773, *nom., nota,* non Wall. (1824). Tahiti = *Alocasia macrorrhiza* (L.) Schott. — There is no botanical description. For *E ape* all that PARKINSON said was: "The root of this plant is as good as the last [*A. esculentum* L.] but considerably larger; the leaves, which are very smooth and extremely large, are used to wrap up, or lay any sort of victuals upon."

Besleria *laurifolia [Soland. ex] Parkins. Jour. 41. 1773, *nom., nota;* Benth. Jour. Linn. Soc. Bot. 1: 98. 1856, *nom. in syn.* Tahiti = *Fagraea berteriana* A. Gray ex Benth. *l.c.* — For *E pooamattapee-pee* PARKINSON said: "The flower of this tree is much admired on account of its sweet scent, for which reason they stick them in their ears and hair, and put them among their garments, and into their monoe [oil]. The wood is very tough and lasting, and of it they make drums, and thwarts across their canoes." This is not a botanical description in any sense of the term. The older *Carissa? *grandis* Bertero ex Guillemin, Ann. Sci. Nat. II Bot. 7: 248. 1837, *nom., nota;* A. DC. Prodr. 8: 336. 1844, *nom. nud.* is an earlier synonym of *Fagraea berteriana* A. Gray ex Benth. but was not validly published. The Tahitian specimen on which BERTERO's name was based was one with immature fruits and no flowers; no description of it was published.

Betonica *splendida Parkins. Jour. 41. 1773, *nom., nota.* Tahiti = *Barringtonia asiatica* (L.) Kurz (*B. speciosa* Forst. f.). — PARKINSON erred in transcribing the generic name, as the original was *Butonica *splendida* Soland. ex Miers, Trans. Linn. Soc. II. Bot. 1: 60, 1875, *nom. in syn.* It was the basis of *Agasta splendida* Miers, *l.c.* which cannot be distinguished from the form LINNAEUS originally characterized as *Mammea asiatica* L. PARKINSON included in his statement that *E hootoo,* the modern *hutu* or *tira-hutu* was a tree with large and "specious white flowers, full of long purple stamina, with which they deck their heads, and sometimes stick them in their ears"; and that the powdered fruit they throw into water to kill fish. It is suspected that this species was man-introduced from islands to the west as the large fruits were useful as floats for nets and the single large seed distinctly useful as a fish poison.

Boerhavia †procumbens [Soland. ex] Parkins. Jour. 41. 1773, *nom., nota.* Tahiti = *B. repens* L. — This is undoubtedly the same form as *B. procumbens* "Herb. Banks" ex Roxb. Fl. Ind. ed. Carey & Wall. 1; 146. 1820, although the ROXBURGH description was based on specimens from India. PARKINSON's statement is merely that "the stalks of this plant [*noonanoona*] are eaten when they have no better food". FORSTER f. Pl. Esculent. 71. 1786, described this same Tahitian form as representing *B. erecta* L.

*Chaitea *tacca [Soland. ex] Parkins. Jour. 38, 1773, *nom., nota* = *Chaitaea tacca* Soland. ex Seem. Fl. Vit. 102. 1865, *descr.* Tahiti

= *Tacca pinnatifida* J. R. & G. Forst. (1776) = *T. leontope-taloides* (L.) O. Kuntze; *see* MERRILL, Jour. Arnold Arb. 26: 85-92. pl. 1-2. 1945. — PARKINSON's entire statement regarding this new genus was: "*Chaitea tacca.* E peea. The root of this plant, properly prepared, makes an excellent strong jelly, like to blanc mange, of the nature of salop, for which it is very justly admired by these islanders." This is the well-known so-called Polynesian arrowroot, but PARKINSON's statement is not a botanical description, the name being a gen-erico-specific one until 1865. FORSTER f. provided a greatly detailed description of the species in his *De plantis esculentis* p. 59-61. 1786.

Convolvulus †alatus [Soland. ex] Parkins. Jour. 37. 1773, *nom., nota*; Soland. ex Seem. Fl. Vit. 172. 1867, *nom. in syn.* Tahiti = *Operculina turpethum* (L.) Silva Manso. — PARKINSON's entire statement was: "The stalks of this plant they give young children to suck." Surely no botanist would accept this as a technical description; and yet from SOLANDER's excellent plate (which PARKINSON prepared) and description (never published) we know where this binomial belongs in synonymy.

Convolvulus †chrysorhizus [Soland. ex] Parkins. Jour. 38. 1773, *nom., nota* = *C. chrysorrhizus* Soland. ex Forst. f. Pl. Esculent. 55. 1786, *descr.*, Prodr. 89. 1786, *nom.* Tahiti = *Ipomoea batatas* (L.) Lam. — This is the exceedingly variable sweet potato*(1)*, the early introduction of which from South America into the Pacific Islands is at least possible. The Polynesians themselves distributed it all over their culture area in pre-Magellan times, except in the low islands where normally it cannot be cultivated successfully. It is rather amusing to note that recently one of our younger neo-geo-graphers, who really should know his elementary geography, has ex-pressed his inability to explain the discontinuous distribution of this cultigen in the Pacific Islands. The explanation is very simple. Most of the Pacific Islands are low sandy ones, the existing conditions thereon forbidding the general culture of this important food plant, except on those islands which happen to be located in regions where the rainfall is well distributed over most months of the year. The sweet potato in Polynesia and Micronesia is largely confined to the widely separated "high" (volcanic) islands and the raised coral ones as contrasted to the much more numerous "low" ones, and even geo-

---

1) It is not generally known that in 1900 the eminent New Zealand botanist T. F. CHEESEMAN, who devoted his life to a study of the New Zealand flora, and who was very familiar with its vegetation and its history, recorded the fact that the Maori people recognized more than fifty varieties of kumara (our sweet potato) in support of his correct contention that they were very skilled agri-culturists as were those of the Polynesian race who occupied the tropical islands of the Pacific. (*See* Trans. New Zeal. Inst. 33: 308. 1901). What they did in the vegetative propagation of their basic food plants, and their distribution of them all over Polynesian islands proper, including the seedless breadfruit, was very remarkable. The latter is another excellent example of how observing they were, for they recognized and named some scores of varieties and forms of the breadfruit. In certain islands, it was one of their most important food plants.

graphers recognize the manifest differences between these categories, even if some of them do not know their botany and ecology.

Cotula *bicolor [Soland. ex] Parkins. Jour. 43, 1773, *nom., nota;* Soland. ex Forst. f. Prodr. 91.1786, *nom. nud.* Tahiti = *Dichrocephala bicolor* (Roth) Schlechtend.; *see* EXELL, Cat. Pl. S. Tomé 223. 1944. — All that PARKINSON said was: "E Vaeenoo. *Cotula-bicolor.* E tooho. *Epipactis purpurea.* Both these plants, bruised, are ingredients of their Erapaow-mai, or plaister to cure sores." EXELL was correct in accepting *Cotula bicolor* Roth, amply described in 1800 = *Dichrocephala bicolor* (Roth) Schlechtend. to replace the widely used *D. latifolia* (Lam.) DC. ROTH's very ample description was apparently based on material from India. He knew nothing about PARKINSON's and FORSTER's use of the same specific name for what manifestly is the same species; yet, neither of the latter validated the binomial. *Cotula latifolia* Pers. (1807) and *Dichrocephala latifolia* Lam. (1813) were both new names for the older *Cotula bicolor* Roth.

Crataeva *frondosa [Soland. ex] Parkins. Jour. 39. 1773, *nom., nota.* Tahiti = *Crataeva religiosa* Forst. f. Pl. Esculent. 45. 1786, *descr. ampl.,* Prodr. 35. 1786. diagn. — The types of both were from Tahiti. PARKINSON's "botanical" description of the species is merely: "The fruit of this shrub they lay upon their corpses and hang it upon their burial whattas, it having an agreeable bitter smell" and further explained that the plant was sacred to their god Tané. The description in FORSTER f. *De plantis esculentis,* p. 45-46 is a very ample one.

Cucurbita †pruriens [Soland. ex] Parkins. Jour. 44. 1773, *nom., nota;* Soland. ex Forst. f. Prodr. 92. 1786, *nom.;* Seem. Fl. Vit. 107. 1865, *descr.* Tahiti = *Benincasa hispida* (Thunb.) Cogn. (*B. cerifera* Savi). — PARKINSON's entire statement was: "E hooe-rorro. *Cucurbita-pruriens.* The fruit of this tree is about the size of a small orange, very hard, and quite round, serving them, instead of bottles, to put their monoe or oil in." This is not a botanical description, and the indicated habit as a tree is an error. It is certain that what PARKINSON saw in use as oil containers were actually small fruits of the common gourd, *Lagenaria siceraria* (Mol.) Standl. (*L. vulgaris* Seringe; *L. leucantha* Rusby) which BANKS and SOLANDER collected in Tahiti and which the latter described as *Cucurbita lagenaria* L. with the Tahitian name E'hooe (SOLANDER MS. p. 335). It is indeed curious to note how field men (particularly in anthropology, but occasionally in botany) are taken in by the phrase "since time immemorial" when they ask a local resident how long they have had this or that plant, animal, artifact or skill. SEEMANN, *l.c.* repeats this for *Cucurbita maxima* Duch. as it occurred in Hawaii. HILLEBRAND (Fl. Hawaii 134. 1888) confused the *ipu nui* with *Cucurbita maxima* Duch.; it is *Lagenaria siceraria* (Mol.) Standl. This in some quarters has been interpreted to mean that *Cucurbita maxima* Duch. occurred in Hawaii before the time of COOK's third voyage, which is not true. Recent anatomical studies of Hawaiian pre-European *ipu nui* vessels*(2)* have shown that they were made from the shells of a very large form of the true gourd (*Lagenaria*).

Cyperus *alatus [Soland. ex] Parkins. Jour. 37. 1773, *nom., nota,* non F. Muell. Tahiti. — There is no description. For *E mohoo* PARKINSON merely said: "The stalks of this plant, stripped of their pulp, which they perform with a sharp shell, make a sort of thread used for several common purposes."

Daphne *capitata [Soland. ex] Parkins. Jour. 39. 1773, *nom., nota.* Tahiti = *Wikstroemia foetida* (L.f.) A. Gray. — There is no description. For *E áwaow*, the modern *oaao* or *avau-ao*, PARKINSON merely said: "This plant is used to poison fish in order to catch them; and, for this purpose, they beat or mash it together and throw it into the rivers and sea within the reefs." SOLANDER (MS. p. 252) said that the leaves and branches of both of his proposed new species of *Daphne* were used for the purpose indicated when mixed with the crushed seeds of *Butonica splendida* Soland. = *Barringtonia asiatica* (L. f.) Kurz. The type of *Daphne foetida* L.f. was from Tahiti. PARK- INSON inadvertently left out the name of the *Butonica* (=*Barring- tonia*), the seeds of which are very widely used for the purpose indi- cated. *Wikstroemia* bast fibers are innocuous.

Epipactis *purpurea [Soland. ex.] Parkins. Jour. 43. 1773, *nom., nota,* non Crantz (1765). Tahiti = *Epidendrum resupinatum* Forst. f. (1786) = *Microstylis resupinata* Drake (1893) = *Malaxis resupinata* (Forst f.) O. Kuntze. — PARKINSON's brief statement regarding the use of this plant is repeated under *Cotula bicolor, supra.* There is no description. This is the form that So- LANDER so amply described (MS. p. 299) and this species was the whole basis of the genus *Malaxis* as originally proposed by him. Yet when SWARTZ (Prodr. 119. 1788) accepted and published *Malaxis* Solander he cited only two Jamaican species. In the margin of the SOLANDER manuscript is pencilled *Microstylis rheedii* Lindl. Mr. CHARLES SCHWEINFURTH, who kindly checked the nomenclatural prob- lem, assures me that F. B. H. BROWN's figure (Occ. Pap. Bishop Mus. 9 (4): 22. fig. 6. 1930), where ample additional descriptive data are given based on Tahiti specimens, represents *Malaxis*, a genus cur- rently accepted as distinct from *Microstylis* and that *Malaxis resupi- nata* (Forst. f.) O. Kuntze is an older name than *Malaxis rhedii* Sw. (1800) which in turn was a new name for *Epidendrum resupinatum* Forst. f. The specific name *rhedii* is usually spelled *rheedii.* The SWARTZ binomial was not published until 1800, so the FORSTER f. name for this Tahitian endemic species has fourteen years priority. SOLAND- ER erroneously thought that RHEEDE's Hort. Malabar. 1: pl. 27, cited with doubt, might represent his Tahitian species.

Euphorbia *develata [Soland. ex] Parkins. Jour. 40. 1773, *nom., nota*; Seem. Fl. Vit. 216. 1867, *nom. in syn.* Tahiti = *E. atoto*

2) EAMES, A. J. and ST. JOHN, H. The Botanical Identity of the Native Hawaiian Ipu nui or Large Gourd. Am. Jour. Bot. 30: 255-259, fig. 1-3. 1943.

Forst. f. Prodr. 36. 1786. — PARKINSON merely stated: "This plant is full of a milky juice with which they dye their garments of an indifferent brown colour." This is not a botanical description.

Ficus †prolixa [Soland. ex] Parkins. Jour. 47. 1773, *nom., nota.* Tahiti = *F. prolixa* Forst. f. Prodr. 77. 1786. — The types of both were from Tahiti. PARKINSON gave a fairly long discussion of the use of the bark of this tree for making a type of tapa cloth, called *ora*, but no botanical description. FORSTER f. certainly knew of SOLANDER's use of the specific name, yet his very short diagnosis is followed by "F".

Ficus †tinctoria [Soland. ex] Parkins. Jour. 46. 1773, *nom., nota.* Tahiti = *F. tinctoria* Forst. f. Prodr. 76. 1786. — The types of both were from Tahiti. There is no botanical description in PARKINSON's work, but he does devote ten lines to an explanation of how the Tahitians used the milky juice of the fruits in the preparation of a red dye and how the bark fibers were used for making twine for the manufacture of seines and nets. FORSTER f., in this case, as with *F. prolixa* Forst. f., followed his brief diagnosis with the letter "F", thus indicating the binomial as his own. As in other cases of this type he certainly took the specific name from the SOLANDER manuscript or from PARKINSON's plate, and it is suspected that he actually saw named BANKS and SOLANDER specimens.

***Galaxa *oppositifolia** [Soland. ex] Parkins. Jour. 38. 1773, *nom., nota.* Tahiti = *Alyxia scandens* (Forst. f.) R. & S. (*Gynopogon scandens* Forst. f.). — SOLANDER's original slips bear the above generic name, proposed as new and on one of them *G. oppositifolia* Soland. appears. In the final copy of his manuscript the generic name was changed to *Alyxia* probably because he thought that *Galaxa* was too similar to the earlier *Galaxia* L. *Alyxia* was originally published as a Banksian genus by ROBERT BROWN in 1810; in the meantime J. R. & G. FORSTER had described the same genus as *Gynopogon* in 1776, based on the two Tahitian species that SOLANDER described but to which he assigned no specific names in his final manuscript, p. 240-242. This generic name like all the other new ones used by PARKINSON falls in the generico-specific group. PARKINSON's entire statement regarding *E maireeo* was: "the leaf of the plant is one of the ingredients in their manoe"; *manoe* = perfumed coconut oil. *Maire* is the name used in Tahiti for *Gynopogon stellatum* Forst. f. = *Alyxia stellata* R. & S., the leaves of which are very fragrant when dry, as are those of all other species of the genus; but in the latter species they are verticillate. The SOLANDER description applies to the opposite leaved species and Mr. STEARN of the British Museum has confirmed this determination by an examination of PARKINSON's unpublished plate.

Galaxa *sparsa Parkins. Jour. 38. 1773, *nom., nota.* Tahiti = *Ochrosia parviflora* (Forst. f.) Henslow. — For *E deva* or *E reva* PARKINSON said: "This plant has a pretty large white flower like that of an oleander. Of the wood of this tree they make their pahaoos, or drums." In the final copy of the SOLANDER manuscript for the second species of *Alyxia* every word of the description except the indication of the species as a tree, applies to *Alyxia stellata* (Forst. f.) R. & S., not at all to *Ochrosia*. Thus SEEMANN, who published SOLANDER's very full description (Fl. Vit. 159. 1866) sub *Ochrosia parviflora* (Forst. f.) Hensl., erred in reducing this taxon to the latter species. SOLANDER recorded for this a curious Tahitian name *ea-eai no the moua* which I felt certain to be a phrase rather than a plant name. Thinking it might possibly be the equivalent of "I told you that before" (and this *has* happened where collectors were unfamiliar with native languages) I appealed to Dr. ST. JOHN of the University of Hawaii. In his consultation with Dr. K. P. EMORY of the Bishop Museum the phrase works out in modern Tahitian as *e a'e a'e no te moua* which means "a vine that grows in the mountains". *Tiare*, in one cognate form or another, is very widely used in Polynesia for *Alyxia*. Thus the species here involved having a definite native name, it merely means that SOLANDER recorded a descriptive phrase rather than an actual plant name. I cannot fully explain the apparent confusion that is involved between what PARKINSON definitely had in mind and what SOLANDER actually described, for the first is surely the *Ochrosia* and the second the *Alyxia*. There is a fruiting specimen of *Ochrosia parviflora* (Forst. f.) Henslow in the British Museum herbarium from the Society Islands, which Mr. STEARN looked up for me. On the verso of the sheet the entry is "Otaheite, J[OSEPH] B[ANKS]." It was apparently the lack of flowers that prevented SOLANDER from placing this particular specimen in its proper place in the Linnaean system; and yet it is clear that PARKINSON saw a flowering specimen. Under the circumstances I credit *Galaxa sparsa* to PARKINSON, not to "[Soland. ex] Parkinson."

Galega †piscatoria [Soland. ex] Parkins. Jour. 43. 1773, *nom., nota.* Tahiti = *Galega piscatoria* Ait. Hort. Kew 3: 71. 1789 = *Tephrosia piscatoria* (Ait.) Pers. = *T. purpurea* (L.) Pers. *sensu lat.* — PARKINSON gave no description for *E hora*, merely stating: "With this plant, beaten small, they poison or stupefy fish, throwing it into the water, by which means they are caught." It is probable, or at least possible, that the living plants at Kew on which AITON's description was based were grown from Tahitian seeds brought back by BANKS and SOLANDER. The *Index Kewensis* entry is *Galega piscatoria* [Dryand. in] Ait. but even if DRYANDER wrote the description, which was undoubtedly the case, the specific name was originated by SOLANDER, MS. 292.

Hibiscus *cuspidatus [Soland. ex] Parkins. Jour. 42. 1773, *nom., nota.* Tahiti = *H. tiliaceus* L. var. *hastatus* (L. f.) Hochr. Ann. Conserv. Jard. Bot. Genève 4: 63. 1900 (*Hibiscus hastatus* L. f.). — PARKINSON provided no description of his *E pooraow*, but his extensive discussion of the uses made of its wood and of the bark clearly indicates that what he had in mind was a form of the very common and widely distributed pantropical strand plant, *Hibiscus tiliaceus* L., the modern name of the latter in Tahiti being *purau*. *Hibiscus* *cuspidatus* Edgw. (1853) is the very different *H. vitifolius* L. The type of *H. hastatus* L. f. was from Tahiti, being a FORSTER specimen received from ABRAHAM BÄCK, LINNAEUS' friend. As pointed out before, it was more or less customary at that time, to indicate the name of the donor of such gifts, not that of the collector. WILLDENOW followed the same practice, as Mr. ALSTON noted in a letter to me from Berlin in 1952, when he observed certain Philippine specimens in the WILLDENOW herbarium indicated as being from HUMBOLDT; they are MALASPINA Expedition collections made by NÉE; HUMBOLDT never was in the Orient.

Hibiscus †tricuspis [Soland. ex] Parkins. Jour. 42. 1773. *nom., nota.* Tahiti = *H. tricuspis* Banks ex Cav. Diss. 3: 152. pl. 55. fig. 2. 1787 = *Hibiscus hastatus* L. f. (1781) = *praec.* — For *E pooraow-toro-ceree* PARKINSON merely stated: "This plant is pretty much like the last [*H. cuspidatus*], and is used for the same purposes." HOCHREUTINER (*op. cit.* 65) in his long discussion mentions an unpublished "*H. tiliaceus* var. *tricuspis*," there being a specimen in the BOISSIER herbarium. He selected the specific name published by the younger LINNAEUS, giving it varietal status, because the description of that taxon appeared earlier than the one published by CAVANILLES.

Jasminum †didymum [Soland. ex] Parkins. Jour. 37. 1773, *nom., nota.* Tahiti = *J. didymum* Forst. f. Prodr. 3. 1786, *descr.* — For *Teatea maowa* PARKINSON said: "Grown upon the hills; has a very sweet smelling white flower, which the natives admire very much." This is not a botanical description, but neither can one claim very much for the younger FORSTER's diagnosis of 1786 which is merely "*I. didymum*, foliis oppositis ternatis, foliolis ovato-lanceolatis acuminatis integerrimis. F. Societatis Insulae." Yet FORSTER, who appropriated SOLANDER's specific name, conformed to the accepted conventions appertaining to the describing of new species: PARKINSON did not do so.

Metrosideros †spectabilis [Soland. ex] Parkins. Jour. 40. 1773, *nom., nota*; Soland. ex Gaertn. Fruct. 1: 172. pl. 34. fig. 9. 1788; Seem. Fl. Vit. 83. 1865, *nom., nota.* Tahiti = *M. collina* (J. R. & G. Forst.) A. Gray. — PARKINSON gave a seven line discussion of his *E ratta* or *E pooratta,* the modern *puarata* in Tahiti. There is no doubt as to what was intended but there is no botanical description. The basis of the accepted name is *Leptospermum collinum* J. R. & G. Forst. (1776), the type from Tahiti.

Pandanus †tectorius(3) [Soland. ex] Parkins. Jour. 46. 1773; Soland. ex Seem. Fl. Vit. 282. 1868, *nom. in syn.*, et in Balf. f. Jour. Linn. Soc. Bot. 17: 56. 1878, *nom. in syn.* Tahiti. (*P. odoratissimus* L. f., 1781, *sensu lat.*). — WARBURG (Pflanzenr. 3 (iv. 9): 46. 1900) accepted *Pandanus tectorius* Soland. as the proper name

3) This binomial, credited to SOLANDER, is, I believe, the only one in this entire list that is correctly entered in Index Kewensis.

for this species, reducing to it, among many other proposed ones, *P. odoratissimus* L. f. The actual type of the former was from Tahiti, that of the latter, a specimen from Ceylon, collected by THUNBERG. The name *Pandanus* was originated by RUMPHIUS in 1743, but under the Linnean system was most casually published by LINNAEUS in 1754 (without a binomial) as *"Pandanus* genus est nondum constitutam. Monoeciae *Bromeliae* forte affine, fructu *Ambrosiae."* Its basis was the pre-Linnaean *Pandanus verus* Rumph. (1743). If this be not acceptable to the taxonomic perfectionists as a proper generic publication, then we would have to accept LINNAEUS f. (1781) as the authority, for he first published a formal generic description about eight years after PARKINSON considered SOLANDER's binomial. In that case *Keura* Forsk. (1775) and *Arthrodactylis* J. R. & G. Forst. (1776) would need to be officially rejected, for both are older than *Pandanus* L. f. (1781) ; strictly, if *Pandanus* L. (1754) be ruled out, *Pandanus* L. f. (1781) would need to be conserved. The type of *Keura* Forsk. (1775) is *K. odoratissima* Forsk. and that of *Arthrodactylis* J. R. & G. Forst. (1776) is *A. spinosa* J. R. & G. Forst. Both of these species are currently placed as synonyms of *P. tectorius* Soland. ex Parkinson = *P. odoratissimus* L. f.; the latter binomial was not based on the earlier one of FORSKÅL. Rules are rules, but here is a case where it is most desirable that *Pandanus* L. should be retained, for the pre-Linnaean description and plate on which it was based impresses me as being amply sufficient to justify its acceptance. As to *Pandanus tectorius* [Soland. ex] Parkinson (1773) it has as good a description as any of the very few worthy of consideration in the PARKINSON document. It consists of eleven lines, and although cursory, rather than technical, can apply to no other plant than *Pandanus.* Yet MARTELLI (Nuovo Giorn. Bot. Ital. 36: 328-337. 1929) after a detailed discussion of the matter rejected *Pandanus tectorius* [Soland. ex] Parkinson (1773) and accepted *P. odoratissimus* L. f. (1781) to replace it. In this discussion (p. 332-334) MARTELLI reproduced in full SOLANDER's very greatly detailed manuscript description and all that PARKINSON published about the species. To be consistent, he should have gone back to *Arthrodactylis spinosa* J. R. & G. Forst. (1776) and should have transferred its specific name to *Pandanus,* as it antedates the publication of *Pandanus odoratissimus* L. f. (1781) by five years, and the specific name is still valid in *Pandanus.* As a matter of fact FORSTER f. in 1786 (Pl. Esculent. 38) reduced *Arthrodactylis spinosa* J. R. & G. Forst. (1776) to *Pandanus odoratissimus* L. f. (1781), publishing a very detailed description occupying more than two and one-half pages, based on the Tahitian form. He added four varieties, each characterized by three to five words with references to RHEEDE's *Hortus Malabaricus.* The botanical characters in PARKINSON's cursory description of the Tahiti plant are that it was a tree growing in sandy places near the seashore, being plentiful on all the low islands, the long leaves "like those of a sedge" have saw-toothed margins, the male and female flowers grow on different plants, the male flowers very fragrant, the white bracts used by the natives to make a sort of garland to put on their heads, the fruit orange, as large as one's head, consisting of a congeries of small cones "like those of the Anana or Pineapple, which they much resemble", that the basal parts of the "cones" (drupes) when fully ripe are sweet and are eaten by children, the leaves being used for thatching houses, and for making mats and baskets. PARKINSON recorded the native name as *E awharra*, the modern *fara* in Tahiti; there is only one species of the genus recorded from Tahiti, this being also the form that FORSTER f. so amply described in 1786. It is a somewhat variable strand form that extends throughout the tropical parts of the Pacific, through Malaysia and the Mascarene Islands to southern Asia. This I frankly interpret as a collective species. No attempt to segregate minor taxa such as varieties and no attempt to segregate local microspecies can be considered as being successful. The species in Polynesia is not man-distributed, but was spread over its vast range by its drupes which float for long periods of time and its habitat is immediately back of the sandy beaches. One form of *Pandanus* (its specific name still unknown) was widely distributed in Malaysia and in Polynesia by early man merely because its leaves have very superior qualities for making fine mats, baskets etc. Captain COOK mentioned this plant as carefully cultivated in Rarotonga. It is suspected that this particular type was a staminate form, thus explaining why no collector ever secured fruiting material. The system of classification within the genus is based almost wholly on fruit characters. As Captain COOK noted, this cultigen was grown in rows and the plants were never permitted to grow very high. When one reads a certain panegyric on the wonderful food possibilities of *Pandanus*, one who knows its limitations is apt to smile rather broadly. It is recommended that the author try the Polynesian form for food and that he extend his field work beyond North and South America!

Phaseolus †amoenus [Soland. ex] Parkins. Jour. 43. 1773, *nom., nota*; Soland. ex Forst. f. Prodr. 91. 1768. *nom. nud.*; Seem. Fl. Vit. 61, 1865, *nom. in syn.* Tahiti = *P. adenanthus* G. W. F. Mey. (1818). — *Phaseolus truxillensis* HBK. (1823), is currently accepted as representing the same species. For *E peepee* PARKINSON merely said: "The stalks of this plant make a very good thread for weaving nets and sein[e]s. Of the flowers, which are very pretty, they make garlands for their heads." This is not a validating botanical description. The species as currently interpreted occurs in both hemispheres, and as I knew it in the Philippines I would judge it to have been a man-introduced plant there. Perhaps a critical study of this particular taxon is in order. As far as I know, it is of no economic importance.

Phyllanthus *anceps [Soland. ex] Parkins. Jour. 44. 1773, *nom., nota*. Tahiti = *P. simplex* Retz. Obs. 5: 29. 1789 = *P. virgatus* Forst. f. Prodr. 65. 1786 (*P. simplex* Retz. var. *virgatus* Muell.-Arg.). — For *Moemoe* all that PARKINSON said was: "The only thing remarkable about this plant is the leaves which shut up at night from whence its [native] name."

Piper †inebrians [Soland. ex] Parkins. Jour. 37. 1773, *nom., nota.,* Bertero ex Miq. Comment. Phyt. 36. 1840, *nom. in syn.*; Seem. Fl. Vit. 262. 1868, *nom. in syn.* Tahiti = *Piper methysticum* Forst. f. Pl. Esculent. 76. 1786, *descr. ampl.,* Prodr. 5. 1786, *diagn.,* non Linn. f. (1781). — Because of the peculiar nomenclatural problems involved in *P. methysticum* Forst. f. versus *P. latifolium* L. f. and *P. methysticum* L. f. versus *P. latifolium* Forst. f., it is most unfortunate that PARKINSON did not validate *P. inebrians* Soland. in 1773. I merely comment in passing that the manuscript name, *P. inebrians,* appearing in synonymy in MIQUEL's *Comment. Phyt.* 36. 1840, undoubtedly came from the SOLANDER manuscript or from PARKINSON's *Journal.* All PARKINSON said about *E ava* was: "The expressed juice of this plant they drink to intoxicate themselves." This is not a botanical description, yet it is well known just which species of *Piper* was intended. J. W. MOORE (Occ. Pap. Bishop Mus. 10(19) : 3-8. 1934) has discussed the nomenclatural problems in detail. See also A. C. SMITH (Jour. Arnold Arb. 24: 349. 1943) and the discussion of *P. latifolium, infra.*

Piper †latifolium [Soland. ex] Parkins. Jour. 42. 1773, *nom., nota.* Tahiti = *P. latifolium* Linn. f. [vel Forst. f. ex Linn. f.] Suppl. [468]. 1781 (*Piper latifolium* Forst. f. Prodr. 42. 1786). — For *E ava-váidái* all that PARKINSON said was: "The juice of this plant has not the intoxicating quality of the other [*Piper inebrians*], so that they prudently make an offering of it to their Eatooas, on whose altars they hang branches of it." Apparently these not exactly unsophisticated aborigines assumed that their gods would not know the difference between the leaves of one *Piper* species and those of another, so why waste the useful *P. inebrians* when the worthless substitute might serve quite as well, when offerings were made. We who sit on the sidelines and watch the *Piper* specialists operate in proposing and describing new species (and nearly 2,000 have been named and described as new in the past 50 years) often wonder if, in many cases, the specialists are much wiser than the Tahitians assumed their gods to be! The author of a volume has the right to correct his own errors and this LINNAEUS f. did, when he realized, because of the younger FORSTER's protest, that what he had described as *Piper methysticum* (Suppl. 91. 1781) was not at all the species to which that name had been originally applied by FORSTER f. Thus in his *Emendanda* [p. 468] he made the entry: "Pag. 91. PIPER *methysticum* lege PIPER *latifolium.*" I agree with Dr. SMITH that in this case *P. methysticum* L. f. (1781) may be interpreted as published in synonymy, and thus has no standing in nomenclature. One might assume that, when the correction was made by the younger LINNAEUS, it was the intent to credit *Piper latifolium* to FORSTER f., but some may prefer to cite the authority as "[Forst. f. ex] Linn. f." The younger FORSTER complained rather bitterly that certain Pacific Islands collections made by his father and himself were credited to ABRAHAM BÄCK by the younger LINNAEUS in 1781, yet he did not hesitate to appropriate many of SOLANDER's binomials, including *Piper latifolium*, and publish them as his own, which is not exactly playing cricket.

Portulaca †lutea [Soland. ex] Parkins. Jour. 41. 1773, *nom., nota;* Forst. f. Pl. Esculent. 72. 1786, *nom., nota;* Prodr. 90. 1786, *nom., nota;* Seem. Fl. Vit. 9. 1865, *descr. ampl.* Tahiti. — This is a valid species, by some authors erroneously reduced to the very different *P. oleracea* L. It is a halophytic strand plant widely distributed in Polynesia, occurring on sandy seashores and both SOLANDER and PARKINSON speak of its use as food; it is never a weed. SEEMANN published the entire SOLANDER description and even FORSTER f. credited the binomial to SOLANDER. PARKINSON did not describe it in 1773, merely stating for *E atooree*: "This sort of purslain grows very common in the low islands, where the inhabitants bake and eat it, and account it very good food."

Psidium †myrtifolium [Soland. ex] Parkins. Jour. 40. 1773, *nom., nota;* Soland. ex Seem. Fl. Vit. 81. 1865, descr. sub *Nelitris forsteri* Seem. Tahiti = *Decaspermum fruticosum* J. R. & G. Forst. (1776). — For *E arrarooá* PARKINSON merely said: "The only use they make of this tree, which has a flower like a myrtle, is to make their totos or clubs, or a sort of lances, being very tough; they call it an iraow paree or the cunning tree." SEEMANN compiled a description from SOLANDER's unpublished manuscript, this appearing in a footnote as *Nelitris forsteri* Seem. which is a synonym of *Decaspermum fruticosum* J. R. & G. Forst. Both the SOLANDER and the FORSTER types were from Tahiti.

Ruellia †fragrans [Soland. ex] Parkins. Jour. 41. 1773, *nom. alt.;* Forst. f. Prodr. 44. 1786, *descr.* Tahiti = *Limnophila fragrans* (Forst. f.) Seem. (*L. serrata* Gaudich.). — See *Stachys dentata* below for PARKINSON's full statement. In 1786 FORSTER f. described *Ruellia fragrans* as his own species, appropriating SOLANDER's specific name.

Saccharum *dulce [Soland. ex] Parkins. Jour. 37. 1773, *nom., nota* Tahiti = *S. officinarum* L. — PARKINSON did not describe *E to* (the *to* of FORSTER f.), his entire statement being: "Of this cane they make no sugar, but content themselves with sucking the juice out of it." This was a form of the common sugar cane, spoken of as such by other members of COOK's first voyage in their journals. It was one of the plants introduced from the west by the Polynesians when they expanded over the Pacific islands. The Polynesians could make no sugar, as they had no earthen or other vessels in which anything could be boiled.

Saccharum †fatuum [Soland. ex] Parkins. Jour. 41. 1773, *nom., nota;* Soland. in Seem. Fl. Vit. 321. 1868, *nom. in syn.* Tahiti = *Erianthus floridulus* Labill. = *Miscanthus floridulus* (Labill.) Warb. — For *E poo-aiho* PARKINSON merely stated: "With bundles of this grass, lit up, they allure fish to the edges of the reefs, carrying them in their hands at night." Even the most extreme searcher for early names would not claim this to be a botanical description. This is widely distributed in Polynesia, Malaysia, etc. and *Miscanthus japonicus* (Thunb.) Anders. is a later name.

*Sitodium *altile [Soland. ex] Parkins. Jour. 45. 1773, *nom., nota*; Seem. Fl. Vit. 255. 1868, *nom. in syn.* Tahiti = *Artocarpus altilis* Fosb. Jour. Wash. Acad. Sci. 31: 95. 1941 = *Artocarpus communis* J. R. & G. Forst. (1776). (*Artocarpus incisa* L.f. (1781), based on *Radermachia incisa* Thunb. (1776)). — In his consideration of *E ooroo*, PARKINSON devoted somewhat more than a quarto page of text. There is no doubt whatever as to what was intended, but about half of the account is devoted to a description of the method of preparing the fruit for use as food. There is no formal description of *Sitodium*, as is also the case with the other new generic names in the paper, and no formal description of the species, the binomial of 1773 being merely a generico-specific one. We learn that it was a tree 30 to 40 ft. high with abundant latex, large palmated [pinnately lobed] leaves, with male and female flowers "at the bottom or joint of each leaf", that "the male flower [inflorescence] fades and drops off", and that the female flowers "swell and yield the fruit"; the gross characters of the fruit are well described. To accept FOSBERG's conclusion would solve one problem, as the specific name *altile* has three years priority over both *Radermachia incisa* Thunb. and *Artocarpus communis* J. R. & G. Forst., both published in 1776. As the preface to the FORSTER's "Characteres" was dated in London "Kalendis Novembribus MDCCLXXV", and the volume was printed in London, it may be assumed that it was published early in 1776, the latter being the title page date. I have not been able to determine the date of publication of *Radermachia* Thunb. to the month, nor could this be determined by Dr. HULTÉN through consultation of the Academy records in Stockholm, but the volume in which it appears was also issued in 1776. Surely *Sitodium altile* [Soland. ex] Parkins. is at least as validly published as is *Pandanus tectorius* [Soland. ex] Parkins.; and yet, neither was provided with a technical botanical description; but *Pandanus* was not a new generic name.

Solanum †latifolium [Soland. ex] Parkins. Jour. 38. 1773, *nom., nota*; Seem. Fl. Vit. 177. 1866, *nom. in syn.* Tahiti = *S. repandum* Forst. f. Prodr. 18. 1786. — For *E booa* or *E pooa* all that PARKINSON said was: "The leaves of this plant they use in making their red dye or mattee." The reduction was made by SEEMANN (Fl. Vit. 177. 1866).

Solanum †viride [Soland. ex] Parkins. Jour. 38. 1773, *nom., nota;* Forst. f. Pl. Esculent. 72. 1786, *nom., nota*, Prodr. 89. 1786, *nom.*; Seem. Fl. Vit. 176. 1866, *nom. in syn.* = *Solanum uporo* Dunal (1852) (*S. anthropophagorum* Seem., 1862). — All that PARKINSON said about *pouraheitee* was: "The leaves of this plant, baked are eaten as greens." FORSTER f. knew *Solanum viride* Soland. merely from what PARKINSON wrote about it, his brief statement no more a description than was the PARKINSON one, but he apparently knew that SOLANDER was the author of the binomial, as in both references he credited it to him.

Spondias †dulcis [Soland. ex] Parkins. Jour. 39. 1773, Tahiti = *S. dulcis* Forst. f. Pl. Esculent. 33. 1786, *descr. ampl.*, Prodr. 34. 1786, *diagn.*, Tahiti. — The PARKINSON description of *E avee*, the modern *vi*, is as near to a technical one as any that he published. It is: "This is a large stately tree, and often grows to the height of forty and fifty feet: the fruit, which I believe is peculiar to these isles, is of an oval shape, yellow when ripe, and grows in bunches of three or four, and is about the size of a middling apple, with a large stringy core; it is a very wholesome and palatable fruit, improving on the taste, which is nearest to that of a mangoe; it is strongly impregnated with turpentine and makes excellent pies when green. The wood serves for building canoes, and for several other purposes." As now interpreted, in a still unpublished treatise, this widely distributed Indo-Malaysian and Polynesian species includes *Mangifera pinnata* L. f. (1781), *Spondias cytherea* Sonn. (1782), *Spondias mangifera* Willd. (1799), *Evia amara* Commers. ex Bl. (1850), *Pourpartia pinnata* Blanco (1837) and *Spondias pinnata* Kurz (1875); there are various other synonyms. FORSTER f. provided a very detailed description of this cultigen in his *De Plantis esculentis* and later in the same year (1786) in his *Prodromus* provided only a six word diagnosis. He manifestly appropriated SOLANDER's binomial. This, in Polynesia proper, is undoubtedly a man-introduced plant from Malaysia but, among the Polynesians, it was a most important fruit tree. The prevalent Polynesian name *vi* is undoubtedly a cognate form of *ehé, ehéu, leé,* and others still in use in the Lesser Sunda Islands for the selected and improved form, for selected forms have apparently long been planted in Indonesia. The fruits of the wild form are smaller, globose, and very inferior, and the seed bearing part is not "stringy." For a greatly detailed description of the cultigen with a colored plate *see Spondias cytherea* Sonn. in OCHSE, Fruits Dutch East Ind. 19.pl. 8. 1931. This form impresses me as being worthy of recognition as a cultigen. (PLATE 91).

Stachys *dentata [Soland. ex] Parkins. Jour. 41. 1773, *nom., nota* Tahiti = *Limnophila fragrans* (Forst. f.) Seem. — For this species PARKINSON gave two binomials, the above an alternate name, and *Ruellia fragrans*, the latter validated as his own binomial by FORSTER f. in 1786, who appropriated SOLANDER's name. All that PARKINSON said about it was: "The juice of this plant, mixed with several others, they use as a plaister to cure any sort of wounds."

†Telopaea [Soland. ex] Parkins. Jour. 44. 1773, *nom., nota;* Soland. ex Baill. Etud. Gén. Euphorb. 345. 1858, *nom. in syn.* = *Aleurites* J. R. & G. Forst. (1776).

Telopaea †perspicua [Soland. ex] Parkins. Jour. l.c., *nom., nota;* Soland. ex Seem. Fl. Vit. 223. 1867, *nom. in syn.* = *Aleurites moluccana* (L). Willd. — I do not here repeat what PARKINSON said about this taxon, as his statement does not include a single botanical descriptive phrase. He said that from the bark soaked in water a gummy substance was produced which was used for waterproofing bark cloth, that the soot from the burned nuts was used in tattooing and that, strung upon sticks, the kernels of the nuts served as candles. This is the well known candlenut. The PARKINSON use of the name in 1773 is, of course, strictly as a generico-specific one, but because BAILLON later published it in synonymy I have above entered it as a generic entity in order to account for the BAILLON one.

Terminalia †glabrata [Soland. ex] Parkins. Jour. 40. 1773, *nom., nota,* Tahiti = *Terminalia catappa* L. *fide* Seemann, Fl. Vit. 93. 1865, *sed pro parte* = *T. glabrata* Forst. f. (1786). — The SEEMANN reduction was made on the basis of the examination of PARKINSON's unpublished plate no. 116; in the margin of the unpublished SOLANDER manuscript is the pencilled entry "no specimen." Mr. EXELL recently examined the plate and informs me that it does look very much like *Terminalia catappa* L. Yet it seems to be evident that the characters of more than one species are involved in the detailed unpublished SOLANDER description. His leaf description does not agree with the characters of *Terminalia catappa* L. It is suspected that there were two species in Tahiti in 1769, the *aowiree* that PARKINSON recorded as being planted in the morais (burial grounds) and near houses (he gave no botanical characters), and the species that was described in great detail as *T. glabrata* Forst. f. (Pl. Esculent. 52. 1786, about a fifty line description), as contrasted to the usually cited and later *Prodromus* entry where the descriptive data are reduced to a four word diagnosis. Here the younger FORSTER appropriated SOLANDER's specific name and incidentally credited the species to both the Society and the Friendly Islands. At any rate what he described is a species not closely allied to *Terminalia catappa* L., although, to confuse the issue, the FORSTER f. taxon has been erroneously reduced to the Linnaean one. It may be noted that while FORSTER f. and PARKINSON both gave the Tahitian name as *e aowiree* or *auwiri* (FORSTER f. adds *eta iri* and *etari-heiriri*) that SOLANDER records only the name *autara.* There might well have been two species in Tahiti in 1769, *T. catappa* L. (introduced) and *T. glabrata* Forst. f. (an indigenous one).

†Thespesia [Soland. ex] Parkins. Jour. 42. 1773, *nom., nota;* Soland. ex Correa, Ann. Mus. Paris. 9 : 290. 1807, *descr.*

Thespesia †populnea [Soland. ex] Parkins. *l.c., nom., nota;* Soland. ex Correa, *l.c., descr.* Tahiti. — Here, as in the case of *Telopaea,* above, I have modified the form of treatment of the Parkinsonian generico-specific names because of CORREA's later and correct use of the SOLANDER taxon. For *E meerro* (the modern *miro* in Tahiti), PARKINSON merely mentioned that this tree was planted in all the *morais,* being sacred to Tané, that its branches were used as an emblem of peace and that its timber was used for various purposes. There is no description nor was the older synonym (*Hibiscus popul-*

neus L.) mentioned. CORREA must have seen the SOLANDER manuscript in London. *Hibiscus bacciferus* Forst. f. Prodr. 48, 1786 (Friendly, Society, and Easter Islands) is a synonym.

Tournefortia *sericea [Soland. ex] Parkins. Jour. 37. 1773, *nom., nota*. Tahiti = *T. argentea* L. f. (1781) = *Messerschmidia argentea* (L. f.) I. M. Johnst. Jour. Arnold Arb. 16: 164. 1935. — For *taihinnoo* (the modern *tahina* in Tahiti), no description was given, the whole statement being: "The leaves of these two plants [*Tournefortia sericea*, and *Cordia sebestena* (non L.) = *C. subcordata* Lam.] are ingredients in their red dye, or mattee, for their cloth."

Urtica †argentea [Soland. ex] Parkins. Jour. 44. 1773, *nom., nota* = *Urtica argentea* Forst. f. Prodr. 65. 1786. Tahiti = seq.

Urtica *candicans [Soland. ex] Parkins. *l.c., nom. alt.* = *Pipturus argenteus* (Forst. f.) Wedd. — For *E roa* PARKINSON merely mentioned its uses, the bast being used for making lines, belts, and seines, seldom for making garments. There is no botanical description. FORSTER f. published *Urtica argentea* as his own binomial, appropriating SOLANDER's name; it was also based on Tahiti specimens.

*Zizyphoides *argentea [Soland. ex] Parkins. Jour. 47. 1773, *nom., nota*, sphalm. "Zezyphoides"; Seem. Fl. Vit. 43. 1865, *nom. in syn.* Tahiti = *Rhamnus zizyphoides* Soland. ex Forst. f. Prodr. 90. 1786, *nom. nud.*; Biehler, Nov. Plant. Herb. Spreng. Cent. 15, May 30, 1807, *descr.*; Spreng. Fl. Halensis Mant. 1: 37. 1807, *descr.*; Syst. Veg. 1: 786. 1825 = *Alphitonia zizyphoides* (Soland.) A. Gray. — PARKINSON merely said for *E toee*, the modern *toe* in Tahiti: "The wood of the tree they make use of for various purposes, such as the sterns of canoes, heightening boards for ditto, and beams to beat their cloth upon." The name is strictly a generico-specific one and is invalid, there being no description. The binomial used by PARKINSON appears on p. 378 of the unpublished SOLANDER manuscript. While he left it in the short appendix, the very last entry, it was undoubtedly his plan to place it in the Pentandria-Monogynia near *Rhamnus* should the manuscript be published. FORSTER f. listed it as *Rhamnus zizyphoides* [Solander] in his *Prodromus* 90. 1786, as a nomen nudum. BIEHLER and SPRENGEL later provided descriptions and finally the latter credited the specific name to SOLANDER; yet Mr. STEARN reports that no original slip can be located under either *Rhamnus* or *Zizyphoides*. Yet when the FORSTERs had access to the BANKS library, manuscripts and herbarium they must have seen the binomial *Rhamnus zizyphoides*, otherwise the younger FORSTER never would have credited the name to SOLANDER. One surmises that SOLANDER originally wrote a description under *Rhamnus* and later decided that what he had represented a new genus. Regarding BIEHLER's *Plantarum novarum ex Herbario Sprengelii Centuria.* 1-46. 1807, FERNALD (Rhodora 47: 197-198. 1948) has shown that this, his doctoral thesis, was published by May 30, 1807. He observed that SPRENGEL, approving of BIEHLER's thesis and finding it worthy, several months later reprinted it as his own paper under the title *Novarum plantarum ex Herbario meo centuria*, this appearing as the second paper, p. 27-58, in his *Flora Halensis Mantissa Prima* (1807). Unfortunately for SPRENGEL the entire paper had been published earlier under BIEHLER's name, and BIEHLER, not SPRENGEL, is the author of the hundred new species published therein. One might, I suppose, consider it strange that in a descriptive flora covering the vicinity of Halle, Germany, a paper should be included containing the descriptions of a hundred new species of plants from all parts of the world. But it should be remembered that a century and a half ago media for the publication of descriptions of new species were mostly limited to individual volumes, which in many cases must have been subsidized. *Alphitonia excelsa* Reisseck, to which this Tahitian species was reduced by many authors, is restricted by BRAID (Kew Bull. 1925: 168-186. 2 pl. 1925) to Australia. This Polynesian species is recorded from Tahiti, Tonga, Rarotonga, Samoa, Tongatabu, and Fiji, and extends westward to the New Hebrides.

ADDITIONAL NOTES

Further Notes on the History of Maize:— Somewhere it is claimed that American maize was recorded from Cebu in PIGAFETTA's account of MAGELLAN's *Primo viaggio intorno al mundo* in 1521. This would be manna to those who believe in the distribution of economic plants between the two hemispheres some 2,000 to 3,000 years ago. But it would be disconcerting to the vast majority who hold that DE CANDOLLE was correct when he stated in 1883 that he had found no evidence that cultivated plants indicated any important associations between the peoples of the Old and the New Worlds before 1492.

DE CANDOLLE's statement is as true today as when it was written over seventy years ago, except for the possibility of a few cultigens which were carried across the Atlantic, both to the east and to the west, a few centuries before COLUMBUS made his crossing in 1492.

I have read through the Italian and the English text of ROBERT-SON's(1) account of 1906 without locating any statement about maize in the Philippines. Because *mais* does not appear in the detailed 88-page index, I scanned, as a last resort, all of the explanatory notes and found the answer in note 370 of the first volume (p. 269). The reference is from "Al panizo" = *dana* [correctly *daua*] = *Panicum* = *Setaria italica* (L.) Beauv. (p. 183, 187). The note is a confused one and reads: "The equivalent of PIGAFETTA's *dana* is *daoa* or *daua*, 'Millet'. *Mais* [our maize], probably the equivalent of *humas*, is the word for 'panicum'." PIGAFETTA correctly recorded *miglio* (p. 186), the classical millet (*Panicum miliaceum* L.) which was widely cultivated in Italy from Roman times on, as well as in India and China and, to a less degree, in Malaysia and the Philippines. We have no modern record of any plant name corresponding to *humas* in the Philippines; but, in 1521, this name was surely used in Negros for *Panicum miliaceum* L., an ancient Old World cultigen.

Incidently, *daua*, very widely used in Malaysia and in the Philippines for *Setaria italica*, is an unmodified Sanscrit name and is probably the word for which the name of the island of Java was derived. It has been noted that there are three excellently executed panels depicting *Setaria italica* on the eighth and ninth century Buddhist stupa of the Borobudur in Java. The identifications are positive ones, and the forms depicted cannot be mistaken for any other plant. Therefore, we may infer that this particular cereal was the most important source of food in eighth and ninth century Java.

---

1) ROBERTSON, J. A. MAGELLAN's Voyage Around the World by ANTONIO PIGAFETTA. The Original Text of the Ambrosian MS. with English Translation, Notes, Bibliography and Index, 2 vols. 1906.

As no rice was depicted on the Borobudur, we are justified in asking whether its cultivation had just commenced or was very limited in Java at that time, even though this cereal was cultivated in Asia from the early times.

The first actual record that I have found of the use of the *word* *mais* (maize) in the Philippines is in the POVEDANO manuscript of 1578. Here are recorded the names of only four cereals which were then cultivated in Negros: rice, the classical millet (*Panicum miliaceum* L.), the so-called Italian millet (*Setaria italica* Beauv.), and the common sorghum. Under his entry *sorgho*, POVEDANO cited the very widely used Philippine name *batad*. He saw no maize. DIEGO LOPE POVEDANO (*2*) was the first *encomiendero* of Negros. His record was made thirteen years after the Spaniards had established themselves at Cebu. Nevertheless, in the interim between 1521 and 1565, Spanish expeditions from Mexico had visited the Philippines (in 1526, 1527 and 1542). The first introduction of maize might well have been by way of any of these expeditions, for it was customary for the Spanish-sponsored exploring expedition, sailing from America, to take maize seeds with them for actual planting (as indicated in the case of QUIROS mentioned on p. 216, 239, 249 & 262.

I have noted two other early records for the introduction of maize into the Old World by QUIROS on the Marquesas Islands in 1595; and on Espiritu Santo (New Hebrides), a decade later. No matter how sterile further investigations of these early maize records may be, they will surely be more profitable than abstract theorizing. Undoubtedly, there were earlier Portuguese introductions of various forms of maize into India, Burma, Siam, and elsewhere in the Old World after 1500 A.D., when direct connections were established between Brazil and the coast of India.

If the truth were known about the provenance of the form (or forms) of maize in Burma, it would doubtless show that this cereal came in over that too often overlooked Portuguese route from Brazil, when a decade or so after establishing themselves at Goa, the Portuguese founded a trading post in Siam. I think that very probably both types could still be found, in cultivation, in the area immediately back of Pernambuco or Natal on the bulge of Brazil.

Maize in Europe:— ANDERSON, in his introduction to the 1950 reprint of FINAN's (*3*) excellent paper on this subject, recognizes two general types of maize. Regarding the second type, he says (p. x of the 1950 reprint) : "Whence had it come? . . . Had it indeed

---

2)   IGNACIO, REBECCA P. An Annotated Translation of the POVEDANO Manuscript (1578). i-ix. 1-78. 1-13. (Index and bibliography). Typewritten thesis, Far Eastern University, Manila, 1951. I am indebted to Dr. KARL J. PELZER of the Department of Geography of Yale University for his courtesy in loaning me a microfilm of Miss IGNACIO's thesis.

3)   FINAN, J. J. Maize in the Great Herbals. Chron. Bot. Co., reprint, i-xiv. 149-181. illus. 1950. The text reprinted from Ann. Missouri Bot. Gard. 35: 149-191. fig. 1-23. 1948.

spread into Europe by the back door of Asia? . . . Or even could it perhaps have been brought over by the Norsemen?"

This Norseman idea is expressed elsewhere in at least one of ANDERSON's other papers, but he did not expand the subject further. Even a farmer would have realized that, because of the very adverse climatic conditions existing in Greenland in the year 1000 and later, maize could not possibly have been grown to maturity in the extreme north.

The Spaniards and Portuguese were early explorers of the east coast of North America, which forms the eastern limits of what is now the United States and Canada. In this connection, we should not overlook another recorded, but now largely forgotten episode. The Spaniards, in the sixteenth century, attempted to establish a colony on Chesapeake Bay prior to the successful attempt of the English at Jamestown in 1607. It is definitely known that at that time four or five varieties of maize were cultivated by the Indians of Virginia and Maryland. It is not impossible that one of these may have been an early introduction into Europe. It seems, therefore, as unnecessary to consider the hypothesis of Viking introduction as it seems incorrect to invoke a possible pre-1500 introduction into Asia, where maize did not occur until after the Portuguese, coming direct from Brazil, established themselves at Goa in 1500 A.D. (see p. 261).

While on the subject of maize it seems well to record that the first figure of maize appearing in European literature is that of OVIEDO in 1535, according to FINAN, and the second that of FUCHS in 1542. In four or five decades of very active exploration in America and an equally active period of trans-Atlantic and trans-Indian Ocean distribution of tropical economic plants and weeds a great deal would have happened. There was more than ample time for the actual introduction of half a dozen varieties before the European herbalists even commenced to have maize illustrations prepared. HERNANDEZ' basic work is generally listed as having been *published* in Rome in 1651, which is of course correct, but his manuscript was prepared between 1571 and 1577 in Mexico (he died in Spain, in 1578). Various Philippine species were included in the 1651 edition of his *Nova plantarum animalium et mineralium Mexicanorum historia* (Rerum medicarum Novae Hispaniae thesaurus) which must have been added by the editor of the first published edition in Rome (*vide* PRITZEL's Thesaurus ed. 2, No. 4,000). There were two issues with different title pages in 1651 (*cf.* FIG. 7).

As to the idea that Asia may have been involved in the introduction and distribution of maize, no one, so far as I am aware, has considered what may well have happened after the Portuguese developed their much traveled Brazil-Goa trade route following 1500 which persisted for 165 years, antedating the Spanish Philippine venture by 65 years. At Goa the Portuguese intersected the ancient, lucrative spice trade route between the East Indies and Europe. Almost any overland caravan to the Mediterranean by way of Asia Minor (where the caravan route connected with the silk route from China), following

1500, may have carried Indian corn northward. From Asia Minor, it would naturally soon reach Europe and perhaps China. Hence, in the early European literature (1535-1658) two of the most commonly used names for forms of maize were *Frumentum turcicum* and *Frumentum indicum*.

One regrets that FINAN did not give more attention to HERNANDEZ' *Nova plantarum animalium et mineralium Mexicanorum historiae*. The latter amply described our common Indian corn as *Tlaolli seu Maizio* and briefly characterized seventeen varieties under their Nahuatl names (FIG. 12). FINAN correctly cited its date of publication as 1651, but does not seem to mention that the manuscript was prepared between the years 1571 and 1577. The difference of three fourths of a century between the time of preparation of this manuscript and its publication is vitally important to those interested in the distributional history of Mexican plant species. The two figures on pages 242 and 243 (FIG. 12) were copied by whomever edited the manuscript in Rome from L'OBEL's work of 1576 (the "cob" was added from some other source, perhaps from OVIEDO's Sevilla edition of his *Historia* of 1535, which I have not seen).

American Fruits on Murals at Pompeii:— In January 1953, another extraordinary paper was published by Dr. CARTER in which Dr. MANGELSDORF's as well as my own opinions were attacked. I did not see this until November 1953 (*4*).

CARTER credited the Romans as knowing the pineapple and the sweetsop (*Annona squamosa* L.), both strictly American endemic species, at the time of the destruction of Pompeii (A.D. 70). His authority was unnamed, but from the reference given it proved to be DOMENICO CASELLA (*5*), merely referred to as "a botanist". I went through CASELLA's paper and find that his reproduction of a fruit on a mural at Pompeii is most certainly based on a pineapple. If we accept this record, the pineapple must have been known to the Romans in the first century of the Christian era. A second record is *Annona squamosa* L. I can express no opinion on the possible correctness of this identification, as CASELLA did not reproduce the figure, and his descriptive data of the fruit, as depicted, are inconclusive.

Neither species will grow in southern Italy today nor elsewhere in the Mediterranean basin, for both belong strictly to tropical climates. There is no indication that the climate of the Mediterranean basin was much warmer two thousand years ago than it is today. There are, furthermore, no records in the extensive literature on Roman botany and horticulture of either species being present in any part of the Mediterranean. No other data exist which might

4) CARTER, G. F. Plants across the Pacific. Mem. Soc. Am. Archaeol. 9: 62-71. Jan. 1953.

5) CASELLA, D. La frutta nelle pitture Pompeiana. Pompeiana. Raccolta di studi per il secondo centenario degli scavi di Pompei. 355-386. fig. 39-46. 1950. Napoli. Gaetano Macchiaroli.

ATE vel AHATE DEPANNVCO, alia Icon.

TEXT FIGURE 22. — *Annona squamosa* L., the Sweet-Sop or Sugar-Apple. — As mentioned on p. 367, the figure of a fruit on a mural at Pompeii has recently been identified as representing this strictly American species. There is no other record of its possible introduction in the Old World until after 1500 and it is strongly suspected that the identification is an error. This species is now universally distributed in the tropics of both hemispheres and was one of the first American plants introduced, probably by the Portuguese, into India following 1500, and by the Spaniards following 1565 into the Philippines. Incidentally, this is one of the most common American species widely naturalized in India. WESTER, in 1913, recorded about 50 different local names for *Ate*, its Philippine form being *Atis*. — From F. HERNANDEZ's *Nova Plantarum . . . Mexicanorum Historiae* (Romae, 1651).

suggest that these species occurred in the Old World tropics before the Portuguese initiated their significant ventures in 1500 A.D. Both species, of course, are grown today in all parts of the tropics where climatic conditions are favorable. In tropical West Africa, the pineapple, according to Dr. CHEVALIER, is naturalized.

We meet here with the old problem of the presence or the absence of the coconut in the Atlantic basin before 1500 in another guise; those who trust O. F. COOK's biased judgment will follow him, but those who read BRUMAN's proofs of its absence there until after 1500 will at least think twice.

There is a remote possibility that the Romans had a knowledge of certain tropical American species, based actually on introduced plants, as they grew on some one of the Macaronesian Islands, with which they were as familiar as were the Greeks and the Phoenicians. These islands were located on the short route between Brazil and Africa. Here we enter a field of pure surmise. I am not competent to say what introduced plant species might or might not have been present on the Macaronesian Islands, about two thousand years ago.

Further conclusions cannot be drawn until after the truly intriguing data presented by Dr. CASELLA have been studied by competent botanists, thoroughly familiar with the history of ancient botany, in coöperation with critical historians of art. They will have to give thought to the possibility that an artist involved in the Pompeii restorations in the past century perpetrated a hoax and an investigation of the pigments used might be in order. We must consider this possibility in view of the very recent exposure of the archeological Piltdown man hoax in England, the Kensington stone in Minnesota and other cases, such as the actual description of an American artifact, a child's toy, as a new species of fossil maize! Certain pre-Spanish carvings in Central America were, at one time, described as representing elephant trunks. This would have been a sensational discovery, were it not that the figures showed only the long tail of the sacred quetzal bird! Then, too, there are the records of American maize found in mummy wrappings in Egyptian tombs which merely prove that some of the caterers to the tourist trade of the last century did not know their botany too well!

Most of CASELLA's identifications are clearly correct, but one cannot agree in all cases. A strangely erroneous one is the common mango (*Mangifera indica* L.). This was perhaps not spectacular enough to attract CARTER's attention, for an Indian, not an American, species was involved. CASELLA was so positive that he referred this ancient painting of a leafy, fruit-bearing branch to the Indian *mulgoba* variety of the common mango. He, fortunately, did reproduce a photograph of the painting (No. 8641 in the National Museum, Naples; figure 45 of *Pompeiana*) which enables me to solve the mystery at a glance. The fruits depicted are *solitary, long pedicelled, ovoid-globose, equilateral,* not at all those of a *Mangifera*. One shows clearly the "superior" position of the calyx. It was an attempt to depict a pomaceous species, probably a pear (*Pyrus*), a genus not unknown in Italy. How critical such paintings should be considered will become clear if one notes that the painter of the mural depicted the narrow entire leaves as strictly opposite which is neither a *Pyrus* nor a *Mangifera* character.

Bixa across the Pacific:— ANDERSON seems to have suggested to CARTER, before investigating the case himself, that the distributional history of *Bixa orellana* L. should be investigated, because this strictly American plant now occurs in all tropical countries. CARTER, in his recent paper, referred to above, could not possibly have selected a better case for the opposition than his notes on *Bixa*. The Portuguese, we can safely assume, would have introduced a Brazilian form of *Bixa* on the Malabar coast of India shortly after 1500. Independently, the Spaniards introduced it in Guam and the Philippines from Mexico after 1565 and, with it, a slight modification of its Nahuatl name *achuetl* as *achuete*.

While CARTER went ahead, ANDERSON thought it advisable to investigate the case and wrote to me to ascertain what I knew about the distribution of *Bixa*. I happened to have much information in my Polynesian card catalogue work, the preparation of which was commenced in Manila in 1918 and continued intermittently up to a few years ago. Here is the Polynesian record which I sent to ANDERSON. *Bixa* presumably was introduced into Hawaii perhaps about 1830; at any rate by 1865 it had become naturalized (*fide* DEGENER) in the Nuuanu Valley east of the Kauaiahao church. There are two other records of the species in Hawaii late in the last century, and two for Samoa. There are also about twenty other records in other mostly high islands, for all of Polynesia, *all within the present century*.

Incidentally, this large-leaved ornamental shrub is not a "shrinking violet" that would be overlooked by casual early collectors and botanists. The pink to white flowers are 4 to 5 cm. in diameter and the reddish capsules covered with curved, rather soft, reddish spine-like processes are equally conspicuous. In the Philippines, the name *achuete* became modified and among the dozen recorded forms it varies, as now used, from *achuete* to *chotis* and *sotis;* but its Nahuatl origin is still apparent after roughly four centuries. CARTER's paper of 1953 certainly shows him as a master in the *argumentum ad hominem* technique (attacking the opposing lawyer, especially in jury trials, to divert attention, when it dawns upon him that his client has not a valid case and no chance whatever of winning before the jury). To master the published records, study the early manuscripts and obtain the necessary botanical knowledge to deal properly with the problems which he now treats would seem to be a more fruitful approach.

Further Notes on Gossypium:— I should still like to refer to SILOW's recent article on *Gossypium* (6) which I received on Decem-

---

6) SILOW, R. A. The Problems of Trans-Pacific Migration Involved in the Origin of the Cultivated Cottons of the New World. Proc. Seventh Pacific Sci. Congr. 5: 112-118. 1953.

ber 11, 1953, when the first proofs of this paper had just been returned to the printers. He follows the views of his co-worker, J. B. HUTCH-INSON, in which I have no confidence. The possible pre-Columbian introduction of African cultigens into America cannot be ignored. Nor should one overlook the trans-Atlantic trade which developed between the Portuguese settlements in West Africa and the Spanish ones in the West Indies, established within the first decade following 1492 and following 1500, when the enterprising Portuguese established their extensive operations between Brazil and India (Goa). The true explanation of the hybridization between the American and Old World cottons may be found in the Portuguese activities in the early introduction of Old World species of *Gossypium* into America over this trade route. A relatively recent introduction of the Old World parent *Gossypium* species, shortly after 1500 and when cotton was in great demand, impresses me as much more logical than its possible American introduction in very ancient time (*cf.* p. 335), before modern man was a factor in plant distribution. There seems to be no more reason for considering an early trans-Pacific migration of cotton through the agency of man than for other American cultigens such as maize, the cultivated species of *Cucurbita* and the grain amaranths.

Concluding Remarks on the Origin of the Sweet Potato:— While in this memoir, as originally prepared, I accepted the almost universally prevalent idea that the sweet potato (*Ipomoea batatas*) was of American origin, I have reason to believe (though no satisfactory proof as yet) that this is erroneous. The plant probably originated through hybridization in Africa and was transmitted by man across the Atlantic to America a few centuries before COLUMBUS reached the West Indies, and perhaps somewhat earlier by way of Madagascar and the Mascarene Islands to Malaysia, Papuasia and Polynesia and even to the west coast of South America. There is no definite proof of this as yet, but the hypothesis is worth further study.

WIENER held that he had "proved" that the Nahuatl name *camotl* was derived from a Filipino word meaning "root". Though but an amateur in comparative philology, I have disproved this idea (*see* p. 316). Yet, WIENER could see no reason for associating the ancient Quechua name *cumar* (*kumar*) of the sweet potato with its Polynesian name *kumara*. Here I could argue against his conclusion, for *kumara* is very widely used in the Polynesian culture area as far to the southwest as New Zealand. I dismiss two records of this name in British New Guinea as probably having been introduced by Polynesian civil service employees after the British took over what became British New Guinea (Territory of Papua) in 1884. Minor variants of the name *kumara* within Polynesia are *kumala* (Fiji), *uala* (Hawaii), *uma'a* (Marquesas), *umala* (Samoa), and *umara* (Tahiti) ; and there are doubtless others. While it seems quite possible that the Polynesians took the sweet potato all the way across the Pacific to Peru, I cannot hazard a guess as to the origin of the

Polynesian name *kumara* or the Quechuan name *kumar*. They are suspiciously similar (*see also* p. 307).

If the idea as to the African origin of the sweet potato be correct, this is the first major cultivated food plant that, through man, extended its range to both hemispheres before the Portuguese and the Spaniards intervened at the close of the fifteenth and the beginning of the sixteenth century — except probably a few tropical species which were carried across the Atlantic Ocean before the European colonial expansion at the end of the fifteenth century. I must, however, leave these interesting problems to others for solution. In discussing the sweet potato problem with Dr. A. E. KEHR of the Louisiana State University in December 1953, I very strongly urged him to investigate the native African species of *Ipomoea* as a possible source of the sweet potato, which is obviously a hexaploid. Dr. KEHR and his assistant Mr. YU CHENG TING failed in all attempts to produce fertilization, using in each case *Ipomoea batatas* as one parent and approximately forty other species of the genus as the other parent, including certain West Indian species which some botanists have suggested as being a potential parent of the sweet potato (*7*).

HORNELL (*8*) reviewed the expressed opinions of those who have considered the sweet potato and favors its transmission from South America to Polynesia by balsa raft or Polynesian canoe. Thus the Quechuan word *kumar* could be linked with the Polynesian form of *kumara*. But the reverse direction is as plausible.

Recently, Mrs. IDA LANGMAN, well known for her bibliographical studies in Mexican botany, kindly informed me: "If WIENER thought, mistakenly, that the term 'camote' was not used by HERNANDEZ and felt that the absence was significant, then the Badianus Ms. offers even more significant data. This work, as you know, was written in 1552, 18 years before HERNANDEZ even came to Mexico. Plate 48 of this work refers to 'tlacacamohtli' which, as Dr. EMMART says, 'doubtless represents a species of *Ipomoea* — perhaps the common sweet potato.... The illustration is too conventionalized to allow the precise identification of the species'. So here is more evidence that the term was used in Mexico before the return of the first galleon from the Philippines."

Colmeiro's Bibliography:— All interested in the distributional history of cultivated plants, particularly those which originated in America, will find it worth while to consult COLMEIRO's remarkable bibliography (characterized by PRITZEL as a *Liber vere egregius*!). This book (*9*) deals well with the writings, published and unpublished, of the early Spanish and Portuguese botanists and botanical explorers. It is a mine of information on early manuscripts and publications of the pioneer explorers of North, Central and South America as well as of parts of the Orient.

---

7) TING, Y. C. and A. E. KEHR. Meiotic Studies in the Sweet Potato. Jour. Hered. 44: 207-211. fig. 24-26. 1953.

8) HORNELL, J. How did the Sweet Potato reach Polynesia? Jour. Linn. Soc. Bot. 53: 41-62. fig. 1-2. 1 map. 1946.

9) COLMEIRO, M. La botánica e los botánicos de la península Hispano-Lusitana. Estudios bibliográficos y biográficos. i-x. 1-216. 1858.

I regret that the pressure of years makes it impossible for me to study the works of the Arab authors which are available in translated form, such as those of ABU-L-QASIM (ABULCASIS), IBN AL-AWWAM (YAHYA B. MUHAMMAD), IBN AL-BAITAR, and others. Bibliographic details regarding their works will be found in COLMEIRO (pages 6 and 7) and in SARTON's *Introduction*. More recent data will be found in the numerous modern accounts and bibliographies of Arab science published in Spain and elsewhere. Studies of the Arab literature and the extensive literature on the history of Arab science and medicine, with which most of us are altogether unfamiliar, might well yield further data as to when maize, the sweet potato, cassava and other economic and medicinal plants first crossed the Atlantic.

Postscript.— I am sorry that I have been unable to make any detailed mention of PAUL WEATHERWAX's *Indian Corn in Old America* (just published by the Macmillan Co.). This interesting, well written and attractively illustrated work is in conformity with my general conclusions.

Dr. WEATHERWAX's book, which includes a reproduction and brief discussion of *Zea* in the *Pen ts'ao kang mu*, the famous Chinese herbal, arrived a few weeks after Dr. VERDOORN lent me his copies of two publications by MESSEDAGLIA which are of some further interest in this connection. I should still like to draw the attention of all interested in the actual dates of introduction of various economic species of American origin (as maize, tobacco, potato, manioc and certain other species) into the Old World, to LUIGI MESSEDAGLIA's "PIETRO MARTIRE D'ANGHIERA e le sue notizie sul mais e su altri prodotti naturali d'America" (Atti Ist. Veneto Sci. Let. Arti 90: 293-346. 1931). MESSEDAGLIA, a well informed though somewhat hasty and uncritical author, was convinced that maize was in cultivation in Spain and in Italy before COLUMBUS discovered America. It seems more logical to assume that the first people to introduce maize into Southern Europe were the Portuguese, who for the last forty years of the fifteenth century persistently explored East Africa in an attempt to circumnavigate that continent. They reached India in 1497 and established their trade route between Lisbon and the Orient via eastern Brazil within the first decade of the 16th Century. There is, it appears now, definite evidence that in pre-Columbian time the natives of Africa had introduced maize from America.

MESSEDAGLIA's more extensive memoir on the subject of maize in Southern Europe is *Il mais e la vita rurale italiana* (Piacenza, 1927). Had the Arabs been involved in this maize introduction into Africa, as some have claimed, it is clear that if this introduction had taken place before they expanded eastward over the Indo-Malaysian region, maize would have been common in cultivation there long before the Portuguese or the Spaniards had introduced it in the Orient between 1500 and 1565. There was certainly no direct introduction of this American species into any part of Asia previous to the arrival of the Portuguese at Goa in 1500.

There is some important evidence in the Oriental literature that no investigator can afford to overlook. All sinologists are in agreement that there exists no mention of maize in the early Chinese writings. There is, *e.g.*, no plant resembling maize in any of the editions, in Dr. VERDOORN's library, of TANG SHEN-WEI's famous, well illustrated herbal (compiled in the 10th century, often reprinted, for 400 years the chief reference work on the Chinese materia medica). The first Chinese maize record, that we know, appeared in the *Pen ts'ao kang mu* by LI SHIH-CHEN. The first of numerous editions was printed in 1590 (see my and WALKER's *Bibliography of Eastern Asiatic Botany*, p. 555. 1938).

Dr. S. Y. HU translated LI's original maize description for me. From this it is apparent that the first maize with which LI became acquainted, in China, was a popcorn, for he states that the seeds are yellow, *edible when popped, and white like popped rice*. This would have been one of the early Portuguese introductions at Goa direct from Brazil, via the Cape of Good Hope (after 1500).

MESSEDAGLIA, as well as WEATHERWAX, reproduce the woodcut of maize which appeared in the early illustrated editions of the *Pen ts'ao kang mu*. The same poor cut is found in the early Japanese editions of the *Pen ts'ao* known as *Honzo Komoku* (Dr. VERDOORN showed me such an edition, by INAU, which seems to antedate the 1714 ed. mentioned in my *Bibliography*). This is hardly a very clear illustration, it is apparent that whoever prepared the drawing did not see the maize plant, but that the drawing was made from descriptive notes prepared by some unnamed person (this cut seems to have been reproduced first, in Europe, in BONAFOUS's *Histoire du Maïs* of 1836). In the well known 1885 edition of the *Pen ts'ao* by CHANG SHAO-TANG (issued in 1885) we find, on the other hand, a perfect illustration of normal maize (though almost all other woodcuts in that edition have been reproduced, without change, from the early editions).

LI further states that he did not know the plant, that it was rare at that time, being cultivated to some extent in Szechuan, and definitely declares that "corn originated in the occident." One may well assume that the first maize to reach China came overland from India because it was the popcorn introduced by the Portuguese from Brazil. (E.D.M. — October, 1954).

INDEX *of* AUTHORS

AIRY-SHAW, 247
AKEMINE, M., *198*, 271, 285, 294
ALDROVANDI, 177
ALEXANDER THE GREAT, 195, 213
ALLAN, H. H., 225, 227
ALLEN, PAUL, 335
ALLISON, R. S., 188
ALSTON, A. H. G., 172, 182, 191, 203, 205, 209, 210, 227, 354
ALVARO DE GUIJO, 267
AMES, BLANCHE, 297
AMES, O., *295* seq., 309
ANDERSON, E., 188, 237, *261*, 271, 276, 278, 285, 286, *289* seq., 312, 341, 342, 365, 366, 370
ARCHBOLD, 323

BÄCK, ABRAHAM, *208*, 347, 354, 357
BACKER, C. A., 227, 230, 238, 275, 290, 305, 306
BACSTRÖM, iv
BADIANUS, 372
BAILEY, L. H., *280*, 281
BAILLON, 361
BAKHUIZEN VAN DEN BRINK Sr., R. C., *303* seq.
BANKS, JOSEPH, 172, 173, 182, *184*, 186, 187, 191, 194, *201* seq., 211, *212* seq., *240* seq., 251, *326* seq., 353, 362, Pls. 80, 81, *82*, 84, *86*, *89*, 90
BARTLETT, *323*
The BAUHINS, 177
BAUSE, I. F., Pl. 85
BECCARI, 266
BERLANGA, Father TOMAS DE, 278
BERTERO, 348
BEST, ELSDON, 271
BIEHLER, 208, 362
BIRD, JUNIUS J., 183, *272*, 276, 279, 281, *291*, 321
BLANCO, M., 313, 314
BOHN, G. W., 280
BOIS, D., 279, 280, 286
BONPLAND, 262
BORROW, GEORGE, 262
BOUCHÉ, 279
BOUGAINVILLE, L. A. DE, 194, 245, 326, Pl. 80
BRADBURY, 210
BRAID, 363

BRASS, L. J., 303, 323
BRAVO DE LAGUNAS, PEDRO, 314
BRETSCHNEIDER, 302
BRITTEN, JAMES, 177, 198/199, Pl. 90
BROWN, F. B. H., *248*, *250* seq., 267, 347, 351
BROWN, ROBERT, 352
BRUMAN, H. J., *258*, *267*, 369
BUCHAN, 326
BUCHENAU, 260
BUCK, PETER, 189, 195, 212, *232*
BUFFON, 280
BURKILL, I. H., 183, *239*, *295*, 333, 341
BYRON, 326, 327

CABRAL, 233, 276
CAMERON, H. C., Pl. 89
CAMUS, J., 177
CANDOLLE, ALPHONSE DE, *179*, 180, 197, 242, 271, 282, 285, *293* seq., 319, 364
CANDOLLE, A. P. DE, 246
CARR, C. E., 172
CARTER, G. F., 222, *236*, *252* seq., 269, 301, 349, *367* seq.
CARTERET, 326, 327
CASELLA, D., *367* seq.
CAVANILLES, 354
CAVENDISH, 233
CHAMISSO, 217
CHAPMAN, 225
CHEESEMAN, T. F., 225, 253, *349*
CHEVALIER, A., *304*, *310*, 369
CHIOVENDA, 266
CHRISTOPHERSEN, 260
CHURCHWARD, 196, 213
CLARKE, C. B., 172
CLAUSEN, 316
CLERKE, 326
COCKAYNE, L., 179, 201, 206
COGNIAUX, 237, 280, 341
COLLINS, G. N., *261*
COLLINS, J. L., *269*
COLLINS, Z., 210
COLMEIRO, M., *372* seq.
COLÓN, 255
COLUMBUS, C., *220*, 255
COMMERSON, 185, 240

COOK, Captain JAMES, 172, 173, *185* seq., *187*, *201*, *218*, *227*, 230, 234, 235, 238, *240*, 243, 249, 262, 266, *269*, *270*, 279, *326*, 327, 347, 350, *356*, Pls. 82, 83, 88, 89, 90, 92
COOK, O. F., 179, 189, *213*, 215, 217, 222, *248*, *253*, 261, *266*, 267, 271, 272, 301, 304, 306, 369
COPELAND, E. B., 183, *275*
CORMACK, MARY, 239
CORREIA DA SERRA, 361, 362
CORTÉS, HERNAN, 267
CRAIGIE, W. A., 180, 181
CRISWELL, E. H., 181

DALRYMPLE, 328
DAMPIER, 240
DAVIS, THOMAS, 214
DEGENER, O., 218, 370
DELESSERT, 171
DIAS, BARTHOLOMEW, 232
DICKINSON, W., Pl. 82
DILLENIUS, 178
DIXON, R. B., 319, 320, 321
DRAKE, FRANCIS, 233
DRAKE DEL CASTILLO, E., 252
DRUCE, 178
DRYANDER, Pl. 90
DU BOIS, CHARLES, 177
DURAND, ELIAS, 210

EAMES, A. J., 264, 351
EAST, E. M., 311
ELLIOTT, STEPHEN, 210
ELLIS, J., 186
ELLIS, WILLIAM, 216, 233, *338*
EMORY, K. P.,
EWAN, JOSEPH, 183, 209
EXELL, A. W., 177, 182, 229, 350, 361

FAXON, C. E., 283
FERNALD, M. L., *175*, 180, 181, 223, 260, 283, 284, 362
FINAN, J. J., 288, *365* seq.
FIRTH, R., 270
FLATT VON ALFÖLD, C., 177

FORSTER, Johann GEORG Adam, 188, *200* seq., *208* seq., 245, 329, 332, *346* seq., Pls. *87, 88*
FORSTER, JOHANN REINHOLD, *200* seq., *208* seq., Pls. *85, 86*, 90
the FORSTERs, 173, 182, 183, 186, *191*, 194, *200* seq., *208* seq., *213*, 220, 227, *245*, 295, 329, 333, *346* seq., Pls. 80, 83, 84, 85, 86, 87, 88, 89
FORSTER Herbarium, *208* seq.
FOSBERG, F. R., 182, 183, 259, *328* seq., 359
FOTHERGILL, JOHN, 327
FUCHS, 366

GAETANO, 233, 317
GAMA, VASCO DA, 232, 255
GAMBLE, J. SYKES, 177, 290
GANDHI, 295
GEMELLI CARERI, G. F., 231
GLADWIN, H. S., *195*
GLEASON, 284
GLÜCK, H., 284
GOODSPEED, T. H., 178, 183, 309, 316
GRAFF, ANTON, Pls. 85, 88
GRAY, ASA, 254, 340
GRIFFITH, W., 172
GUPPY, 257, 258

HÄCKEL, M., Pl. 88
HADDON, A. C., *309*, 312, 316
HAMMEN, TH. VAN DER, *273*
HANCE, 286
HARLAND, S. C., *338*
HARRIS, ROBERT S., *287*
HAWKESWORTH, J., 327, 328, 330, Pls. 80, *92*
HEALY, A. J., 225, 227
HERDER, F. VON, 203
HERNANDEZ, FRANCISCO, *224*, 226, 288, 292, 298, 300, 308, *317* seq., 337, 366, 367, 368, 372
HEYERDAHL, T., 189, *212* seq., 232, 248, 250, 251, 252, 261, 262, *263* seq., 269, 291
HEYNE, 323, 324
HILLCOAT, D., 338
HILLEBRAND, W., *252*, 259, 260, 264, 265, 350
HOCHREUTINER, 260
HODGES, WILLIAM, Pls. 83, 84
HOEHNE, 296

HOFFMAN, 319
HOLMES, Chief Justice, 185
HOOKER, W. J., 211
HOOPS, 319
HORNELL, J., 372
HORNIUS, G., 280
HRDLICKA, 243
HUERTAS G., G., *273*
HUERTO, GERONIMO DE, 224
HULBERT, J. R., 180, 181
HULTÉN, 359
HUMBOLDT, 252, 254, 273, 354
HUTCHINSON, J. B., 258, 265, 279, 291, *337* seq., 371

IGNACIO, REBECCA P., 365
INGLETON, G. C., Pl. 81
IRVING, WASHINGTON, 197, 280

JEFFREYS, M. D. W., *319*
JEPSON, W. L., 225
JOHNSTON, I. M., 245, 246, 266
JONES, G. N., 181
JUEL, H. O., 208

KAMEL, J. G., *313*
KEHR, A. E., 372
KERR, R., 327
KING, G., 290
KING, L. J., 284
KINSEY, A. C., 284
KOBUSKI, C. E., 182
KOZLOFF, I. V., 286
KUNTH, 262
KUNZE, 209

LAM, H. J., *312*
LAMARCK, 260
LAMBERT, 203, 209
LANDAUER, WALTER, 277
LANGMAN, IDA, 372
LASKI, HAROLD, 185
LATCHAM, 276, 277
LAUFER, B., 194, 290, 307, *309* seq., 313, *341* seq.
LEE, JAMES, 327, Pl. 90
LEGASPI, 233
LEPEL, VON, 209
LEWIS, A. B., 310, 313
LI, H. L., *340*
LINK, 260
LINNAEUS, C., *186*, 208, 234, 332, 333, 347, 348, 355, Pls. 85, 89
LINNAEUS *f.*, C., 208, 347, 354, 355, 357
LOBELIUS, 288, 367
LOUREIRO, 210, 343
LOYASA, 233, 317

MACDANIELS, 343

MAGELLAN, 188, 189, 213, 233, 235, 241, 255, 307, 339, 364
MAIDEN, J. H., Pl. 90
MALASPINA, 354
MANGELSDORF, P. C., 179, 182, *188*, 258, *261*, 265, 275, *287*, 289, 342, 367
MARCGRAVE, 228, 322, 334
MARTELLI, U., 328, *355*
MARTIRE D'ANGHIERA, P., 280, 373
MARTIUS, 171
MELVILLE, HERMAN, 215
MENDAÑA, 230, 233, 235, 241, 246, 251, 270
MERCADO, I., *313*
MERRILL, E. D., 188, 206, 221, 237, *248, 250*, 265, *289* seq., 313, 314, *331*, 367
MEYER, F. G., 246
MICHELI, 284
MIKI, S., 283
MIKLOUHO-MACLAY, A. DE, 313
MILLSPAUGH, 310
MIQUEL, 324, 357
MOE, HENRY ALLEN, *183*
MOORE, J. H., 327
MOORE, J. W., 357
MOQUIN, 302
MORISON, R., 178
MUELLER, FERD. VON, 313
MUHLENBERG, 210

NÉE, 354
NELSON, DAVID, 246
NEUHAUS, HENRIETTE A., *323*
NEWTON, JA., Pl. 90
NORDENSKIÖLD, 276
NOUHUYS, J. W. VAN, *309* seq., 313
NUTTALL, THOMAS, 209

OCHOTERENA, I., 224
OCHSE, 360
OLIVER, D. L., 179, *188*, *261*, 265, 289, 342
OVIEDO, G. F. DE, *220*, 254 seq., *266, 278*, 366, 367
OWNBEY, G. B., 220, *259*

PALLAS, 208, 211
PARKINSON, STANFIELD, *326* seq.
PARKINSON, SYDNEY, 173, 175, 186, *187*, 191, 200, 203, 205, 206, 217, 241, *326* seq., *332* seq., *346* seq., Pls. 81, *90, 91*
PARLATORE, 338
PARRY, WM., Pl. 89
PAX, 319
PELZER, KARL J., 365
PENNANT, Pl. 90

PENROSE, B., 232
PERRY, LILY M., 182
PERSOON, 347
PICHARDO, 255
PIERCE, W. D., *321*
PIGAFETTA, A., 270, 307, 316, 317, 341, *364*
PISO, 228, 322, 334
PLINIUS, 224
POIRET, 314, 337
POLO, MARCO, 289, 316
POVEDANO, DIEGO LOPE, 317, *365*
PRADO Y TOVAR, DIEGO DE, 324
PRAIN, D., *214*, 244, 259
PRITZEL, 372
PUNNETT, R. L., *277*

QUIRÓS, P. F. DE, *215* seq., *219*, 230, 233, 235, *239*, 241, 246, *249*, 251, *262*, 270, 324, *365*
QUISUMBING, E., 317

RAFINESQUE, 210
RAMOS, 247
RAMSBOTTOM, J., 177, 182, Pl. 89
RATZEL, 273
RECCHI, 224
REICHE, K., 179
REYNOLDS, 326
REYNOLDS, JOSHUA, Pls. 82, 92
RHEEDE, 313, 351, 355
RIDLEY, 284
ROBERTSON, J. A., 364
ROBERTY, G., *338*
ROCK, 266
ROGGEVEEN, 269
ROIG Y MESA, J. T., 255
ROSS, A. S. C., 270
ROXBURGH, WILLIAM, *171*, 198, 220, 237, 294, 348
RUEHLE, GEO. D., 298
RUMPHIUS, 256/257, 268/269, *303* seq., *343*, 355

SAAVEDRA, 233, 317
SAHAGUN, B. DE, 318
ST. JOHN, HAROLD, 183, 260, 264, 351, 353
SAINT-LAGER, J. B., 177
SAN AGUSTÍN, GASPAR DE, 314
SANDWICH, Earl of, 203, 206

SAPPER, 273
SAUER, C., *271* seq., 289, 293, *345*
SAUER, J. D., *301* seq.
SAVAGE, SPENCER, 182, 208
SAVIGNY, 184
SAWYER, F. C., Pl. 90
SCHKUHR, 209
SCHUBERT, BERNICE, 334
SCHULTES, R. E., 182, 273
SCHUMANN, K., 305
SCHURZ, W. L., 231
SCHWEINFURTH, CHARLES, 351
SEEMANN, B. C., 175, 216, 217, *221*, 264, 265, 266, 329, 332, 350, 358, 359, Pl. 80.
SEITZ, C. H. A., 258
SETCHELL, 260
SHEPHERD, JOHN, 209
SILOW, R. A., 258, 265, *337* seq., *370*
SKOTTSBERG, C., 252, 269
SLOANE, HANS, 177, 324
SMITH, A. C., 217, 252, 357
SMITH, EDW., 184
SMITH, G. ELLIOT, 244
SMITH, JAMES E., 182, 186, 208
SMITH, S. PERCY, 271
SOLANDER, D. C., iv, 172, 173, 175, 182, *184*, *186* seq., 191, 194, *198/199*, *200* seq., 208, 211, *212* seq., *240* seq., 251, *326* seq., *332* seq., *346* seq., Pls. 80, 81, 84, *89* seq., Pls. 80, 81, 84, *89*
SPRENGEL, KURT, 208, 209, 362
STANSFIELD, H., 182, *209* seq.
STEARN, W. T., 182, 352, 353, 362
STEBBINS, 337, 339
STEENIS, C. G. G. J. VAN, 179, 182, 185, 227
STEINER, G., Pl. 88
STEPHENS, S. G., 258, 265, *337* seq.
STEVENS, H. N., *324*
STEWARD, J. H., 272
STONOR, 188, 237, *261*, 278, *289*, 341, 342
SWARTZ, 351

SWIFT, Pl. 92

TAYLOR, GEORGE, 182, 329
TAYLOR, W. R., 266
THUNBERG, C. P., 208, 355
TING, Y. C., 372
TISCHBEIN, Pl. 88
TORRES, 230, 233, 235
TOWLE, M. A., 257
TOWNSEND, A. C., 182, 328
TOXOPEUS, H. J., 304
TRUMBULL, 254

VASEY, G., 283
VAUPEL, 282
VAVILOV, N. I., 262
VERDOORN, F., 182, 270
VERDOORN, JOH., 182
VINES, 178
VLEKKE, B. H. M., 236

WALLICH, N., 171
WALLIS, S., 194, 212, 216, 218, 235, 245, 265, 326, 327, Pl. 80
WARBURG, E. F., 177
WARBURG, O., 328
WATSON, JAMES, Pl. 92
WATT, G., *337* seq.
WATTS, W., Pl. 84
WEBB, BARKER, 171
WERDERMANN, 209
WESTER, P. J., 295, 368
WETMORE, A., 276
WETTSTEIN, R., 338
WHARTON, 327
WHEELER, HELEN - MAR, 309
WHITAKER, T. W., 258, 280 seq.
WIENER, LEO, 276, 278, 313, *316* seq., 340, 341, *371* seq.
WILDER, G. P., 216
WILLDENOW, K. L., 209, 347, 354
WILLIAMS, L. O., 183, *276*, 307
WITTHOFF, 311
WOODSON, 314
WORMINGTON, H. M., 243
WRIGHT, C. H., 284

YANOVSKI, E., 274

ZOFFANY, JOHN, 201, Pl. 89

INDEX of COMMON, LATIN, and VERNACULAR
PLANT NAMES

Abelmoschus, 195, 216, 291
Abrus, 195, 216
Abrus precatorius, 332
Acacia farnesiana, 220
achuete, 370
achuetl, 370
Achyranthes, 219
Acorus, 282
Acorus calamus, *282*
Adenostemma, 219
Adenostemma lavenia, 303
adlai, 295
Aeschynomene speciosa, *347*
Aeschynomene indica, 347
Agasta splendida, 348
ages, 255
ajes, 254, 255
Aleurites, 195, 216, 330, 360
Aleurites moluccana, *360*
Alocasia, 195, 216, 235
Alocasia macrorrhiza, *348*
Alphitonia, 330
Alphitonia excelsa, 363
Alphitonia zizyphoides, *362*
Alyxia, 330, 332, 352, 353
Alyxia scandens, *352*
Alyxia stellata, 352, *353*
amara Batata, 318
amaranth, see *Amaranthus*
Amaranthus, 195, 216, *265*, *301* seq.,
  328, 340, *341*, 371
Amaranthus cruentus, *260*
Amaranthus gangeticus, 251
Amaranthus paniculatus, *260*
Amaranthus spinosus, 302
Amaranthus viridis, 302
Amorphophallus, 195, 216, 286
Amorphophallus campanulatus, 335
Amylotheca forsteriana, 342
Ananana sativa, 269
Ananas comosus, 251, *267* seq., *367* seq.
Ananas sativus, 269
anatto tree, see *Bixa*
Andropogon, 219
Aniotum, 328, 330, 347
Aniotum fagiferum, 329, 330, *347*
Annona squamosa, *367*, *368*
e aowiree, 361
e ape, 348
Apios, 340
Arachis diogoi, 296
Arachis hypogaea, 174, 192, 238, 265,
  276, *295* seq., 315, 319
araroetoe, 324
Araucaria, 306
Argemone, 173, *220*, *259*, 269
Argemone alba, 220, 259
Argemone glauca, 220, 259
Argemone mexicana, 220, *259*, 291
arraroet, 324

e arraroóá, 358
arrow-root, see *Maranta*
Arthrodactylis, 355
Arthrodactylis spinosa, 355
Artocarpus, 195, *216*, 219, 235, 249, 265,
  275, 286, 328, 329, 330
Artocarpus altilis, 359
Artocarpus communis, 329, 359
Artocarpus incisa, 329, 359
Arum costatum, *348*
Arum esculentum, 332, 348
Arundo bambos, 332
arurú, 323, 324
Asclepias curassavica, 291
Astilbe, 340
e atae, 335
ate, 368
atis, 368
e atooree, 358
e atoto, 351
autara, 361
auwiri, 361
e ava, 357
avau-ao, 351
e ava-váidái, 357
e avee, 360
Averrhoa bilimbi, 301
Averrhoa carambola, 301
e áwaow, 351
e awharra, 356

babaku, 309
Baccaurea, 286
Bacopa monnieria, 250, 254
Bactris, 266
bako, 307
Bambos arundo, 332
banana, see *Musa*
barley, see *Hordeum*
Barringtonia, 251
Barringtonia asiatica, *348*, 351
batad, 365
Batata montana, 318
Batata purgativa, 318
Batata venenata, 317
batatas, 317
battatas, 307
bean, see *Phaseolus*
Benincasa, 216, 281
Benincasa cerifera, 350
Benincasa hispida, *350*
Besleria laurifolia, *348*
Betonica, 330, 332
Betonica splendida, *348*
bhako, 307
Bidens pilosa, 246
Bixa orellana, *300*, *301*, *370*
Boerhavia, 249
Boerhavia procumbens, 348
Boerhavia repens, 303, *348*

boniato, 255
e booa, 359
Brassica, 338
breadfruit, *see Artocarpus*
Bromelia comosa, 269
Broussonetia, 195, 216, 217
Broussonetia papyrifera, 342
Buckleya, 340
Butonica, 330, 332
Butonica splendida, 348, 351

cacamotic, 318
Caesalpinia, 250
Caesalpinia bonduc, 250
Caesalpinia bonducella, 250
Cajanus cajan, 296
calabaza de España, 219
calabaza de Peru, 219
Calophyllum, 251
Calophyllum inophyllum, 332
camaranbaya, 334
camopatli, 317
camote, 316 seq., 321, 341
camotic, 318
camotl, 317 seq., 371
camotli, 317, 318
Campsis, 340
Canarium album, 286
Canarium pimela, 286
Canavalia, *296*, 340, 341
Canavalia ensiformis, 341
Canavalia gladiata, 341
Canavalia rosea, 222, 341
Canna, *272*
Canna edulis, *273*
Capsicum, 249
cara brasiliensibus, 334
Cardiospermum, 219, 222
Cardiospermum halicacabum, 251
Carica papaya, 251, 267
Carissa grandis, 348
Carya, 340
cassava, *see Manihot*
Cassia, 220, 246
Cassia sophora, 246
Cassia tora, 303
Cassytha filiformis, 222, 254
castor bean, *see Ricinus*
Casuarina, 251, 330, *332* seq.
Casuarina equisetifolia, 332, 333
Casuarina litorea, 333
Catalpa, 340
Ceiba caribaea, 304, 305
Ceiba guinensis, 304
Ceiba occidentalis, 304, 305
Ceiba pentandra, *304* seq.
Ceiba pentandra var. *caribaea*, 304, 305
Ceiba pentandra var. *indica*, 305
Ceiba thonningii, 304
Cenchrus, 219
Cenchrus calyculatus, 219
Cenchrus echinatus, *219*
Centotheca, 219
Centrolepidaceae, 306
Chaitaea, 330
Chaitaea tacca, 348

Chaitea, 330
Chaitea tacca, 348
Chenopodium ambrosioides, 262
Chenopodium sandwichensis, 260
Chenopodium sandwicheum, 260
chichiccamotic, 318
chotis, 370
cigarro, 309
Citrus, 281, 338
Cladrastis, 340
coconut, *see Cocos*
Cocos nucifera, *194* seq., 217, 223, 241, 248, 249, *258*, 265, *266* seq., 274, *275*, 330, 333, 339, 369
Coix lachryma-jobi, 246, *295*
Colocasia, 195, 216, 274
Colocasia esculenta, 235, 265, 274, 332
Colubrina asiatica, 251
Convolvulus alatus, *349*
Convolvulus brasiliensis, 333
Convolvulus chrysorhizus, *349*
Convolvulus chrysorrhizus, 349
Conyza albida, 260
Conyza bonariensis, 260
Cordia sebestena, 333, 362
Cordia subcordata, 249, 251, 333, 362
Cordyline fruticosa, 335
Cordyline terminalis, 335
Coronilla coccinea, 347
cotton, *see Gossypium*
Cotula bicolor, *350*, 351
Cotula latifolia, 350
cozabba, 310
Crataeva frondosa, 350
Crataeva religiosa, 350
Croomia, 340
Cucumis, 216
Cucurbita, 192, 216, *218*, *237*, 249, *265*, 274, *279* seq., 290, *296*, 301, 315, 338, *340* seq., 371
Cucurbita ficifolia, 192, 238, 265, *279*, 281
Cucurbita lagenaria, 350
Cucurbita maxima, 218, 219, *264*, *281*, 319, 350
Cucurbita moschata, 282
Cucurbita pepo, 218, 219, *280* seq., 319
Cucurbita pruriens, *350*
culong tsjutsju, 313
cumar, 371
Curcuma, 217, 294
Cyathula, 219
Cyperus, 222
Cyperus alatus, *351*
Cyperus esculentus, *282*
Cyrtosperma, 195, 217, 235, 286

Dahlia, 198, 285, *294*
dana, 364
daoa, 364
Daphne capitata, *351*
Daphne foetida, 351
daua, 364
Decaspermum fruticosum, *358*
Dentella repens, 220, *246* seq.
Dentella serpyllifolia, 247
Derris, 262

Desmodium, 219
e deva, 352
Dichrocephala, 219
Dichrocephala bicolor, *350*
Dichrocephala latifolia, 350
Digitaria, 219, 285
Dioscorea, *194*, 195, 217, 255, 258, 265, 274, 278, 307, *323*, *334*
Dioscorea alata, *254*, *323*, *333* seq.
Dioscorea cayanensis, 333, 334
Dioscorea esculenta, 323
Dodonaea viscosa, 222, 335
Dorstenia lucida, 206
Dracaena, 195, 216
Dracaena terminalis, 335
Dracontium polyphyllum, 335

Echites costata, 206
Eleocharis dulcis, 286
elephant's ear, *see Alocasia*
Eleusine, 219
Embothrium, 178
Epidendrum resupinatum, 351
Epigaea, 340
Epipactis purpurea, 350, *351*
Eragrostis mauiensis, 260
Eragrostis mexicana, 260
Erianthus floridulus, 358
Erigeron albidus, *260*
Erigeron bonariensis, 260
Erigeron linifolius, 260
Eriochloa, 219
Ervatamia divaricata, 314
Erythoina, 332, 335
Erythraea spicata, *229*
Erythrina, 332
Erythrina corallodendron, 335, Pl. 80
Erythrina indica, 251, 335, *Pl. 80*
Erythrina variegata var. *orientalis*, 335
eta iri, 361
etari-heiriri, 361
Eugenia, 216
Eugenia malaccensis, 335
Eugenia uniflora, 301
Euphorbia, 198
Euphorbia develata, *351*
Euphorbia heterophylla, 291
Euryale ferox, 286
Evia amara, 360
ewavai, 337

Fagraea berteriana, *348*
fara, 356
Ficus prolixa, 206, *352*
Ficus tinctoria, 206, *352*
Fimbristylis, 219, 222
Fleurya, 219
Flos convolutus, 303
Flos manhilanos, 314
Folium mensarium album, 305
Forstera, Pl. 85
Frumentum indicum, 367
Frumentum turcicum, 367
Frutex lintearius, 343

Galaxa, 330, 332
Galaxa oppositifolia, *352*

Galaxa sparsa, *352* seq.
Galaxia, 352
Galega piscatoria, 353
gamot, 317
gamut, 317
ganda, 294
gandasuli, 294
Garcinia mangostana, 286
Gardenia florida, 335
Gardenia taitensis, 222, 335
genda, 294, 295
genda rojia, 295
gendu, 294
gisia, 310
Glycine lucida, 206
Glycine rosea, 206
gol-mariyam, 295
Gossypium, 178, 189, 241, 258, 265, *279*, 281, *291* seq., 295, 310, *335* seq., *370* seq.
Gossypium hirsutum, *336*
Gossypium hirsutum var. *punctatum*, 337
Gossypium purpurascens, 337, 338
Gossypium religiosum, 335, 337
Gossypium taitense, 335, 337, 338
gourd, *see Lagenaria*
common gourd, *see Lagenaria*
large gourd, *see Lagenaria*
Malabar gourd, *see Cucurbita*
ornamental gourd, *see Cucurbita*
Siamese gourd, *see Cucurbita*
true gourd, *see Lagenaria*
wax gourd, *see Benincasa*
guava, *see Psidium*
Guettarda speciosa, 342
gumbili, 317
Gymnocladus, 340
Gynopogon, 330, 352
Gynopogon scandens, 352
Gynopogon stellatum, 352

habanos, 309
hala kahiki, 269
Halesia, 340
Hamamelis, 340
Hedychium, 295
Hedychium coronarium, 294
e hee, 347
Helianthus annuus, 226
Heliconia, *305*
Heliconia austro-caledonica, 305
Heliconia bihai, 305, 306
Heliconia buccinata, 305
Heliconia edwardus rex, 305
Heliconia illustris, 305
Heliconia indica, *305*
Heliconia micholitzii, 305
Heliconopsis amboinensis, 305
Heliotropium indicum, 229
Hemionitis reticulata, 206
Hernandia ovigera, 342
Hernandia peltata, 342
Hibiscus, 195, 291
Hibiscus bacciferus, 206, 362
Hibiscus bifurcus, 260
Hibiscus cuspidatus, *353* seq., 354

Hibiscus furcellatus var. *youngianus*, 260
Hibiscus hastatus, 353, 354
Hibiscus populneus, 206, 361
Hibiscus rosa-sinensis, 216, 335, 342
Hibiscus tiliaceus, 222, 248, 251, 253, 254, 304, 353
Hibiscus tiliaceus var. *hastatus*, *353* seq.
Hibiscus tiliaceus var. *tricuspis*, 354
Hibiscus vitifolius, 354
Hibiscus youngianus, 260
e hooe-rorro, 350
e hootoo, 348
e hora, 353
Hordeum vulgare, 242
humas, 364
hutu, 348
Hydrocotyle moschata, *Pl. 87*
Hyptis, 220

Ietica brasiliensibus, 322
Illicium, 340
Ilysanthes, 219
inhame, 334
inhame de S. Thome, 334
Inocarpus, 195, 216, 248, 328, 329, 330, 347
Inocarpus edulis, 329, *347*
Inocarpus fagiferus, *347*
Ipomoea, 340
Ipomoea acetosaefolia, 260
Ipomoea batatas, 194, 195, *213* seq., 216, *220*, 223, 235, 238, 241, *243*, 248, *253*, 255, 258, *264*, 265, 274, *276* seq., 290, *306* seq., *316* seq., *321* seq., *341*, 349, *371* seq., 373
Ipomoea bona-nox, 222
Ipomoea pes-caprae, 222, 249, 254, 260, 303, 333
Ipomoea stolonifera, *260*
ipu nui, 350, 351
Itea, 340

Jack bean, *see Canavalia*
Jambosa, 195
Jasminum didymum, 206, *354*

kalachuche, 313
kaoliang, 286
kapok, *see Ceiba*
kau-sun, 286
kemaki, 309
Keura, 355
Keura odoratissima, 355
kumala, 371
kumar, 371
kumara, 307, 349, 371, 372
kurintagos, 317
Kyllinga, 219, 222

Lagenaria leucantha, 350
Lagenaria siceraria, *194*, 195, 212, 216, 217, 218, 219, 223, 235, 241, *255* seq., 258, *264*, 271, 281, 339, 350, 351
Lagenaria vulgaris, 350
Lansium, 286

Lantana camara, 220
Lepargyrea, 209
Leptospermum collinum, 354
Leucaena glauca, 220
Leucas, 219
Limnophila fragrans, *358*, *360*
Limnophila serrata, 358
Liriodendron, 340
Lomatia, 178
Lonchocarpus, 262
Lonicera japonica, 225, 283
Loranthus forsterianus, 342
Loranthus stelis, 342
lotus, *see Nelumbo*
Lusitanis Batata, 322
Lycopersicum, 224, 249
Lycopodium myrtifolium, 206
Lycopodium squarrosum, 206

maire, 352
e maireeo, 352
mais, 364, 365
maize, *see Zea*
maizio, 367
Malaxis, *351*
Malaxis resupinata, *351*
Malaxis rhedii, 351
Malus, 338
Malva parviflora, *286*
Malvastrum coromandelianum, 229
Mammea asiatica, 348
Mangifera, 286
Mangifera indica, 266, *369*
Mangifera pinnata, 360
mangosteen, *see Garcinia*
Manihot, *319*
Manihot esculenta, 212, 278, 318, 319, 373
Manihot utilissima, 317
Maranta arundinacea, *323* seq.
marigold, *see Tagetes*
Mariscus, 219
ma tai, 286
e meerro, 361
Melastoma denticulatum, 342
Melastoma malabathricum, 342
Menispermum, 340
Mentha arvensis, 251
Messerschmidtia argentea, 362
Metrosideros collina, *354*
Metrosideros spectabilis, *354*
Microstylis, 351
Microstylis resupinata, 351
Microstylis rheedii, 351
miglio, 364
Mimosa, 220
Mimosa pudica, *228*, 229
miro, 361
Miscanthus floridulus, *358*
Miscanthus japonicus, 359
moemoe, 356
e mohoo, 351
Morinda, 248, 251
Morinda citrifolia, 342
Morus papyrifera, 342
Mucuna, 219
Musa, 216, 217, *272* seq., *278* seq., 338

Musa acuminata, 345
Musa balbisiana, 345
Musa bihai, 305, 343
Musa coccinea, 343
Musa ensete, 273
Musa fehi, 343
Musa mexicana, 345
Musa paradisiaca, 195, 249, 272, 274,
    277, *278* seq., 281, *343* seq.
Musa sapientum, 281, 345
Musa troglodytarum, 343 seq.
Musa uranoscopos, 343

ñames, 255
Nauclea forsteri, 345
Nauclea forsteriana, 345
Nauclea orientalis, 345
Nelitris forsteri, 358
Nelumbium lotus, 284
Nelumbo, 263
Nelumbo lutea, 262, 284
Nelumbo nucifera, 263, 284, 286
Neonauclea forsteri, 345
niames, 255
Nicotiana, 178, 274, 290, 293, 299, 306,
    316
Nicotiana paniculata, 316
Nicotiana rustica, 178, *308* seq., *316*
Nicotiana silvestris, 316
Nicotiana suaveolens, 311
Nicotiana tabacum, 178, *307* seq., *316,*
    323
Nicotiana tomentosa, 316
Nicotiana undulata, 316
nono, 248
Nothofagus, 306

oaao, 351
Ochrosia, 353
Ochrosia parviflora, 352, 353
Ocimum, 251
Oldenlandia repens, 246
e ooroo, 359
Operculina turpethum, 222, *349*
Oplismenus, 219
Orites, 178
Oryza latifolia, 275
Oryza minuta, 275
Oryza sativa, 275, 281, 365
oufai, 347
e owhaee, 347
Oxalis, 219
Oxalis repens, 227

Pachyrrhizus, 217, 218
Pachyrrhizus erosus, 217
Pachyrrhizus trilobus, 217
pallares, 239
Pandanus, 269, 275, 306, 330, *355,* 359
Pandanus odoratissimus, 328, 354, 355
Pandanus tectorius, 249, 328, 330, *354*
    seq., 359
Pandanus verus, 355
Panicum, 364
Panicum miliaceum, 364 seq.
papaya, *see Carica*
Paspalum, 219
peanut, *see Arachis*

e peea, 349
e peepee, 356
petum, 310
petun, 310
Petunia, 310
Phalaris, 227
Phalaris canariensis, 227
Phalaris minor, 227
Phaseolus, 249, 281, 340, 341
Phaseolus adenanthus, 356
Phaseolus amoenus, 356
Phaseolus coccineus, 249
Phaseolus pallar, 239, 249
Phaseolus truxillensis, 356
Phyllanthus, 219
Phyllanthus anceps, 356
Phyllanthus simplex, 356
Phyllanthus simplex var. *virgatus,* 356
Phyllanthus virgatus, 356
Physalis, 219, 224
Physalis peruviana, 260
Physalis philadelphia, 224
picielt, 310
Pieris, 340
pigeon pea, *see Cajanus*
pineapple, *see Ananas*
Piper inebrians, 357
Piper latifolium, 357, 358
Piper methysticum, 357
Piper pallidum, 206
Piper tetraphyllum, 206
Pipturus argenteus, 362
plantain, *see Musa*
platano, 278
Plumbago, 219
Plumeria, 294, 303
Plumeria acuminata, 313
Poa annua, 303
Poa latifolia, 206
Podophyllum, 340
Polygonum, 219
e pooa, 359
e poo-aiho, 358
e pooamattapeepee, 348
e pooraow, 353
e pooraow-toro-ceree, 354
e pooratta, 354
popcorn, *see Zea*
Portulaca lutea, 249, *260, 358*
Portulaca oleracea, 260, 358
Potamogeton foliosus var. *macellus, 260*
Potamogeton pauciflorus, 260
pouraheitee, 359
Pourpartia pinnata, 360
Proteaceae, 178, 306
Psidium guajava, 220, 290, *296* seq.
Psidium myrtifolium, 358
Pteridium aquilinum var. *esculentum,*
    235
Pteris comans, 206
puarata, 354
Pueraria, 195, *217*
Pueraria lobata, 217, 218
Pueraria thunbergiana, 217, 218
pumpkin, *see Cucurbita*
purau, 353
Pyrularia, 340
Pyrus, 338, 369

quantyetl, 310
quauhcamotli, 317, 318
quingombo, 334

Radermachia, *359*
Radermachia incisa, 329, 359
e ratta, 347, 354
Remirea maritima, 303
e reva, 352
Rhamnus, 362
Rhamnus zizyphoides, 362
rice, see Oryza
Ricinus communis, 294
e roa, 362
Rosa, 293
rosa de ouro, 295
Roupala, 178
Ruellia fragrans, 206, *358*, 360

Saccharum, 217
Saccharum dulce, *358*
Saccharum fatuum, *358*
Saccharum officinarum, 235, 274, *358*
Sagittaria, *284*
Sagittaria cuneata, 284
Sagittaria sagittifolia, *284*
Sagittaria sinensis, 284, 286
sakapa, 309
sakape, 309
sakupe, 309
Sandoricum koetjape, 286
Saururus, 340
Schizostachyum glaucifolium, 332
Scoparia, 220
sepuke, 309
Sesbania, 195, 216
Sesbania coccinea, *347*
Sesbania grandiflora, 347
Sesbania speciosa, *347*
Sesuvium portulacastrum, 240, 249, 303
Setaria faberi, 225, *283* seq.
Setaria italica, 364, 365
Shepherdia, 209
Shortia, 340
Sida rhombifolia, 246
Siegesbeckia, 219
silk-cottontree, see Ceiba
Sitodium, 328, 330
Sitodium altile, 328, 330, *359*
sitrube, 309
sokuba, 309
Solanum, 219, 340, 341
Solanum anthropophagorum, 222, 359
Solanum latifolium, *359*
Solanum melongena, 341
Solanum nigrum, 219, 227, 303
Solanum nodiflorum, 219, 227
Solanum repandum, *359*
Solanum tuberosum, 341
Solanum uporo, 222, *359*
Solanum viride, *359*
Sonchus oleraceus, 246
Sophora tomentosa, 222
sorgho, 356
Sorghum, 274, 278, *286*, 307
sotis, 370
Spathiphyllum, 306
Sphacele hastata, 246

Spondias, 195, 216
Spondias cytherea, 360
Spondias dulcis, 206, 207, 330, *360*, Pl. 91
Spondias mangifera, 360
Spondias pinnata, 360
squash, see Cucurbita
summer squash, see Cucurbita
Stachys dentata, 358, *360*
Stachytarpheta, 220
sugar cane, see Saccharum
suguba, 309
sukaba, 309
Suriana maritima, 254
sweet potato, see Ipomoea
sweetsop, see Annona
Syzygium, 216
Syzygium malaccense, 335

tabaco, 307, 309, 310, 311, 323
tabacos, 307
tabak, 309, 323
tabaka, 307, 309
tabake, 309
tabaku, 309
tabaok, 309
Tabernæmontana divaricata, 314
Tacca, 216, 217, 330
Tacca leontopetaloides, *349*
Tacca pinnatifida, 349
tafaki, 309
Tagetes, 192, 198, 247, 285, *292*, 294, *301*
Tagetes erecta, *292*
tahina, 362
taihinnoo, 362
taitu, 323
tambako, 307
tamok, 309
tampaku, 309
tamuk, 309
tamuku, 309
tapioca, see Manihot
taro, see Colocasia
giant taro, see Cyrtosperma
tavo, 309
tavora, 309
teatea maowa, 354
tebak, 307
Telopaea, 330, *360*, 361
Telopaea perspicua, *360*
tembako, 307
tembaku, 309
temuka, 309
tepecamotli, 318
Tephrosia, 251
Tephrosia piscatoria, 353
Tephrosia purpurea, 353
Terminalia, 249, 251
Terminalia catappa, *361*
Terminalia glabrata, 206, *361*
Theobroma cacao, *314*
Thespesia, 206, 330, *361*
Thespesia populnea, 222, 251, 254, *361*
tiale feutu, 335
tiale tofe, 335
tialo, 335
tiare, 335, 353

tiare tahiti, 335
tira-hutu, 348
tlacacamohtli, 372
tlaolli, 288, 367
e to, 358
e toa, 333
tobacco, *see Nicotiana*
toe, 362
e toee, 362
tomatl, 224
e tooho, 350
Tournefortia sericea, 362
Trapa, 283, 286
Trapa bicornis, 283
Trapa natans, 225, *282* seq.
Trichomanes demissum, 207
Trichomanes elatum, 207
Trichomanes gibberosum, 207
turmeric, *see Curcuma*

uala, 371
uma'a, 371
umala, 371
umara, 371
Uncinia, 306
uppuwoc, 310
upwoc, 310
Urena, 219
Urena lobata, 345
Urtica argentea, 207, *362*
Urtica candicans, 362
Urtica virgata, 207
Ustilago, 286
Ustilago esculenta, 286
Ustilago sorghi, 286

e vaeenoo, 350
Vandellia, 219
vi, 360
Vigna lutea, 250

Vigna marina, 250, 303

waherút, 323
Waltheria, 238
Waltheria americana, 245
Waltheria indica, 245
wa-waka, 217
e wavai, 337
e wawei, 335
Wedelia biflora, 250
Weinmannia parviflora, 207
Wikstroemia foetida, 351
Wisteria, 340

Xanthosoma, 274
Ximenia, 249
Ximenia americana, 254, 303
Ximenia elliptica, 304

yaka, 217
yam, *see Dioscorea (& Ipomoea)*
Chinese yam, *see Dioscorea*
greater yam, *see Dioscorea*
true yam, *see Dioscorea*
ycheaxvitl, 336
yelt, 310
yoli, 310
yuca, 317
yu shu shu, 290

Zea mays, 188 seq., 192, 212, *216, 237,*
239, 249, *261* seq., 265, 274, 276, 277,
278, 281, *288* seq., 319, 338, 341, 342,
364 seq., 371, 373
Zingiber, 217
Zizania, 340
Zizania caduciflora, 286
Zizyphoides, 330, 362
Zizyphoides argentea, 362

Contents of Chronica Botanica, Volume 14 (1950/1954)

List of Editors ii
From Emerson's Wood Notes v
The Harvard Botanic Garden, Cambridge, Mass., in the 1880's vi
Dedication of Volume 14 (*to the* Founders and Leaders of the former Botanic Garden and the Gray Herbarium of Harvard University) vii

Nuttall's Travels into the Old Northwest: An Unpublished 1810 Diary, *edited by* Jeannette E. Graustein (Chronica Botanica 14, 1/2; issued Autumn 1951) 1-88
    Contents, *see* 4
    List of Illustrations 4
    Appendices 77

Plant Genera: Their Nature and Definition: A Symposium *by* G. H. M. Lawrence, I. W. Bailey, Arthur J. Eames, Reed C. Rollins, Marion S. Cave, and Herbert L. Mason, with an introductory essay on generic synopses and modern taxonomy *by* Th. Just (Chronica Botanica 14, 3/4, *nec* No. 3 as stated on the cover and halftitle, *cf.* the running heads; issued Autumn 1953) 89-160
    Contents, *see* 92
    Editor's Foreword 93
    Generic Synopses and Modern Taxonomy (Just) 103
    Plant Genera, their Nature and Definition: the Need for an Expanded Outlook (Lawrence) 117
    The Anatomical Approach to the Study of Genera (Bailey) 121
    Floral Anatomy as an Aid in Generic Limitation (Eames) 126
    Cytogenetical Approaches to the Study of Genera (Rollins) 133
    Cytology and Embryology in the Delimitation of Genera (Cave) 140
    Plant Geography in the Delimitation of Genera: The Role of Plant Geography in Taxonomy (Mason) 154
    List of Illustrations and Tables 160

The Botany of Cook's Voyages *by* E. D. Merrill (Chronica Botanica 14, 5/6; issued Autumn 1954) .... i-iv, 161-384
    Contents, *see* 164
    List of Illustrations 170

Contents and Plates of Chronica Botanica, Volume 14 (1950/1954) 384

Position of the Plates of Chronica Botanica, Volume 14

Plate 68: Thomas Nuttall .... p. 2
Plates 69/79: Nuttalliana (*cf.* p. 4) .... *after* p. 88
Plate 80: The *Endeavour* at Anchor in Matavai Bay, Tahiti .... *after* p. 384
Plate 81: The *Endeavour* coming to Anchor in Botany Bay .... *after* p. 384
Plate 82: Sir Joseph Banks .... *after* p. 384
Plate 83: H. M. S. *Resolution* and H. M. S. *Adventure* in Matavai Bay .... *after* p. 384
Plate 84: View of Tahiti, after a painting by W. Hodges .... *after* p. 384
Plate 85: Johann Reinhold Forster .... *after* p. 384
Plate 86: Extracts from a Financial Statement prepared by J. R. Forster ...... *after* p. 384
Plate 87: *Hydrocotyle moschata*, unpublished drawing by G. Forster .... *after* p. 384
Plate 88: Johann Georg Adam Forster .... *after* p. 384
Plate 89: Daniel Carl Solander .... *after* p. 384
Plate 90: Sydney Parkinson .... *after* p. 384
Plate 91: *Spondias dulcis*, unpublished drawing by S. Parkinson .... *after* p. 384
Plate 92: John Hawkesworth .... *after* p. 384
Plate 93: The *Endeavour*, pencil drawing by Hilde de Vries after a recent reconstruction by R. Langmaid (*courtesy Endeavour*) .... *after* p. 384

The title page and other front matter (pp. i-viii) of vol. 14 (1950/54) will be found bound at the beginning of the first number of the volume.

The *Endeavour* at anchor in Matavai Bay, Tahiti, where BANKS, SOLANDER and the FORSTERs collected the materials with which this memoir is mainly concerned. — Engraving from J. HAWKESWORTH's *Account of the Voyages ... Southern Hemisphere* (1773): "Called by Captain WALLIS, Port Royal Harbour in King George the Third's Island. The view is taken from One Tree Hill, and the tree is a new species of the *Erythrina*". — SOLANDER called it *Erythrina corallodendron* L. (which is wrong). It is *E. indica* Lam. according to SEEMANN who examined the BANKS and SOLANDER specimen. In the background (left of the tree) the temporary "fort" construction with BANKS's personal tent (*not* a Polynesian construction), at right. — Captain WALLIS, as outlined on p. 212, discovered Tahiti, the center of the Polynesian culture area, in 1767. In 1769, the *Endeavour* reached Tahiti. Between 1767 and 1769, the French exploring expedition under L. A. DE BOUGAINVILLE visited the island with *l'Etoile* and *la Boudeuse*.

H. M. BARK ENDEAVOUR.

H. M. Bark *Endeavour*, the ship of Cook's first voyage, in which BANKS, SOLANDER and PARKINSON took part, coming to anchor in Botany Bay, Australia, April 29, 1770. — Etching ("Botany Bay Welcome") by G. C. INGLETON (ca. 1948). — *From the Chronica Botanica Archives.*

Sir JOSEPH BANKS (1743-1820), the chief naturalist of COOK's first voyage, to whose energy and influence, we owe most of the 18th Century Pacific Islands collections discussed in this memoir. — Mezzotint by W. DICKINSON (1774) after a painting by Sir JOSHUA REYNOLDS. — *Courtesy of the British Museum (Natural History).*

H. M. S. *Resolution* (left) and H. M. S. *Adventure*, the two ships of COOK's second voyage, in which the FORSTERS took part, lying in Matavai Bay, Tahiti, August 26, 1773. — Detail from a painting by WILLIAM HODGES, lent by the British Admiralty to the National Maritime Museum. — *Courtesy of the National Maritime Museum, Greenwich, England.*

VIEW OF TAHITI ("bearing S.E. distant one League"), looking into Matavai Bay from the South. — The highest mountain on Tahiti, the double peaked Orohena, rises to ca. 7350 ft. BANKS and SOLANDER collected to about 2500', while the FORSTERS reached the mossy forest (perhaps 4000'). — At right, two double canoes or catamarans; at left, an outrigger canoe. The possible rôle in plant distribution played by these primitive boats is discussed in Chapter I. — Engraving by W. WATTS (1777) after a painting by W. HODGES.

JOHANN REINHOLD FORSTER (1729-1798), German botanist, naturalist to COOK's second voyage (1772-1775), the father of GEORG FORSTER. Able and hard working botanists, the FORSTERS often disregarded the principles of scientific ethics, thereby becoming involved in a variety of quarrels. — Engraving by I. F. BAUSE (1781), after a portrait by ANT. GRAFF. — The explanation referring to the plant shown at the bottom states: "Diese Pflanze in nämlicher Grösse, hat Herr Prof. FORSTER in Neu-Seeland entdeckt, und LINNÉ ihm zu Ehren *Forstera* benennt"; Ivy leaves have been utilized as an ornament around the upper border of the portrait.

Two extracts from a financial statement which J. R. FORSTER submitted to Sir JOSEPH BANKS (cf. p. 205). It appears from this account of the 4000 pounds due to the FORSTERS, as per their agreement with the British government, that BANKS gave the elder FORSTER 200 pounds for unspecified purposes, in addition to 400 guineas for the FORSTER drawings (perhaps for miscellaneous natural history and ethnological specimens, curios, etc., collected by the FORSTERS on COOK's second voyage?). — *Courtesy of the British Museum (Natural History).*

Hydrocotyle moschata T. Austr. p. 22. n. 135.

Hydrocotyle moschata.

Hydrocotyle moschata Forst. f., an Australian Water Pennywort. — One of the unpublished drawings made by GEORG FORSTER while in New Zealand. From the folio volumes of original pencil and water color sketches made by the FORSTERS during COOK's second voyage (cf. p. 203). — *Courtesy of the British Museum (Natural History).*

JOHANN GEORG ADAM FORSTER (1754-1794), the son of JOHANN REINHOLD FORSTER, whom he accompanied on COOK's second voyage (1772-1775), was only 17 years old when the *Resolution* left England. Published a journal of his voyage in H.M.S. *Resolution*, antedating COOK's official account, by some months, in 1777. Returned thereafter with his father to Germany. — If one be interested in following up GEORG FORSTER's later, mainly non-botanical career *see* G. STEINER and M. HÄCKEL, FORSTER: Ein Lesebuch für unsere Zeit. i-xxii. 1-506. illus. Weimar: Thüringer Volksverlag. 1952. — Painting by ANTON GRAFF ("hat mich herrlich getroffen. TISCHBEINS ist kein Schatten davon. Ich bin hier ganz mit meinem Charakter bis auf die kleinsten Züge und Nuancen"). This formal portrait is almost a reversed version of an informal portrait drawing (original at Kew, copy in Chronica Botanica Archives), made at Tahiti.

DANIEL CARL SOLANDER (1736-1782). — LINNAEUS's favourite
pupil who came to England in 1760. Accompanied Sir JOSEPH BANKS
on COOK's first voyage (1768-1771) and prepared numerous mss. based
on the plants and animals collected on the voyage of the *Endeavour*.

SOLANDER, a prolific writer, actually finished his manuscript accounts of such floras as those of Tahiti, New Zealand, Australia, Java,
Cape of Good Hope, Saint Helena, Madeira, Brazil, and Terra del
Fuego. He also prepared manuscripts on the plants collected on
COOK's third voyage, but left the plants of the second voyage to the
FORSTERS. Particularly in his later years, SOLANDER had a tendency
to procrastinate (LINNAEUS, also on behalf of SOLANDER's mother,
often complained about not hearing from him at all for extended
periods) and while the manuscript flora of Tahiti, with which this
memoir is particularly concerned, and several other floras were completed, many other of his numerous botanical and also zoological
manuscripts remained unfinished (often in the form of a preliminary
card index) and nearly all unpublished. It should be remembered that
SOLANDER's fate as a publishing botanist was not wholly in his own
hands. Though a very large number of plates were actually engraved
(plans had been made, before the Second World War to publish the
New Zealand icones) for several of SOLANDER's floras, BANKS, his
principal, lost interest after he became President of the Royal Society.

An extensive biography of SOLANDER is being prepared at present
by Dr. O. SELLING (*cf.* also FRIES, R. E. DANIEL SOLANDER. Levnad-
steckningar K. Sv. Vet. Akad. Ledamöter 114. 1940).

Oil painting, in the possession of the Linnean Society of London.
— *Courtesy of the Linnean Society of London.*

"Although it is generally stated that the artist is unknown, it has
appeared in print several times that he was JOHN ZOFFANY (the artist
who was to have accompanied BANKS and SOLANDER on Captain COOK's
second voyage). The authority for this statement is unknown to me.
However, if we consult *Joseph Banks* by H. C. CAMERON (Batchworth
Press, 1952) we find a plate, opposite p. 236, the upper figure of which
shows a painting of "OMAI, SOLANDER and BANKS." This should read
OMAI, BANKS and SOLANDER, for BANKS is the centre figure and the
right hand figure, seated, seems identical with the Linnean Society
portrait. The legend states "By WILLIAM PARRY . . . in the possession
of General JOHN VAUGHAN, of Nannau, Dolgelley." The exact connection between the two portraits is not clear to me, but I am inclined
to attribute both to the same artist." (J. RAMSBOTTOM, *in ep.*).

SYDNEY PARKINSON (ca. 1745-1771) one of the draughtsmen who accompanied BANKS on COOK's first voyage, frontispiece engraving by JA. NEWTON to *A Journal of a Voyage to the South Seas in his Majesty's Ship the Endeavour . . . from the papers of the late* SYDNEY PARKINSON (1784).

"The biography of SYDNEY PARKINSON, the draughtsman to whom the figures of the plants and animals observed on COOK's First Voyage are due, is sufficiently recorded in the preface to his 'Journal . . .', but a few words may be said with special reference to his connection with BANKS. His brother tells us that he was put to the business of a woollen-draper; but, taking a particular delight in drawing flowers, fruits, and other objects of natural history, he became so greatly proficient in that style of painting, as to attract the notice of the most celebrated botanists and connoisseurs in that study. In consequence of this, he was, some time after his arrival in London, recommended to JOSEPH BANKS, Esq., 'whose very numerous collections of elegant and highly-finished drawings of that kind, executed by SYDNEY PARK-INSON, is a sufficient testimony of both of his talents and application' . . . It was by the advice of JAMES LEE (not 'an artist', but the well-known nurseryman of Hammersmith) that PARKINSON was engaged by BANKS to accompany the voyage to the South Seas. He died during the return voyage on January 26*th*, 1771. . . . The total number of drawings made by PARKINSON during the voyage was 955, of which 675 were sketches and 280 finished drawings. All the Australian and most of the New Zealand ones are sketches; those from Brazil, Madeira, Tierra del Fuego, and the Friendly Islands are nearly all finished drawings; of the Java plants there are 44 finished drawings and 72 sketches — in a few cases there are both sketch and finished drawings of the same plant. On the back of each drawing are pencil notes by PARKINSON, indicating the colour of the leaves, flowers, &c., and the locality is added in BANKS' hand" (J. H. MAIDEN, Sir JOSEPH BANKS. Sydney and London. 1909, p. 62 — *after* JAS. BRITTEN, Illustrations of Australian Plants . . . *Endeavour*. London. 1900-1905).

A detailed account of PARKINSON's *Journal* will be found on p. 326. *See also:* F. C. SAWYER. Some Natural History Drawings made during Captain COOK's First Voyage Round the World. Jour. Soc. Bibl. Nat. Hist. 2: 190-193. 1 fig. 1950. In the appended bibliography are references to various lists of subjects in the works of DRYANDER and PARKINSON with references to zoological publications and manuscripts of SOLANDER, PENNANT, J. R. FORSTER and others.

SYDNEY PARKINSON

Spondias dulcis

Spondias dulcis Parkinson, the Otaheite-Apple, a beautiful, unpublished drawing of a cultivated variety, made by SYDNEY PARKINSON during the *Endeavour*'s visit to Tahiti. PARKINSON first used this binomial in 1773 (*cf.* p. 360). — *Courtesy British Museum (Natural History).*

John Hawkesworth (ca. 1715-1773), author and editor, edited Swift's works (1755) and compiled the account of Captain Cook's and other voyages to the South Seas, described on p. 327; became a director of the East India Company shortly before his death. — Engraving by James Watson after a painting by Sir Joshua Reynolds. — *Courtesy of the Trustees of the British Museum.*

Due